Heinemann BIOLOGY 1

2ND EDITION

Student Workbook

Yvonne Sanders

VCE Units 1 & 2

- Written for the VCE Biology Study Design 2016–2021
- Key knowledge and key skills study notes
- Worksheets and practical activities
- Area of Study 3 investigation model and guide

Pearson Australia
(a division of Pearson Australia Group Pty Ltd)
707 Collins Street, Melbourne, Victoria 3008
PO Box 23360, Melbourne, Victoria 8012
www.pearson.com.au

First published 2005 by Harcourt Education
2019 2018 2017 2016
10 9 8 7 6 5 4 3 2

Publisher: Alicia Brown
Project Editors: Jane Sunderland and Hannah Turner
Editor: Fiona Maplestone
Cover Designer: Anne Donald
Designer: Lauren Statham
Copyright & Pictures Editors: Isabel Angus, Amirah Fatin
Illustrator/s: Dimitrios Prokopis, Andrew Louey, Claire Wilson, Pearson India
Printed in Malaysia (CTP-PJB)

ISBN 978 1 4886 1200 8

Pearson Australia Group Pty Ltd ABN 40 004 245 943

Acknowledgements
We thank the following for their contributions to our text book:

123RF: pp. 75tl, 77t1l, 77t3l, 77bcr; Gajus, p.123t; jdeks, p.63t; Viktoriya Kirillova, p.123cl; Shihina, p.64t. Age Fotostock: Auscape/UIG, p.91t1r. Alamy: Blickwinkel/McPHOTO/VLZ, p.77bcl. Amana Images: Joe McDonald, p.63b. Avita Medical Ltd: pp.144tl, 144bl. Copyright Agency Ltd (CAL): The Age: 'Changing Conceptions' by Rachel Browne, 26 November 2004, p.181. Fotolia: Susan Flashman, p.77br; Glen Gaffney, p.77t2l; Dave Hanlon, p.64bl; Swapan, p.139. Getty Images: Norbert Probst, cover; Terry Whittaker, p.63c. Yvonne Sanders: p.58cr. Pearson Australia: MIXA Co., Ltd, pp.124,125,147,178,179. Science Photo Library: Ammrf, University of Sydney, pp.1,47,121; Dr Keith Wheeler, p.64br. Shutterstock: Jason Benz Bennee, p.138b; bstoltz, p.77t4l; Andrew Burgess, p.50tl; Clearviewstock, p.90; Philip Ellard, p.77t1r; Vitalii Hulai, p.91t2r; Piotr Krzeslak, p.77t3r; Janelle Lugge, p.50tr; John McQueen, p.64c; Milosz_M, p.77bl; Nata-Lia, p.77t4r; PRILL, p.123cr; Eugene Sergeev, p.77t2r; Joanne Weston, p.75tr. Victorian Curriculum and Assessment Authority (VCAA): Selected extracts from the VCE [Biology] Study Design (2016-2021) are copyright Victorian Curriculum and Assessment Authority (VCAA), reproduced by permission. VCE® is a registered trademark of the VCAA. The VCAA does not endorse this product and makes no warranties regarding the correctness or accuracy of its content. To the extent permitted by law, the VCAA excludes all liability for any loss or damage suffered or incurred as a result of accessing, using or relying on the content. Current VCE Study Designs and related content can be accessed directly at www.vcaa.vic.edu.au pp. 46, 47, 121, 125, 147, 179.

Every effort has been made to trace and acknowledge copyright. However, should any infringement have occurred, the publishers tender their apologies and invite copyright owners to contact them.

Contents

Unit 1 How do living things stay alive?

AREA OF STUDY 1
How do organisms function?

AREA OF STUDY 2
How do living systems sustain life?

AREA OF STUDY 3
Practical investigation

Contents

Unit 2 How is continuity of life maintained?

AREA OF STUDY 1
How does reproduction maintain the continuity of life?

AREA OF STUDY 2
How is inheritance explained?

AREA OF STUDY 3
Investigation of an issue

INTRODUCTION

To the student

The *Heinemann Biology 1 Student Workbook* 2nd edition has been created to help you achieve your best possible performance in VCE Biology Units 1 and 2. It is designed to be used in conjunction with your textbook and class notes. This workbook will be an important reference document throughout the course and in preparation for the examinations. The workbook is divided into six Areas of Study—three in Unit 1 and three in Unit 2. The workbook has four main sections:

- Key knowledge
- Worksheets
- Practical activities
- Research and practical investigation skills.

KEY KNOWLEDGE

Key knowledge is a set of summary notes that covers the key knowledge set out in each Area of Study of the Study Design. It is useful for highlighting information essential to your understanding of the themes covered in the textbook, and provides a ready reference for completing the worksheets and for exam preparation. As this is your workbook, you are encouraged to make your own notes and highlight key points directly onto the pages as you work.

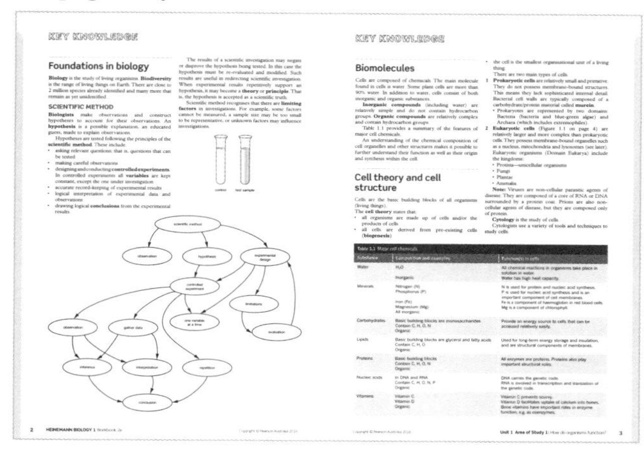
KEY KNOWLEDGE

Foundations in biology

Biomolecules

Cell theory and cell structure

WORKSHEETS

Each Area of Study includes a range of worksheets designed to consolidate and test your understanding of the essential knowledge required, and to further your understanding of the key concepts. Once completed, they will become an important part of your revision notes. You can check your answers to these by visiting ProductLink at pearsonplaces.com.au.

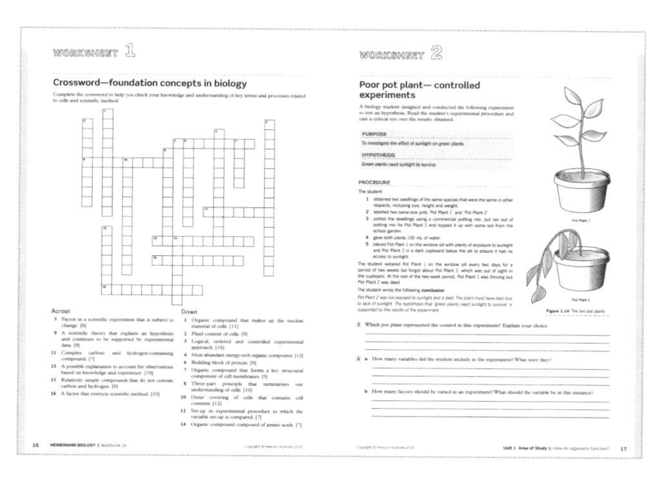
WORKSHEET 1

Crossword—foundation concepts in biology

WORKSHEET 2

Poor pot plant— controlled experiments

PRACTICAL ACTIVITIES

Each Area of Study includes a range of activities related to the various themes covered in this course. These investigations include several practical activities designed to satisfy the requirements of the Area of Study Outcomes. The activities offered help you develop the skills of scientific enquiry outlined in the Study Design. They give you practise in designing, conducting and evaluating scientific investigations, as well as gathering and analysing data. Discussion, results and conclusions can be recorded directly into your workbook. The activities in this section of your workbook support and extend the key skills relevant to Units 1 and 2, and the key concepts within each Area of Study.

This symbol indicates that the activity includes hazards and your teacher will discuss these with you.

This symbol indicates that you should wear safety glasses.

In other practical activities your teacher may require you to complete the risk assessment yourself. In this case you will be required to sign the risk assessment data sheet, to indicate that you have read and understood it, before completing each activity.

INTRODUCTION

To the teacher

The *Heinemann Biology 1 Student Workbook* 2nd edition has been created wholly with a view to meeting the requirements of the Study Design in this subject and is designed to be used in conjunction with the textbook. This workbook helps students check their understanding of key knowledge, consolidate ideas, extend their thinking, address technologies, apply key skills, undertake practical activities and assessment tasks.

KEY KNOWLEDGE

These summary notes cover the key knowledge in each Area of Study and so offer a convenient and succinct set of study notes. They are highly illustrated and written in a straightforward and easy-to-understand style to assist students of all reading abilities.

WORKSHEETS

The multiple intelligence worksheets cater for a range of learning styles. The worksheets provide opportunities to revise, consolidate and extend the student's knowledge and understanding of the key biological principles prescribed in the VCE Unit 1 and 2 Study Design. Answers can be found at ProductLink pearsonplaces.com.au.

PRACTICAL ACTIVITIES

The activities and investigations included here offer a range of opportunities for exploration of the themes covered in Units 1 and 2 of this course. The practical activities represent the most popular and effective activities relevant to the VCE Biology course. They provide students with an opportunity to develop and demonstrate skills of scientific enquiry and method, including experimental design and evaluation, constructing and testing hypotheses, gathering and analysing data as well as opportunities to consider technological advances in Biology. The range of tasks deliberately illustrates different kinds of approaches to assessment items. Each activity has been carefully designed for completion within the suggested timeframes for this course. Risk assessment advice as well as teacher notes to support each practical activity are available on the Pearson Reader. The practical investigations focus on the key knowledge outlined in the Study Design with a view to contributing to the assessment requirements of the course.

RESEARCH AND PRACTICAL INVESTIGATION SKILLS

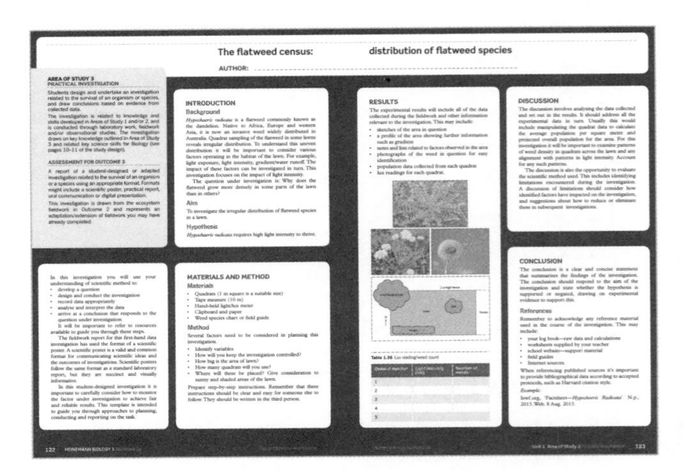

The Study Design for Area of Study 3 in Units 1 and 2 focuses on developing crucial scientific skills around research and practical investigation.

A suggested template for the presentation of a research investigation as well as a practical investigation has been provided for students. There are also skill development worksheets to assist students in beginning to develop or consolidate the skills of analysing sources and conducting practical investigations. The templates and worksheets provided are designed to be used multiple times to allow students to practise developing these skills using different sources and practical investigations.

PRODUCTLINK

Heinemann Biology 1 5e ProductLink supports all Heinemann Biology texts and resources including *Heinemann Biology 1* (5th edition) and *Heinemann Biology 2* (5th edition) and the student workbooks *Heinemann Biology 1 Student Workbook* (2nd edition) and *Heinemann Biology 2 Student Workbook* (3rd edition). It includes:

- course advice and a week-by-week work program that integrates the text and student workbook
- practical notes and advice
- additional practical activities
- risk assessments
- chapter tests and solutions
- answers to the student worksheets contained in the student workbook
- assessment advice.

UNIT 1

How do living things stay alive?

AREA OF STUDY 1

How do organisms function?

Outcome 1

Investigate and explain how cellular structures and systems function to sustain life.

Key knowledge

Cell size, structure and function

- cells as the basic structural feature of life on Earth, including the distinction between prokaryotic and eukaryotic cells
- surface area to volume ratio as an important factor in explaining the limitations of cell size and the need for internal compartments (organelles) with specific cellular functions
- the ultrastructure of plant and animal cells in terms of their organelles and identification of these organelles using the light microscope and electron micrographs.

Crossing the plasma membrane

- the characteristics of the plasma membrane as a semi-permeable boundary between the internal and external environments of a cell
- modes of transport of soluble substances across the plasma membrane including simple diffusion, facilitated diffusion, osmosis and active transport.

Energy transformations

- the distinction between photosynthetic autotrophs, chemosynthetic autotrophs and heterotrophs
- photosynthesis as a chemical process in which solar energy is captured and transformed to chemical energy by fixing carbon to produce a carbohydrate and releasing oxygen as a by-product
- aerobic and anaerobic cellular respiration as a chemical process that commonly uses glucose to produce energy for the cell in both autotrophs and heterotrophs.

Functioning systems

- a study of one selected vascular plant with reference to how its cells are specialised and organised (cells into tissues, and tissues into organs) for the intake, movement and loss of water from the plant
- a study of one selected mammalian system (circulatory, digestive, excretory or respiratory) with reference to how cells in the system are specialised and organised (cells into tissues, tissues into organs and organs into systems), how a specific malfunction can lead to biological consequences and how the system is interconnected to other systems for the survival of the organism.

Foundations in biology

Biology is the study of living organisms. **Biodiversity** is the range of living things on Earth. There are close to 2 million species already identified and many more that remain as yet unidentified.

SCIENTIFIC METHOD

Biologists make observations and construct hypotheses to account for their observations. An **hypothesis** is a possible explanation, an educated guess, made to explain observations.

Hypotheses are tested following the principles of the **scientific method**. These include:

- asking relevant questions; that is, questions that can be tested
- making careful observations
- designing and conducting **controlled experiments**. In controlled experiments all **variables** are kept constant, except the one under investigation
- accurate record-keeping of experimental results
- logical interpretation of experimental data and observations
- drawing logical **conclusions** from the experimental results.

The results of a scientific investigation may negate or disprove the hypothesis being tested. In this case the hypothesis must be re-evaluated and modified. Such results are useful in redirecting scientific investigation. When experimental results repetitively support an hypothesis, it may become a **theory** or **principle**. That is, the hypothesis is accepted as a scientific truth.

Scientific method recognises that there are **limiting factors** in investigations. For example, some factors cannot be measured, a sample size may be too small to be representative, or unknown factors may influence investigations.

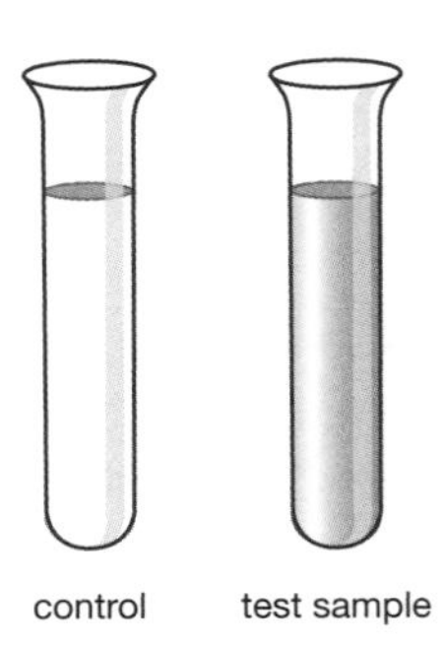

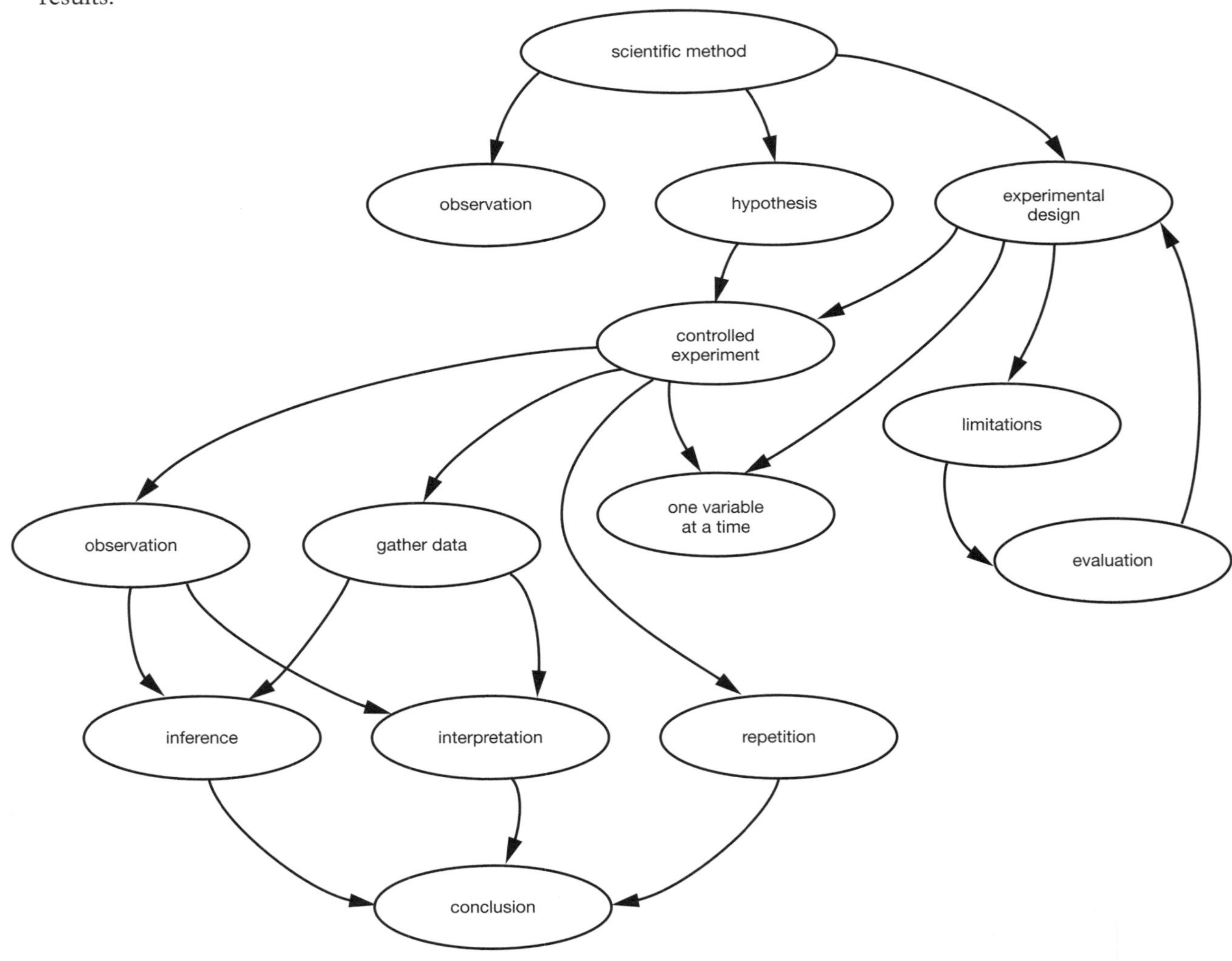

KEY KNOWLEDGE

Biomolecules

Cells are composed of chemicals. The main molecule found in cells is water. Some plant cells are more than 90% water. In addition to water, cells consist of both inorganic and organic substances.

Inorganic compounds (including water) are relatively simple and do not contain hydrocarbon groups. **Organic compounds** are relatively complex and contain hydrocarbon groups.

Table 1.1 provides a summary of the features of major cell chemicals.

An understanding of the chemical composition of cell organelles and other structures makes it possible to further understand their function as well as their origin and synthesis within the cell.

Cell theory and cell structure

Cells are the basic building blocks of all organisms (living things).

The **cell theory** states that:

- all organisms are made up of cells and/or the products of cells
- all cells are derived from pre-existing cells (**biogenesis**)
- the cell is the smallest organisational unit of a living thing.

There are two main types of cells.

1. **Prokaryotic cells** are relatively small and primitive. They do not possess membrane-bound structures. This means they lack sophisticated internal detail. Bacterial cell walls are typically composed of a carbohydrate/protein material called **murein**.
   - Prokaryotes are represented by two domains: Bacteria (bacteria and blue-green algae) and Archaea (which includes extremophiles).
2. **Eukaryotic cells** (Figure 1.1 on page 4) are relatively larger and more complex than prokaryotic cells. They possess membrane-bound organelles such as a nucleus, mitochondria and lysosomes (see later). Eukaryotic organisms (Domain Eukarya) include the kingdoms:
   - Protista—unicellular organisms
   - Fungi
   - Plantae
   - Animalia.

Note: Viruses are non-cellular parasitic agents of disease. They are composed of a core of RNA or DNA surrounded by a protein coat. Prions are also non-cellular agents of disease, but they are composed only of protein.

Cytology is the study of cells.

Cytologists use a variety of tools and techniques to study cells.

Table 1.1 Major cell chemicals

Substance	Composition and examples	Function(s) in cells
Water	H_2O Inorganic	All chemical reactions in organisms take place in solution in water. Water has high heat capacity.
Minerals	Nitrogen (N) Phosphorus (P) Iron (Fe) Magnesium (Mg) All inorganic	N is used for protein and nucleic acid synthesis. P is used for nucleic acid synthesis and is an important component of cell membranes. Fe is a component of haemoglobin in red blood cells. Mg is a component of chlorophyll.
Carbohydrates	Basic building blocks are monosaccharides Contain C, H, O, N Organic	Provide an energy source to cells that can be accessed relatively easily.
Lipids	Basic building blocks are glycerol and fatty acids Contain C, H, O Organic	Used for long-term energy storage and insulation, and are structural components of membranes.
Proteins	Basic building blocks Contain C, H, O, N Organic	All enzymes are proteins. Proteins also play important structural roles.
Nucleic acids	In DNA and RNA Contain C, H, O, N, P Organic	DNA carries the genetic code. RNA is involved in transcription and translation of the genetic code.
Vitamins	Vitamin C Vitamin D Organic	Vitamin C prevents scurvy. Vitamin D facilitates uptake of calcium into bones. Bone vitamins have important roles in enzyme function, e.g. as coenzymes.

KEY KNOWLEDGE

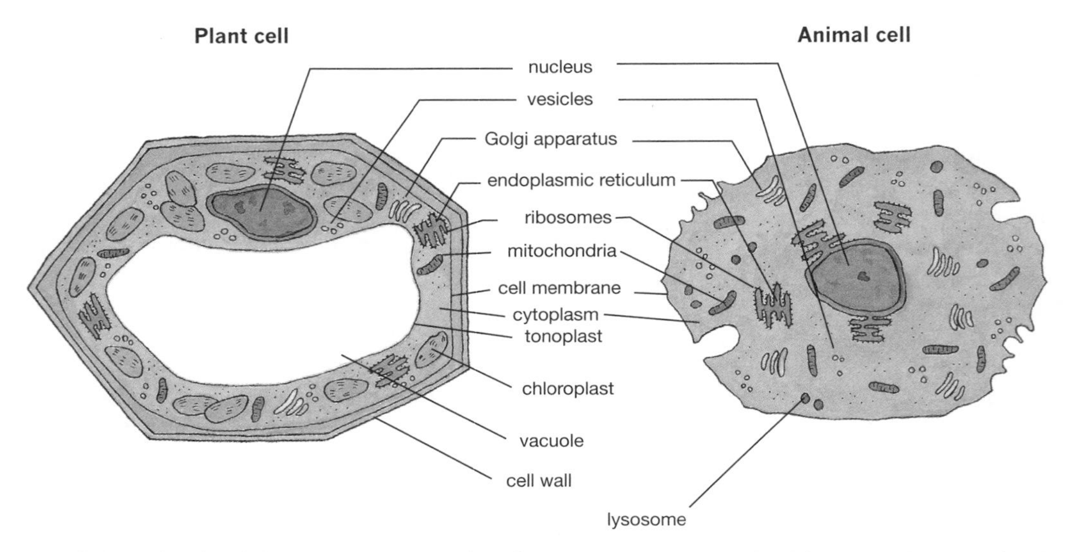

Figure 1.1 In unicellular and multicellular organisms, many of the functions that are essential to life occur within specialised structures and organelles of individual cells.

The main tool used by cytologists is the microscope. There are many different types of microscope but the two main types are the **light microscope** and the **electron microscope**.

Table 1.2 is a summary comparison of these two types of microscopes:

Table 1.2 Comparison of microscopes

Feature	Light microscope	Electron microscope
Magnifying power	Low	High
Cost	Low	High
Expertise needed	Low	High
Can living specimens be observed?	Yes	No

Organelles are distinct structures within cells that perform specific functions. Some organelles are visible using the light microscope while some are not.

The details of many cell organelles are only visible when using the electron microscope.

Some cells display:

- **Cilia**: short and hairlike; generally present in large numbers; rhythmic waves create movement of substances over cell surface, *or* movement of the cell
- **Flagellum**: long and hairlike; generally singular or present in small numbers; rhythmic contractions enable movement of cell.

Prokaryotic cells lack the membrane-bound structures listed in Table 1.3 on page 5. However, prokaryotic cells are capable of controlling their functions. They are also capable of generating energy. Some are even capable of photosynthesis, because they contain photosynthetic pigments.

Prokaryotic cells contain a single, coiled chromosome that contains all of the DNA (genes) necessary to control and direct all the activities of the cell. In addition, there are specialised regions within prokaryotic cells where cellular respiration can occur.

Functioning organisms

LEVELS OF ORGANISATION

Many organisms consist of single cells. These are called **unicellular organisms**, and include *Amoeba, Paramecium* and bacteria.

Some organisms consist of a mass of cells that are capable of living independently but have evolved to live together in a group. These are called **colonies**.

Other organisms are **multicellular** but are very simple and do not possess organs or organ systems.

Some organisms are **multicellular** and very complex in structure—they are composed of many different kinds of cells.

- **Cells may be specialised**. This means they have features that make them well suited to carrying out a particular function; e.g. muscle cells contain contractile fibrils that allow cell contraction (see Figure 1.2 on page 6).

KEY KNOWLEDGE

Table 1.3 Cellular organelles and their functions

Organelle	Description and function	Found in both plants and animals
Nucleus	Large spherical organelle Controls cell activities (contains DNA)	Yes
Mitochondrion	Features folded inner membrane Site of aerobic stages of cellular respiration (contains some DNA)	Yes
Ribosomes	Tiny spherical organelles Site of protein synthesis	Yes
Endoplasmic reticulum (ER)	Network of membranes involved in protein transport within cells ER encrusted with ribosomes is called 'rough' ER	Yes
Golgi apparatus	Stacks of flattened membranous sacs Modifies and packages substances in preparation for secretion from cell	Yes
Chloroplast	Site of photosynthesis (contains chlorophyll)	Plant cells only
Lyosomes	Membrane-bound organelles that produce digestive enzymes Break down complex compounds into simpler molecules	Animals Plants (some evidence)
Vacuoles	Membrane-bound compartments that keep a variety of substances separate from cell contents (large in plant cells, small in animal cells)	Yes
Cell wall	Rigid structure surrounding cell; composed of cellulose in plants Limits cell expansion when fully turgid; contributes to structural support of plant	Plant cells only
Plasma membrane	Partially permeable, flexible barrier Controls cell inputs and outputs	Yes

- A group of cells that work together to achieve a particular function is called a **tissue**. For example, a group of muscle cells is called muscle tissue.
- A group of tissues that work together to perform an overall function is called an **organ**. For example, the stomach is composed of muscle tissue and vascular tissue.
- A group of organs that work together to perform an overall function form a **system**. For example, the digestive system is composed of the mouth, stomach, liver and intestine.

Multicellular organisms may be composed of many systems, e.g. the digestive, respiratory, excretory and nervous systems.

Internal and external environments of cells

The **internal environment** of cells is the intracellular fluid—the medium inside cells.

The **external environment** of cells is the extracellular fluid—the watery medium surrounding cells.

PLASMA MEMBRANE

The plasma membrane controls entry and exit of substances into and out of cells. (Table 1.1 looks at the major substances that affect cell functionality.) It controls which substances leave and enter, when and how much. It responds to instructions from the nucleus. It can detect and respond to external stimuli.

The plasma membrane is described as being **semi-permeable** (also called partially permeable) because it is permeable to some substances but not others.

The composition of the plasma membrane is basically the same as that of all membranes within cells (including the membranes of the nuclear envelope, mitochondria, Golgi, endoplasmic reticulum, vacuoles, lysosomes and chloroplasts).

The plasma membrane consists of a double layer of special lipid molecules called **phospholipids**. This is called the phospholipid bilayer. The bilayer has **protein molecules** scattered through it in a random pattern. The total structure is **fluid**. This means that the molecules can move around relative to each other. The structure of the cell membrane is described as **fluid-mosaic**.

In summary, the plasma membrane is a flexible, partially permeable barrier between the **intracellular** and **extracellular** environments.

KEY KNOWLEDGE

Function carried out by specialised cells	Plant cells	Animal cells
Exchange	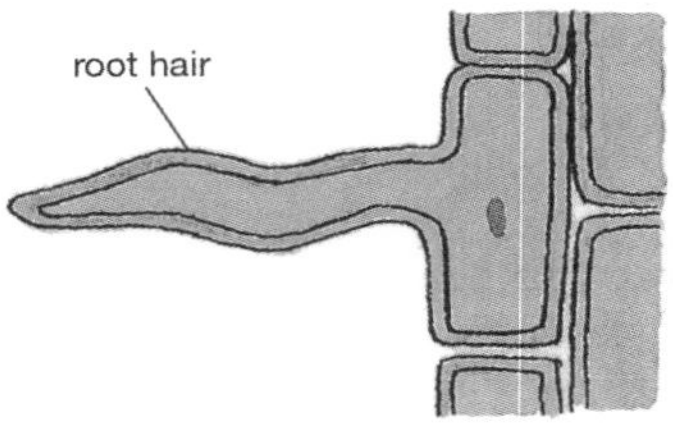 root hair	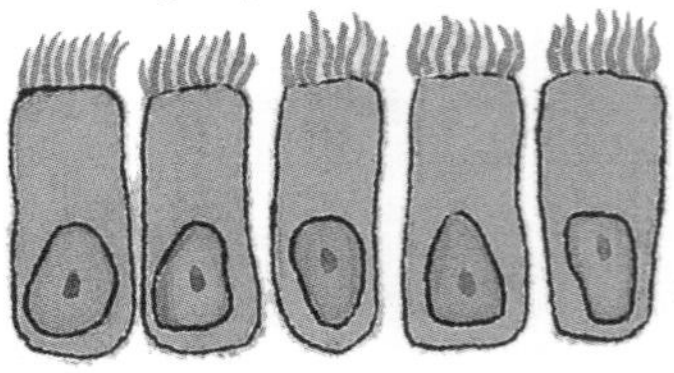 gut epithelium cells
Transport	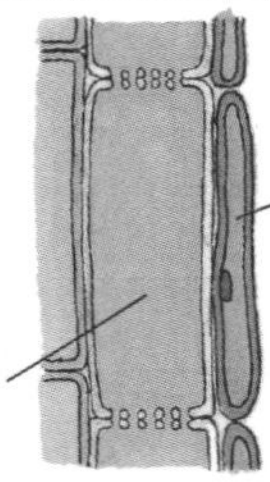 companion cell sieve cell	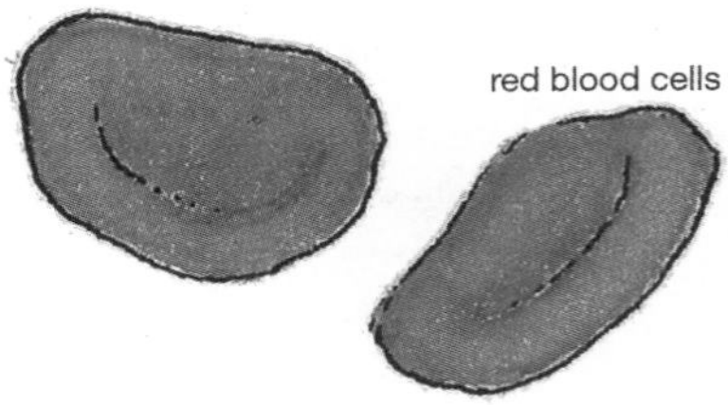 red blood cells
Strength/ support	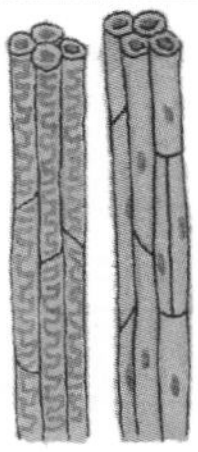 fibres (xylem, phloem)	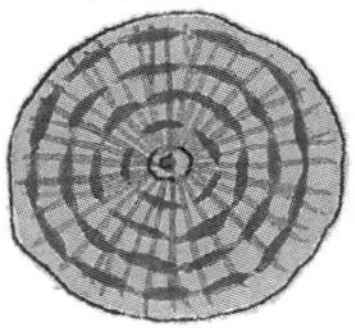 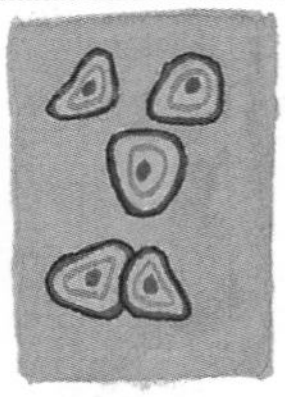 bone cells cartilage cells
Protection/ defence	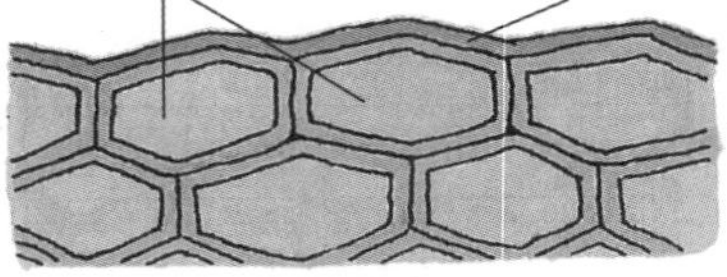 epidermal cells cuticle	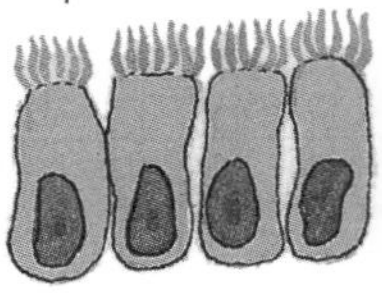 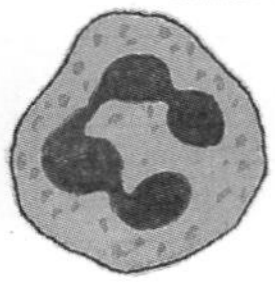 ciliated epithelium cells white blood cells
Photosynthesis	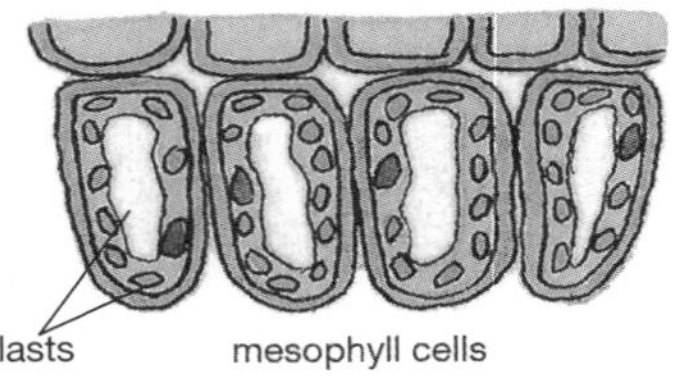 chloroplasts mesophyll cells	
Movement		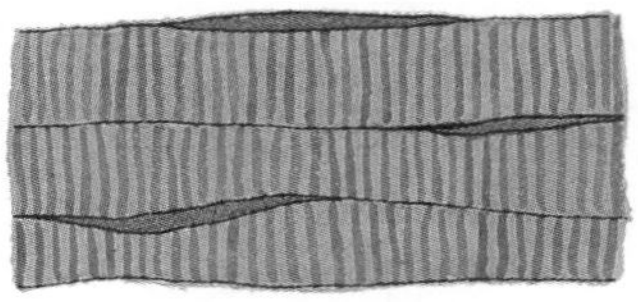 muscle cells
Communication		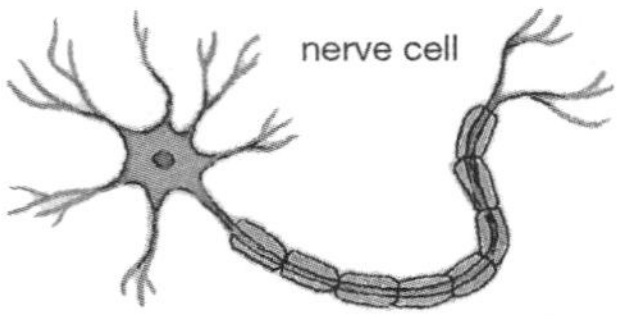 nerve cell

Figure 1.2 Some different types of specialised cells in plants and animals, their appearance and function

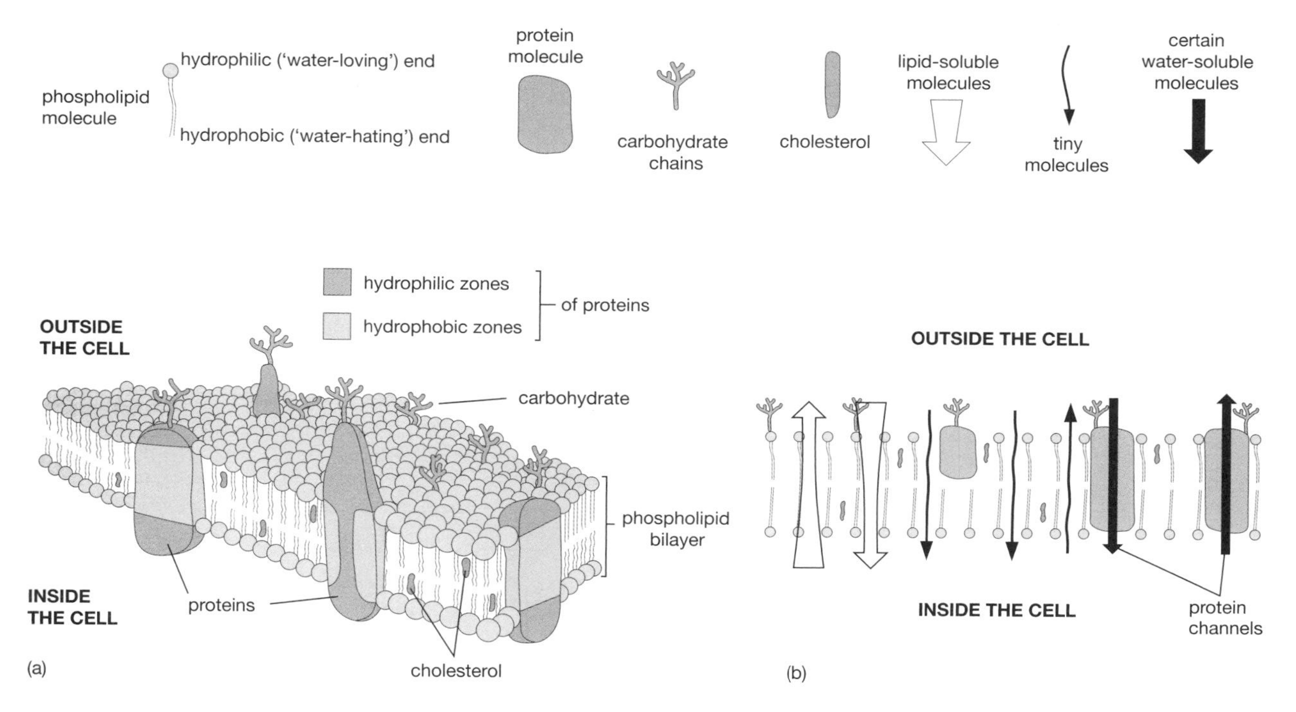

Figure 1.3 (a) Biological membranes are composed of a phospholipid bilayer with large protein molecules embedded in the bilayer. These proteins provide channels for the passive and active movement of certain molecules across the plasma membrane. **(b)** Short carbohydrate molecules attached to the outside of the membrane are involved in cell adhesion and cell recognition.

MOVEMENT ACROSS THE MEMBRANE

For a substance to leave or enter a cell, its size, configuration and concentration all have to be considered (see Figure 1.3).

Simple diffusion

For very small molecules and lipid-soluble substances, movement directly through the lipid bilayer is possible. The concentration of the substance determines its net movement. This is known as simple diffusion. Diffusion is a passive process in which particles move from an area of high concentration to an area of low concentration along a concentration gradient.

Osmosis

Diffusion of water is a special case. It is called osmosis. Osmosis is a process in which water molecules move across a semi-permeable membrane from a region of high concentration of water molecules to a region of low concentration of water molecules. Osmosis is a passive process—water molecules move along a concentration gradient. The rate of osmosis is determined by the relative concentration of solutes on either side of a partially permeable membrane. As the membrane is fully permeable to water (simple diffusion), the only factor that can 'control' its passage is the osmotic pressure exerted by the concentration of solutes such as sugars and salts on either side of the membrane.

Facilitated diffusion and active transport

For larger molecules (not too large!) that are not lipid soluble, e.g. glucose and mineral ions, movement through the plasma membrane is made possible by special protein molecules embedded in the lipid bilayer. These proteins act as channels or carrier molecules. If the substance moves through the membrane from an environment of high concentration to one of lower concentration (i.e. along the concentration gradient), the movement is called facilitated diffusion. If the substance moves against the concentration gradient, the movement is called active transport and requires an expenditure of energy by the cell.

It is also possible for very large substances to move through the plasma membrane. This type of movement requires a physical disruption to the membrane. Entry to the cell under these circumstances is called endocytosis. Exit is called exocytosis.

Table 1.4 on page 8 summarises entry to and exit from cells.

KEY KNOWLEDGE

Table 1.4 Summary of movement into and out of cells

Outside the cell		Inside the cell	Type of movement
Higher concentration of oxygen	→	Lower concentration of oxygen	Simple diffusion
Lower concentration of water (high concentration of solute)	←	Higher concentration of water (low concentration of solute)	Osmosis
Higher concentration of magnesium ions	→	Lower concentration of magnesium ions	Facilitated diffusion
Low concentration of glucose	→	High concentration of glucose	Active transport
Bacterium	→		Endocytosis
	←	Hormone	Exocytosis

[Arrow indicates direction of movement of particles.]

SURFACE AREA TO VOLUME RATIO

When substances enter or leave cells, the rate at which they move is determined by a number of factors. These include:

- concentration (steep concentration gradient causes faster diffusion)
- temperature (higher temperature increases the rate of movement of molecules)
- surface area to volume ratio (SA : V).

Consider the two cells in Figure 1.4.

Which cell has the larger SA : V? Cell B, of course. Although Cell A has a larger volume, Cell B has a larger surface area compared to its volume. This means it will be more efficient at taking in and exporting substances through its plasma membrane per unit time.

In general, the surface area to volume ratio of an organism decreases as size increases. Cells and organisms have structural adaptations to overcome this. Such adaptations include microvilli on absorptive cells, and ribbon-like body shape of tapeworms.

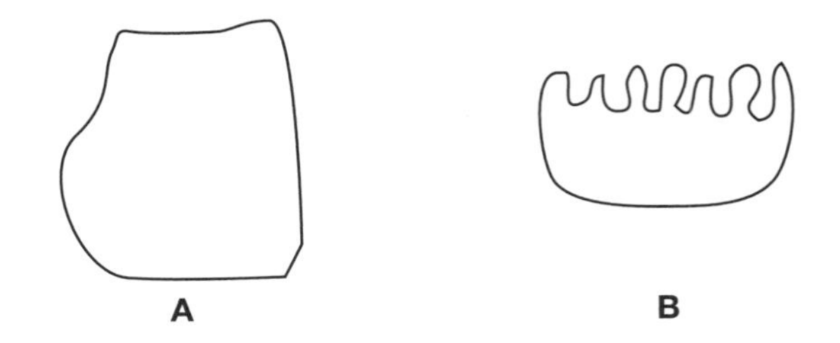

Figure 1.4 Two cells (A and B) with a different volume but similar surface area

PLANT TRANSPORT

Vascular plants feature a series of tubes called **vascular tissues** for the transport of substances throughout the plant (see Table 1.5 and Figure 1.5 on page 9).

Vascular tissues

- **Xylem:** composed of non-living tissue; remnants of cells reinforced with lignin

Table 1.5 Characteristics of transport in plants

Vascular tissue	Xylem	Phloem
Substances involved	• Water • Inorganic nutrients	• Organic nutrients, e.g. sugars
Direction of transport	• From roots up through the plant	• From leaves to rest of plant in both directions (upwards and downwards)
Processes involved	• Transpiration and root pressure draw water upwards • No energy expenditure by the plant	• Active process requiring energy

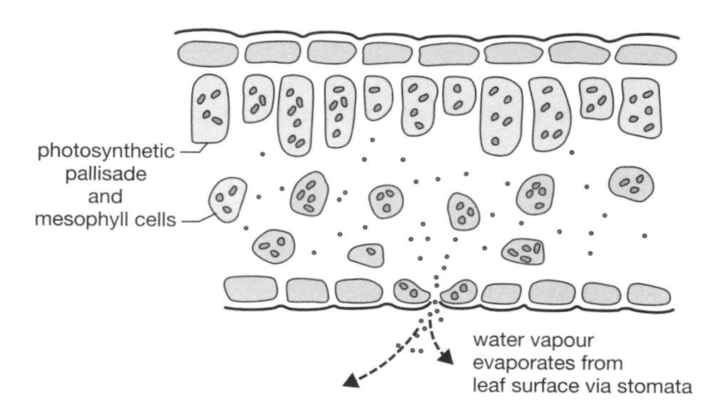

Figure 1.5 Cross-section of leaf tissue

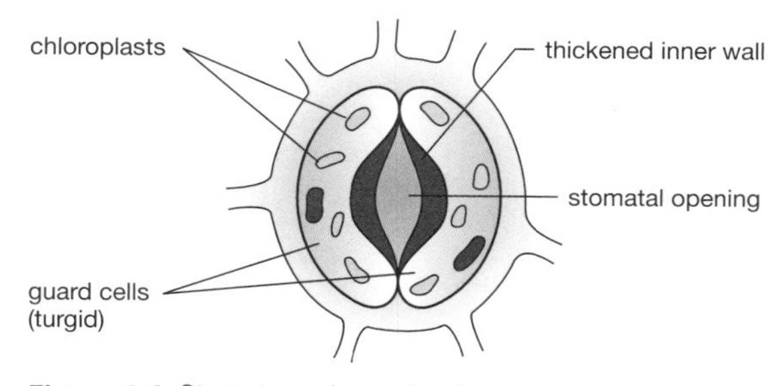

Figure 1.6 Stomata and guard cells

- **Phloem:** living cells; end plates of cells sieve-like; associated with companion cells that control activities of nucleus-free sieve cells
- **Plasmodesmata:** fine channels that link plant vascular cells, allowing lateral movement of nutrients from cell to cell.

WATER REGULATION IN PLANTS

Plants control some aspects of their internal environment, e.g.

- water loss
- concentration of salts.

Stomata, pores bounded by **guard cells** in the epidermis of leaf and stem tissue, are responsible for the:

- rate of water loss through transpiration
- exchange of carbon dioxide and oxygen from plants.

Transpiration is the loss of water from plants through evaporation, mainly via stomata.

When guard cells are **turgid**, under pressure from the water they contain, their outer elastic walls bend more than the thickened inner walls, causing the stomatal pore to increase in size and the stomata to open.

Table 1.6 Features of plants adapted to hot, dry environments

Function	Features
Reduce water loss	• Thick cuticle • Leaves with reduced surface area • Decreased number of stomata • Sunken stomata, hairy leaves, and ability to roll leaves create a pocket of humid air around the stoma; this decreases the water–vapour gradient between the intercellular spaces and the external environment, thereby reducing the rate of water loss by evaporation
Increase water uptake	• Shallow, spreading root system
Store water	• Succulent leaves/stems

Energy transformations in cells

Some cell functions have already been listed and described above. The preferred term for cell functioning is **metabolism**, and it is controlled by the nucleus. Metabolism can be divided up into two main types of processes:

- **endergonic** processes that result in a net input or use of energy
- **exergonic** processes that result in a net output or release of energy.

Processes in which energy is changed from one form to another are **energy transformations**. Photosynthesis and cellular respiration are examples of energy transformations that occur in living organisms.

- **Photosynthesis** is an example of an endergonic process.
- **Cellular respiration** is an example of an exergonic process.

PHOTOSYNTHESIS

This process is performed by plant cells that contain chlorophyll (see Figure 1.7). It requires light and involves the conversion of light energy into chemical energy.

A word equation for photosynthesis is as follows:

$$\text{carbon dioxide} + \text{water} \xrightarrow[\text{chlorophyll}]{\text{light}} \text{glucose} + \text{oxygen}$$

A balanced chemical equation for photosynthesis is:

$$6CO_2 + 12H_2O \xrightarrow[\text{chlorophyll}]{\text{light}} C_6H_{12}O_6 + 6O_2 + 6H_2O$$

- Organisms that produce their own organic compounds are called **autotrophs**. Autotrophs can be photosynthetic (plants) or chemosynthetic (some prokaryotes).
- Organisms such as fungi and animals that obtain their organic compounds from other organisms are called **heterotrophs**.

KEY KNOWLEDGE

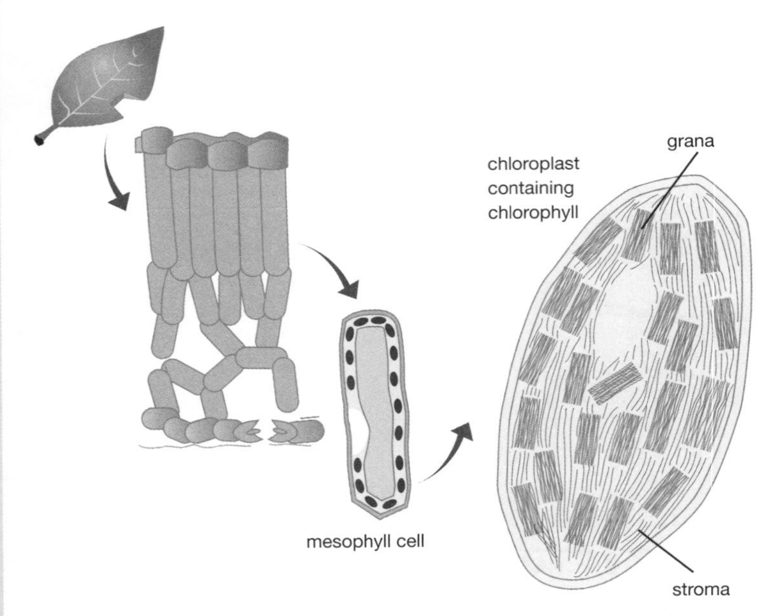

Figure 1.7 Leaves, and some stems, are green because the mesophyll cells contain many chloroplasts (the organelles in which photosynthesis takes place).

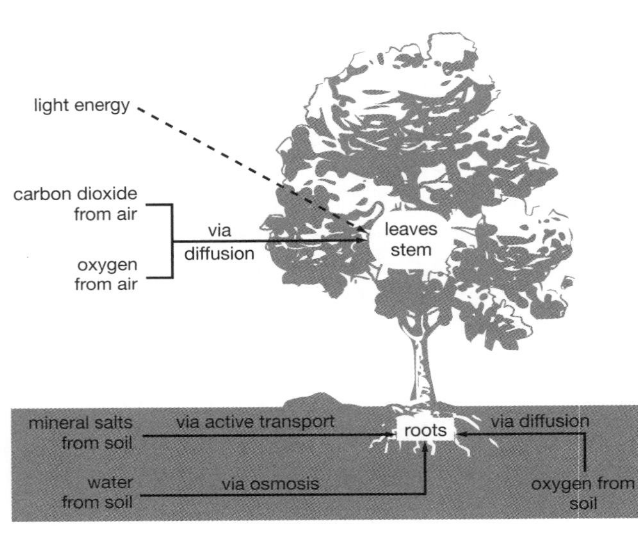

Figure 1.8 Overview of how plants obtain nutrients

Photosynthesis occurs in two stages: the **light-dependent** stage occurs in **grana**; the light-independent stage occurs in the stroma (summarised in Table 1.7).

Adaptions such as smaller leaves and orientation of leaves can reduce water loss. Some plants are adapted to hot, dry conditions by closing stomata during the day and opening them at night to take up the carbon dioxide needed for photosynthesis.

Factors that may limit the rate of photosynthesis include light intensity, carbon dioxide concentration and temperature. Photosynthesis and cellular respiration occur simultaneously in green plants during periods of light exposure. The point at which the products of photosynthesis are consumed in the process of cellular respiration is called the **light compensation point**.

CELLULAR RESPIRATION

This process occurs in all living cells all the time. It results in the production of a molecule called **adenosine triphosphate** (ATP). This molecule is energy for the cell in a 'usable' form. Energy in glucose cannot be used immediately by cells. It must first be transferred to ATP. This involves the splitting of the glucose molecule in a process called **glycolysis**. When glucose breakdown is carried out in the presence of oxygen, **aerobic respiration** occurs.

Aerobic respiration

A word equation for aerobic cellular respiration is as follows:

glucose + oxygen → carbon dioxide + water + energy

The energy released is used to synthesise ATP from ADP (adenosine diphosphate) and an additional phosphate. ATP then moves around the cell to wherever energy is needed; it loses its third phosphate group to release energy that can be used immediately.

A balanced chemical equation for cellular respiration is:

$$C_6H_{12}O_6 + 6O_2 + 36\text{—}38\ (ADP + P_i) \rightarrow 6CO_2 + 6H_2O + 36\text{—}38\ ATP$$

Table 1.7 Overview of stages involved in photosynthesis

1st stage	2nd stage
Light-dependent	Light-independent
Occurs in grana Red and blue light absorbed Light absorbed by chlorophyll Energy used to split water molecule Create O_2 (by-product) and H^+ ions ATP also produced (used in 2nd stage)	Occurs in stroma Carbohydrate produced • in the form of glucose • stored as starch H^+ ions and CO_2 (from air) combined ATP from 1st stage consumed in glucose manufacture

Anaerobic respiration

If oxygen is not available to meet the cell's energy requirements, **anaerobic respiration** will occur (fermentation). End products differ. Lactic acid is produced in animal cells. Ethanol and carbon dioxide are produced in plant and yeast cells. Less ATP is produced during anaerobic respiration. (A lot of energy is still bound up in the end products.) Anaerobic respiration is less efficient than aerobic respiration.

Mammalian systems

CIRCULATORY SYSTEM

Single-celled organisms, due to their size (and high surface area to volume ratio), have no need for specialised systems to deliver nutrients to, and remove wastes from, all parts of the organism. Large multicellular organisms rely on complex systems to complete these tasks.

Larger **multicellular** organisms cannot simply rely on diffusion of substances or fluid around the organism, so that each cell receives nutrients and removes wastes at a sufficient rate. These organisms have **transport systems** to ensure all substances are moved throughout an organism to meet its particular demands.

For complex multicellular animals, such as mammals, circulatory systems are characterised by:

- efficient carrying capacity
- large surface area for exchange
- effective movement of fluid
- ability to regulate movement of fluid according to needs.

BLOOD

Closed circulatory systems involve movement of **blood** that is separated from the cells of the body and the **interstitial fluid**.

Intracellular fluid: fluid inside cells (cytosol)
Extracellular fluid: all fluid outside cells
Interstitial fluid: extracellular fluid surrounding cells and separate from blood

Blood contains both intracellular and extracellular fluid and is surrounded by interstitial fluid where **diffusion** takes place between **capillaries** and body cells (see Figure 1.9).

Mammalian transport systems include the blood **circulatory** and the **lymphatic** drainage systems.

Lymphatic drainage system:

- fluid is called **lymph**
- helps maintain osmotic and fluid balance in tissues
- collects leaked proteins from blood capillaries
- returns lymph to veins near heart.

Blood circulatory system:

- closed system
- double circuit involving pulmonary and systemic circulation
- consists of blood vessels—**arteries** (carry blood away from heart), **veins** (carry blood to heart) and **capillaries** (smallest blood vessels; site of exchange)
- muscular pump called a **heart**.

Pulmonary circulation is the transport of deoxygenated blood from the right side of the heart to the lungs and the return of oxygenated blood back to the left side of the heart (see Figure 1.10).

Systemic circulation is the transport of oxygenated blood from the left side of the heart to the rest of the body and the return of deoxygenated blood back to the right side of the heart (see Figure 1.10 on page 12).

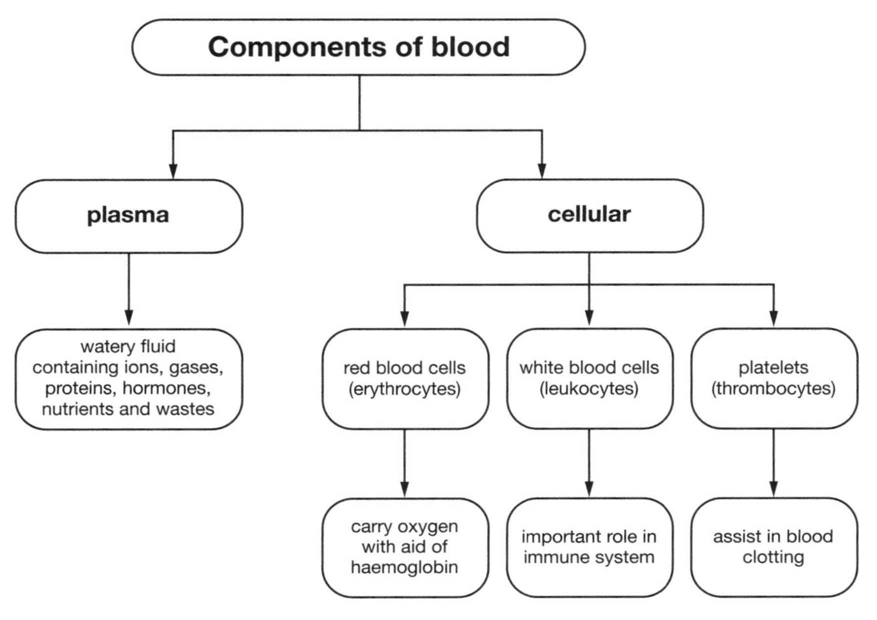

Figure 1.9 Components of blood

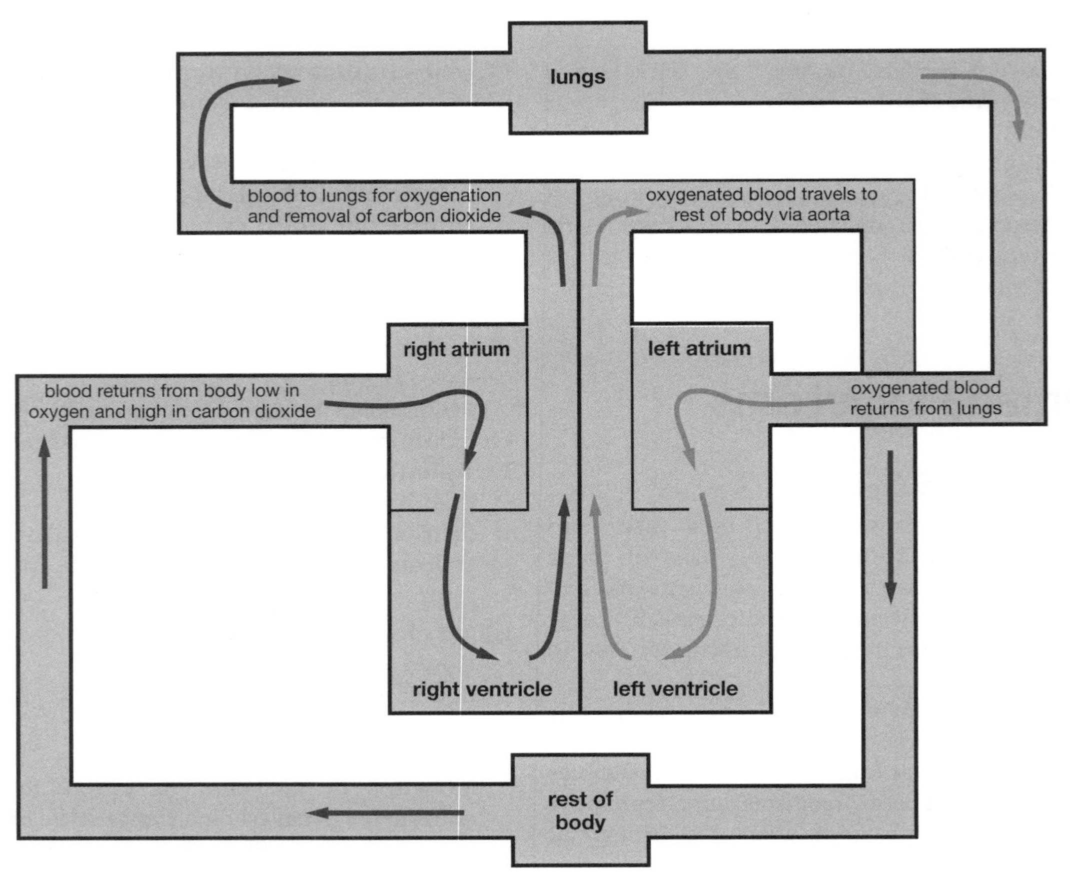

Figure 1.10 Schematic diagram showing circulation in mammals

DIGESTIVE SYSTEM

The foods consumed by heterotrophs are useful on a cellular level. However, most organic nutrients ingested in the diet are in a form that is too large to enter cells. This organic matter needs to be broken down into simpler forms so that it can ultimately pass across **plasma membranes** and into cells. This process of breaking large food molecules into smaller ones is called **digestion** (see Table 1.8).

Different kinds of heterotrophs have different digestive structures depending on their diets.

Larger, complex animals need to ensure digestion occurs efficiently enough to meet generally higher energy demands. These systems have the following characteristics:

- adaptations for acquiring food
- reliance on physical breakdown of food
- appropriate structures for handling and mastication of food
- one-way gut is compartmentalised into different sections each providing an optimal environment for different digestive enzymes
- high surface area for absorption of nutrients from gut into circulatory system
- movement of food along the system and removal of undigested material.

FEATURES OF MAMMALIAN DIGESTIVE SYSTEMS

Simple animals rely primarily on chemical processes involving **enzymes**. Larger animals (e.g. humans) also utilise mechanical processes during digestion. Mammalian digestive systems primarily consist of:

- mouth
- oesophagus
- stomach
- small intestine
- large intestine
- rectum
- anus
- associated **organs** such as salivary glands, liver, gall bladder and pancreas that release enzymes and other chemicals into digestive tract (see Figure 1.11).

KEY KNOWLEDGE

Table 1.8 Comparison of physical and chemical digestion

	Physical digestion	Chemical digestion
Type of process	• Mechanical breakdown of larger food pieces into smaller pieces	• Chemical change of complex molecules into simpler ones
Purpose	• Smaller pieces have a relatively larger surface area that allows enzymes to work more effectively	• Simpler molecules can pass through plasma membranes and into cells
Requires	• Teeth and muscles	• Enzymes and appropriate pH conditions
Where it occurs	• Mouth and stomach	• Mouth, stomach and small intestine • Rumen and caecum in herbivores
Examples	• Teeth chewing food, muscles of stomach churning food into semi-liquid paste called chyme	• Lipases act on lipids • Proteases act on proteins • Amylases act on carbohydrates • Gastric lipase begins converting fats into fatty acids and glycerol

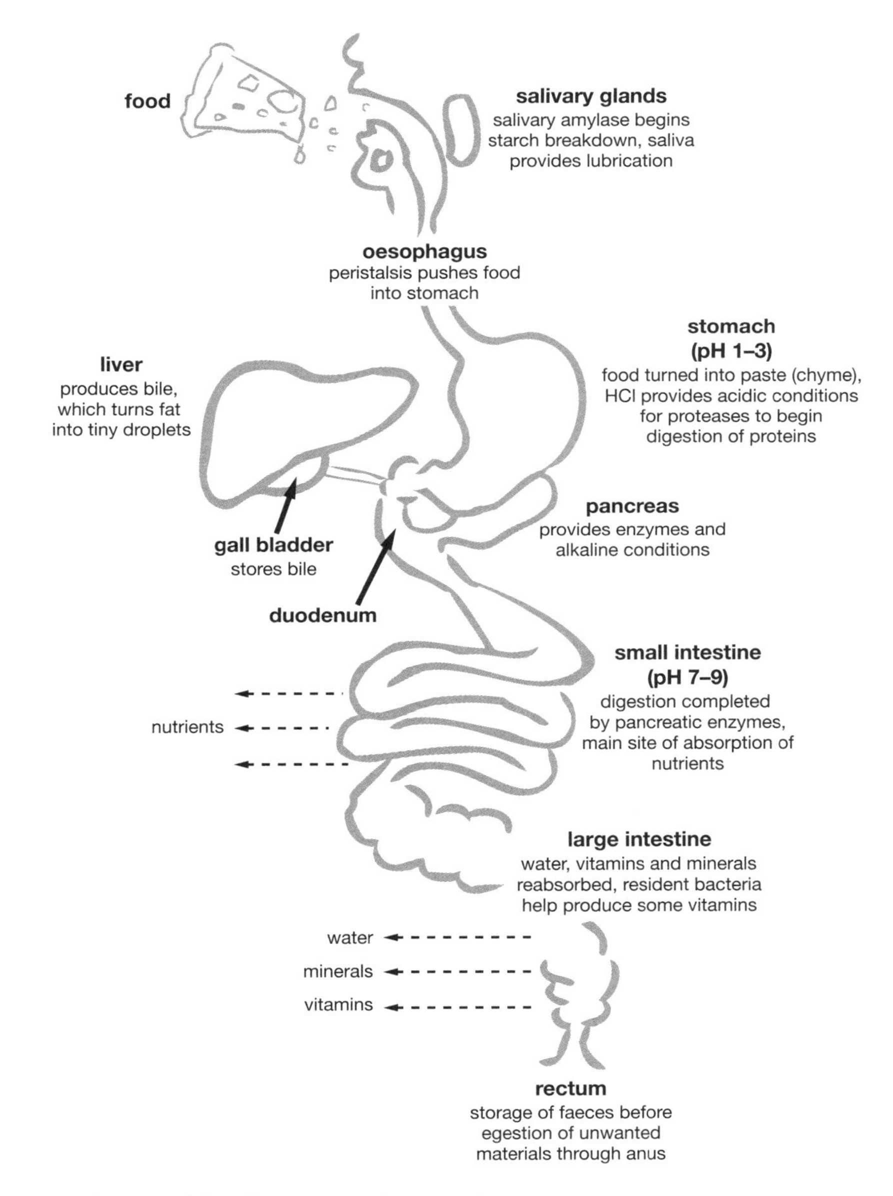

Figure 1.11 Schematic diagram of digestive processes in mammals

KEY KNOWLEDGE

EXCRETORY SYSTEM

Animals produce a variety of substances that they no longer need or can tolerate. **Excretion** is the removal of these substances. The main waste products are **carbon dioxide** and **nitrogenous waste**.

Nitrogenous waste is continually produced as a result of the breakdown of proteins. The main waste product is **ammonia** (NH_3). This is a highly toxic, soluble compound that must be removed by animals.

Kidney

The **kidney** is the main excretory organ in vertebrates. It is concerned with removing nitrogenous wastes and maintaining water balance.

Features of the mammalian kidney (an amazing organ for effective filtration and water conservation):

- divided into cortex and medulla region
- functional unit is the **nephron**
  - nephron is made up of glomerulus, Bowman's capsule, proximal tubule, loop of Henle, distal tubule, collecting duct
- key waste is urea
- able to reabsorb most of the primary filtrate, e.g. glucose, ions, amino acids and water
- capable of producing concentrated urine (low water concentration).

The **nephron** is a tube with specialised regions for carrying out various functions so that, ultimately, concentrated **urine** is produced.

The kidneys of desert-adapted mammals feature a relatively long loop of Henle, which results in greater water reabsorption and therefore a smaller volume of concentrated urine (see Table 1.9 and Figure 1.12).

In insects, a series of tubules called the Malpighian tubules are adapted for removing nitrogenous wastes in the form of uric acid.

Dialysis

In instances of kidney failure, nitrogenous wastes are artificially removed from the blood by passing it through a dialysis machine. The dialysis membranes are set up with a concentration gradient that moves nitrogenous wastes out of the blood circulation along a concentration gradient.

Table 1.9 Major components of the mammalian kidney and their functions

Structure	Function	Location
Glomerulus	Network of capillaries carrying blood under high pressure in Bowman's capsule of the nephron	Cortex
Bowman's capsule	Collects primary filtrate (nitrogenous waste and other small soluble molecules) forced by the high pressure in the glomerulus	Cortex
Proximal tubule	Site of selective reabsorption of useful substances such as water, glucose, amino acids, salts	Cortex
Loop of Henle	Active transport is used to establish salt concentration gradient to enhance water reabsorption	Medulla
Distal tubule	Tubular resorption of substances such as sodium by active transport (water follows by osmosis)	Cortex
Collecting duct	Reabsorption of water by osmosis so that concentrated urine leaves the nephron	Cortex and medulla

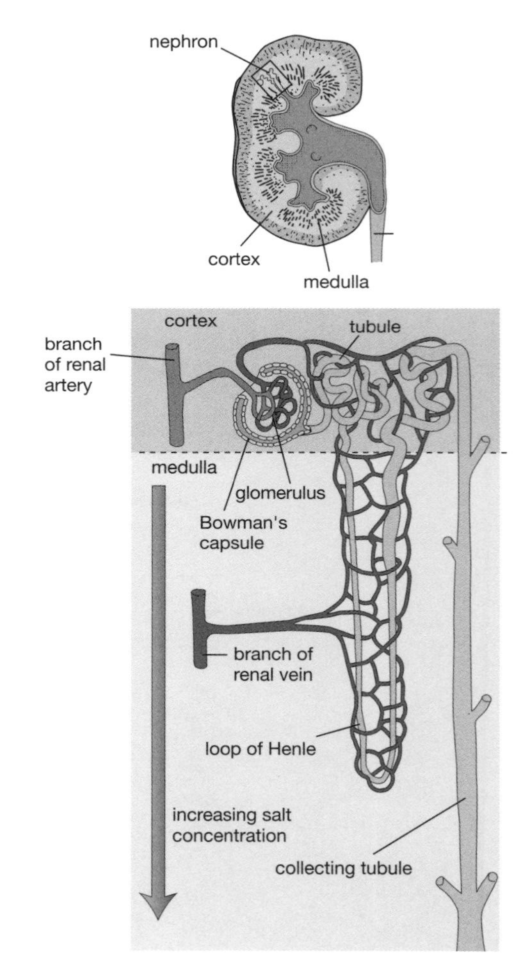

Figure 1.12 Mammalian kidney and nephron

KEY KNOWLEDGE

RESPIRATORY SYSTEM

Oxygen and carbon dioxide need to be exchanged with the environment for **cellular respiration** and **photosynthesis**. The process of gas exchange is always by **diffusion** between the external and internal environment of an organism (see Figure 1.13). These gases need to be exchanged continuously so that an organism is able to function efficiently.

For single-celled and small organisms, diffusion of gases is not a problem due to their high **surface area to volume ratio**. Large multicellular animals, such as mammals, rely on specialised **respiratory surfaces** for adequate gas exchange.

The mammalian **respiratory system** features structures and processes that result in the efficient exchange of oxygen and carbon dioxide. It is composed of:

- **lungs**
- **respiratory passages—nasal passages, trachea, bronchi**, and **bronchioles** that end in sacs called **alveoli** (the site of gaseous exchange).

The alveoli increase the surface area for gas exchange.

Contraction and relaxation of the diaphragm muscle results in changes in pressure within the lung cavity, forcing air in and out.

The epiglottis prevents food from travelling down the trachea and blocking the passage of air.

Gas exchange relies on diffusion; therefore, **concentration gradients** need to be maintained. For oxygen to continually diffuse into capillaries around **alveoli**, oxygen needs to be transported away from the site. Respiratory pigments such as **haemoglobin** carry oxygen in the blood from **lungs** and release oxygen into cells. Rhythmic pumping of the heart ensures continuous flow of blood along capillaries surrounding the alveoli.

Haemoglobin and oxygen bind in a reversible reaction:

$$\text{Hb} + 4\text{O}_2 \rightleftharpoons \text{Hb(O}_2)_4$$
$$\text{haemoglobin} + \text{oxygen} \rightleftharpoons \text{oxyhaemoglobin}$$

The reaction proceeds to the right in areas of high oxygen concentration, such as when oxygen diffuses into the capillaries in the lung. The reaction proceeds to the left in areas of low oxygen concentration, such as in capillaries near body cells. The released oxygen can now diffuse into nearby cells. Diffusion of each gas occurs down its concentration gradient, whether it is in the alveoli of the lungs or in capillaries near body cells.

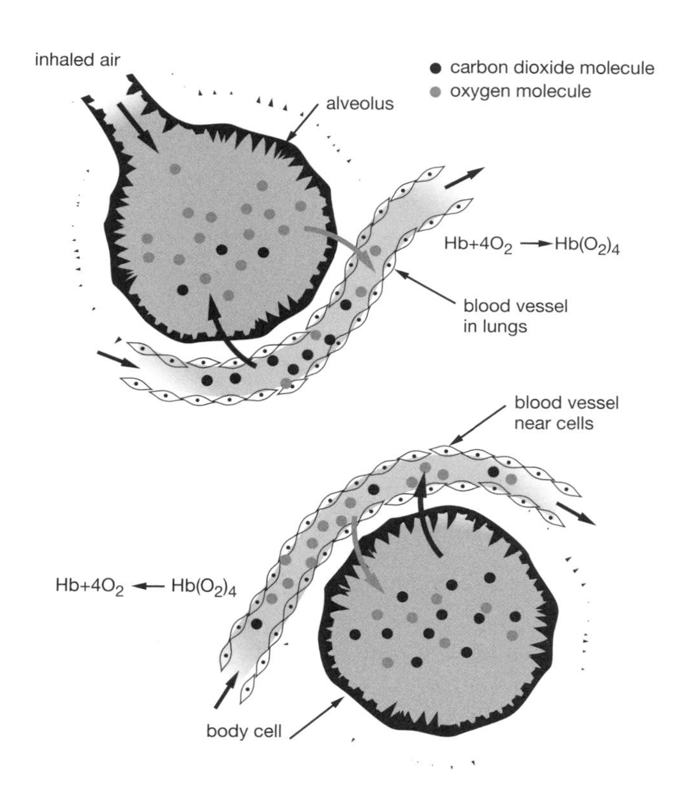

Figure 1.13 Diffusion of gases in the lungs and body cells

WORKSHEET 1

Crossword—foundation concepts in biology

Complete the crossword to help you check your knowledge and understanding of key terms and processes related to cells and scientific method.

Across

5 Factor in a scientific experiment that is subject to change. [8]

9 A scientific theory that explains an hypothesis and continues to be supported by experimental data. [9]

11 Complex carbon- and hydrogen-containing compound. [7]

13 A possible explanation to account for observations based on knowledge and experience. [10]

15 Relatively simple compounds that do not contain carbon and hydrogen. [9]

16 A factor that restricts scientific method. [10]

Down

1 Organic compound that makes up the nuclear material of cells. [11]

2 Fluid content of cells. [9]

3 Logical, ordered and controlled experimental approach. [16]

4 Most abundant energy-rich organic compound. [12]

6 Building block of protein. [9]

7 Organic compound that forms a key structural component of cell membranes. [5]

8 Three-part principle that summarises our understanding of cells. [10]

10 Outer covering of cells that contains cell contents. [12]

12 Set-up in experimental procedure to which the variable set-up is compared. [7]

14 Organic compound composed of amino acids. [7]

WORKSHEET 2

Poor pot plant—controlled experiments

A biology student designed and conducted the following experiment to test an hypothesis. Read the student's experimental procedure and cast a critical eye over the results obtained.

PURPOSE

To investigate the effect of sunlight on green plants.

HYPOTHESIS

Green plants need sunlight to survive.

PROCEDURE

The student:

1. obtained two seedlings of the same species that were the same in other respects, including size, height and weight.
2. labelled two same-size pots 'Pot Plant 1' and 'Pot Plant 2'.
3. potted the seedlings using a commercial potting mix, but ran out of potting mix for Pot Plant 2 and topped it up with some soil from the school garden.
4. gave both plants 100 mL of water.
5. placed Pot Plant 1 on the window sill with plenty of exposure to sunlight and Pot Plant 2 in a dark cupboard below the sill to ensure it had no access to sunlight.

The student watered Pot Plant 1 on the window sill every two days for a period of two weeks but forgot about Pot Plant 2, which was out of sight in the cupboard. At the end of the two-week period, Pot Plant 1 was thriving but Pot Plant 2 was dead.

The student wrote the following **conclusion**:

Pot Plant 2 was not exposed to sunlight and it died. The plant must have died due to lack of sunlight. The hypothesis that 'green plants need sunlight to survive' is supported by the results of the experiment.

Pot Plant 1

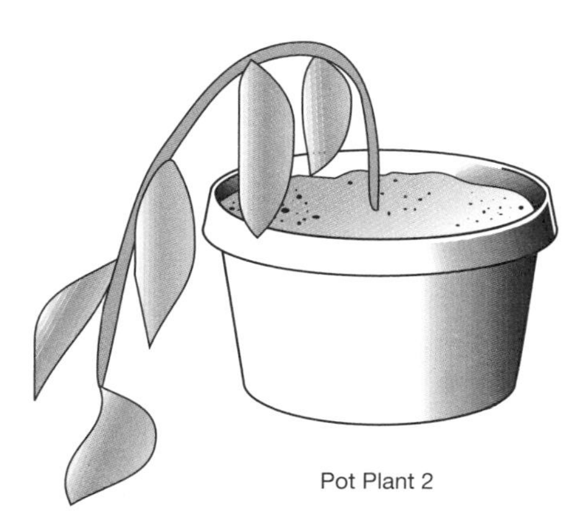

Pot Plant 2

Figure 1.14 The two pot plants

1 Which pot plant represented the control in this experiment? Explain your choice.

______

______

______

2 **a** How many variables did the student include in the experiment? What were they?

______

______

______

b How many factors should be varied in an experiment? What should the variable be in this instance?

______

______

______

3 Are the student's conclusions accurate? Explain.

____

____

____

4 Outline the conclusions that could be drawn from the student's experiment.

____

____

____

5 **a** Describe the changes you would make to this experiment to make it a properly controlled experiment.

____

____

____

____

b In the light of the changes you would make, outline the results you would expect and the conclusions you could draw.

____

____

____

____

____

WORKSHEET 3

Matchmaker—considering cells

1 Read the definitions listed in the boxes on the right of the page. Choose the correct term from the list below to match each definition. Write each term in the box corresponding to its definition.

protista	cytoplasm	light microscope	extremophile	cytology	ribosome	prokaryotes
plasmid	eukaryotes	cell theory	murein	DNA	electron microscope	biogenesis

Term	Definition
	collective term describing cell contents, including fluid, dissolved ions, salts, enzymes and organelles
	the idea that cells arise from pre-existing cells
	organisms that live in extreme conditions
	the study of cells
	organisms whose cells feature a distinct nucleus and membrane-bound organelles
	carbohydrate/protein compound of which the cell wall of bacteria is composed
	Kingdom containing algae, unicellular and colonial organisms
	organelle responsible for protein production in cells
	organisms in the Kingdom Monera; cells do not have membrane-bound organelles
	circular thread of DNA found in bacterial cells

2 There are four terms remaining. For each of these write a sentence summarising its meaning.

Term 1: ______________________________

____

Term 2: ______________________________

____

Term 3: ______________________________

____

Term 4: ______________________________

____

WORKSHEET 4

The inside story on cell structure

1 Identify each of the specified organelles for the plant cell and the animal cell shown.

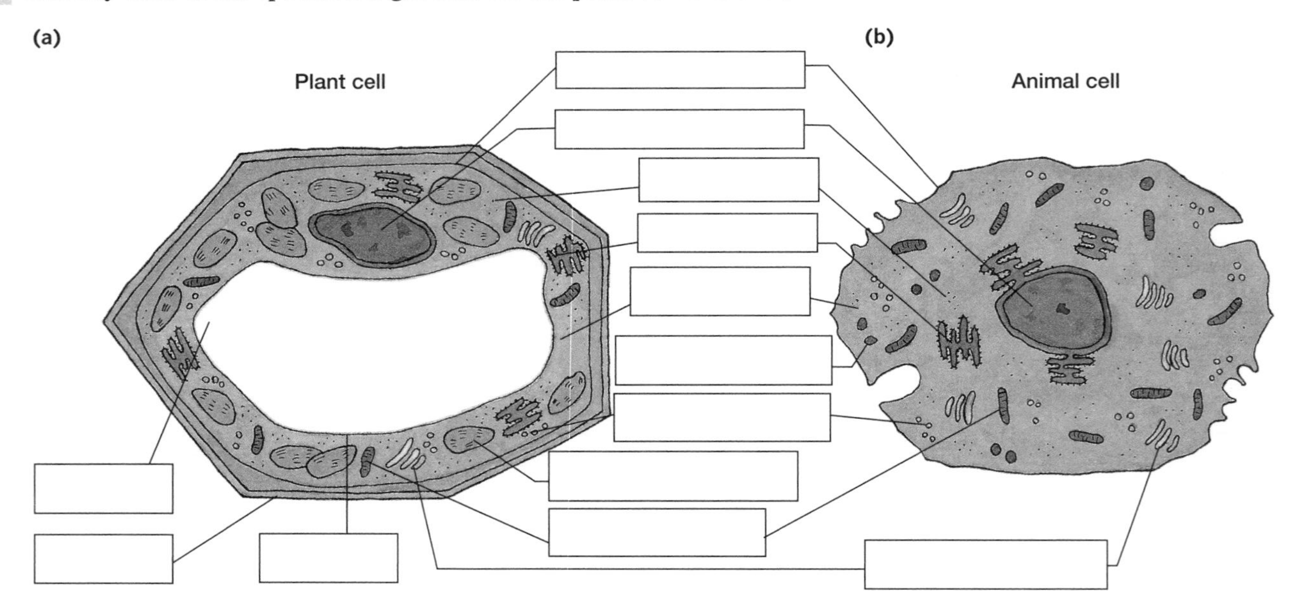

2 Describe the function of each cell organelle in the table.

Organelle	Function
Nucleus	
Cell membrane	
Cytoplasm	
Endoplasmic reticulum	
Ribosomes	
Golgi apparatus	
Mitochondria	
Cell wall	
Vacuole	
Chloroplast	

3 **a** Describe two similarities between plant and animal cells.

____

____

b Describe two differences between plant and animal cells.

____

____

WORKSHEET 5

Selective cells—cell membranes and selectivity

Cell membranes act as the 'border guards' of cells, selectively determining which molecules enter and leave. The route taken by different kinds of molecules as they enter and leave cells depends on the type of molecule and whether or not it is soluble in the phospholipid bilayer of the membrane. Some very small molecules cross the cell membrane by passing between the lipid molecules within the membrane. Larger water-soluble molecules make their way through protein channels embedded across the phospholipid bilayer. Other molecules are actively taken up by cells through the protein channels against a concentration gradient. Yet others simply dissolve into the lipid of the cell membrane to enter cells.

1 Look carefully at Figure 1.15 and the different kinds of molecules represented, and their respective concentrations inside and outside of the cell. Decide on the process by which each enters the cell, giving reasons for your choice. Write your answers in the spaces provided.

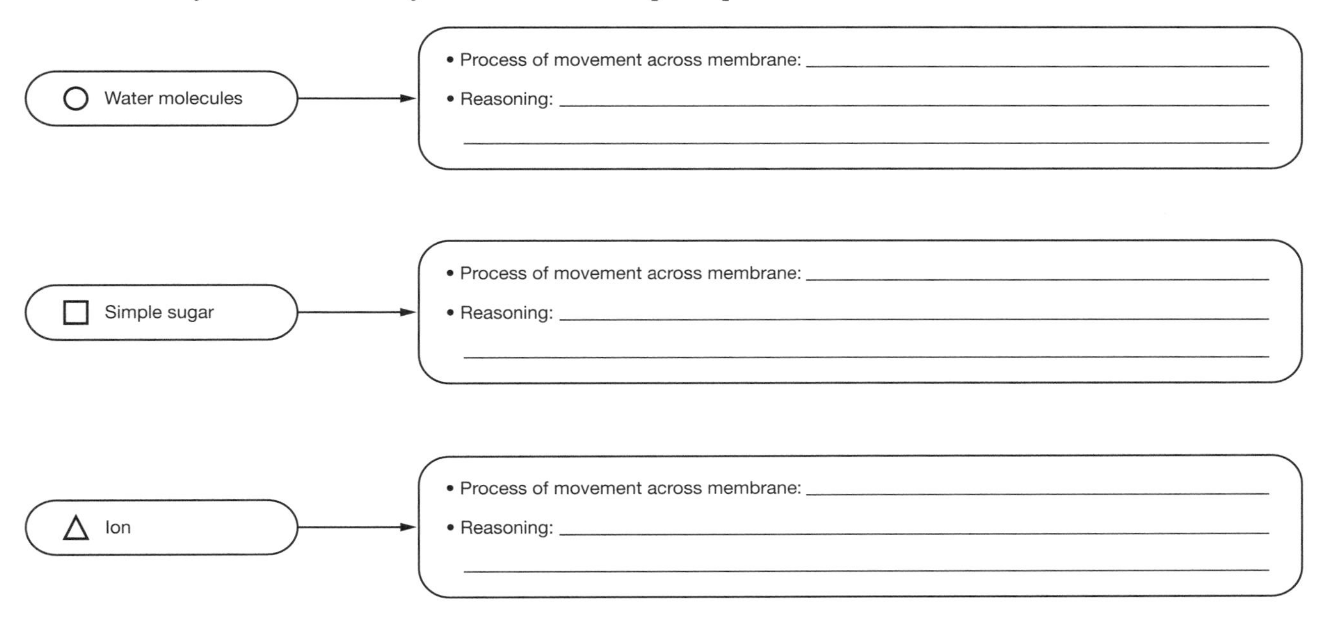

2 Molecule L enters the cell by dissolving into the lipid bilayer.

a What kind of molecules are represented by L?

___

b Name two different kinds of molecules that enter cells in this way.

___

3 The cell membrane is composed of different kinds of molecules. Identify the various parts of the cell membrane indicated, providing information as directed.

4 Suggest why the cell membrane is described as a 'fluid-mosaic'.

___
___
___
___
___

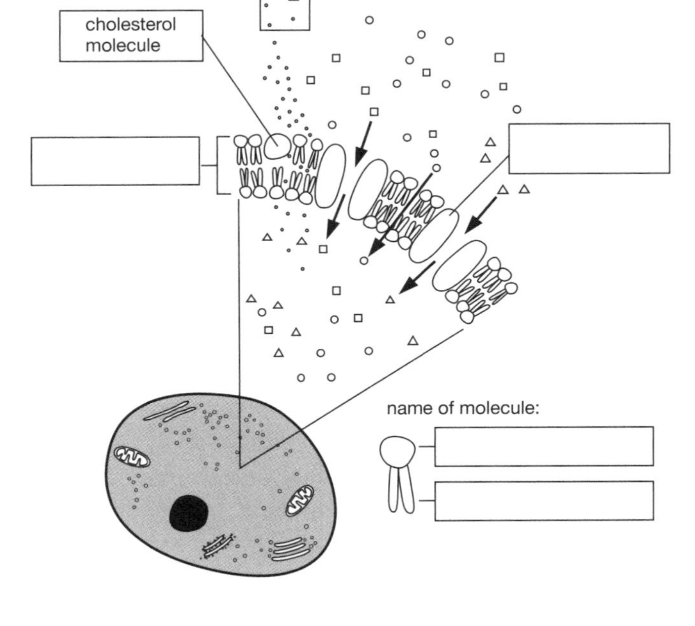

Figure 1.15 Zooming in on the cell membrane

WORKSHEET 6

Crossword—autotrophs and heterotrophs

Complete the crossword to help you check your knowledge and understanding of autotrophs, heterotrophs and their requirements.

Across

2 Organism that produces its own energy-rich compounds from inorganic ones. [9]

4 Photosynthetic pigment contained inside the chloroplasts of green plants. [11]

5 Organism that does not make its own organic compounds, feeding instead on other organisms to acquire these. [11]

7 Organelle that is the site of cellular respiration. [13]

9 A raw material for photosynthesis. [13]

10 Process in which some autotrophic bacteria produce organic compounds from inorganic ones. [14]

11 An alternative name for the anaerobic pathway in cellular respiration. [12]

13 Describes cellular respiration in the absence of oxygen. [9]

14 The first stage of cellular respiration in which glucose molecules are split. [10]

15 Complex carbon and hydrogen containing compound that is rich in energy. [12]

Down

1 Point at which the products of photosynthesis are consumed in cellular respiration. [22]

2 Describes cellular respiration in the presence of oxygen. [7]

3 Process in which green plants harness sunlight to produce organic compounds from inorganic compounds. [14]

6 Energy-rich molecule that is the raw material for cellular respiration. [7]

8 Organelle that is the site of photosynthesis. [11]

12 The ability to do work. [6]

WORKSHEET 7

Reciprocal reactions—photosynthesis and cellular respiration

In photosynthesis, plant cells harness sunlight to drive a reaction in which carbon dioxide and water are combined to produce energy-rich organic molecules. These energy-rich organic molecules are, in turn, broken down to make energy available to meet the life-sustaining activities of cells.

1 Fill in the missing terms, definitions and equations in the spaces provided to construct a complete picture of the processes of photosynthesis and respiration.

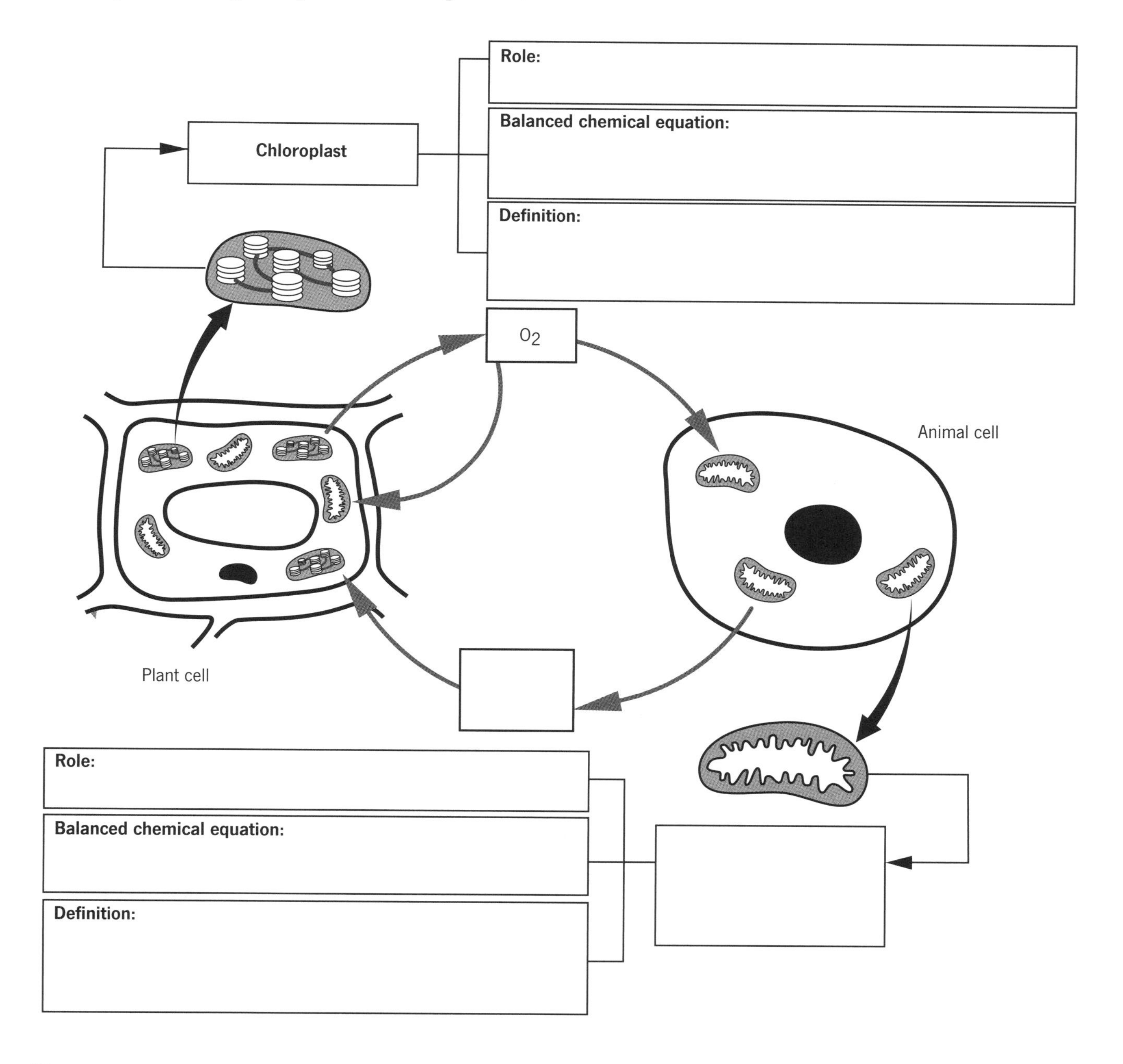

2 Summarise the relationship between the processes of photosynthesis and cellular respiration.

____

____

WORKSHEET 8

Cells on a mission—cell specialisation

1 Consider the examples of specialised cells shown in the table below. For each cell type shown, suggest its function and outline the features that make it well-suited to this role. Also, identify the cell types represented by **b–e**.

	Cell type	Diagram	Function	Feature
a	Nerve cell			
b				
c				
d				
e		chloroplast		
f	Root hair cell			

2 Summarise the relationship between the structure and features of cells and their function.

Lifeline—the mammalian circulatory system

The following diagram illustrates the circuit that blood takes as it moves around a mammalian body. Follow the instructions below to complete the diagram to produce an information chart about the circulatory system of mammals.

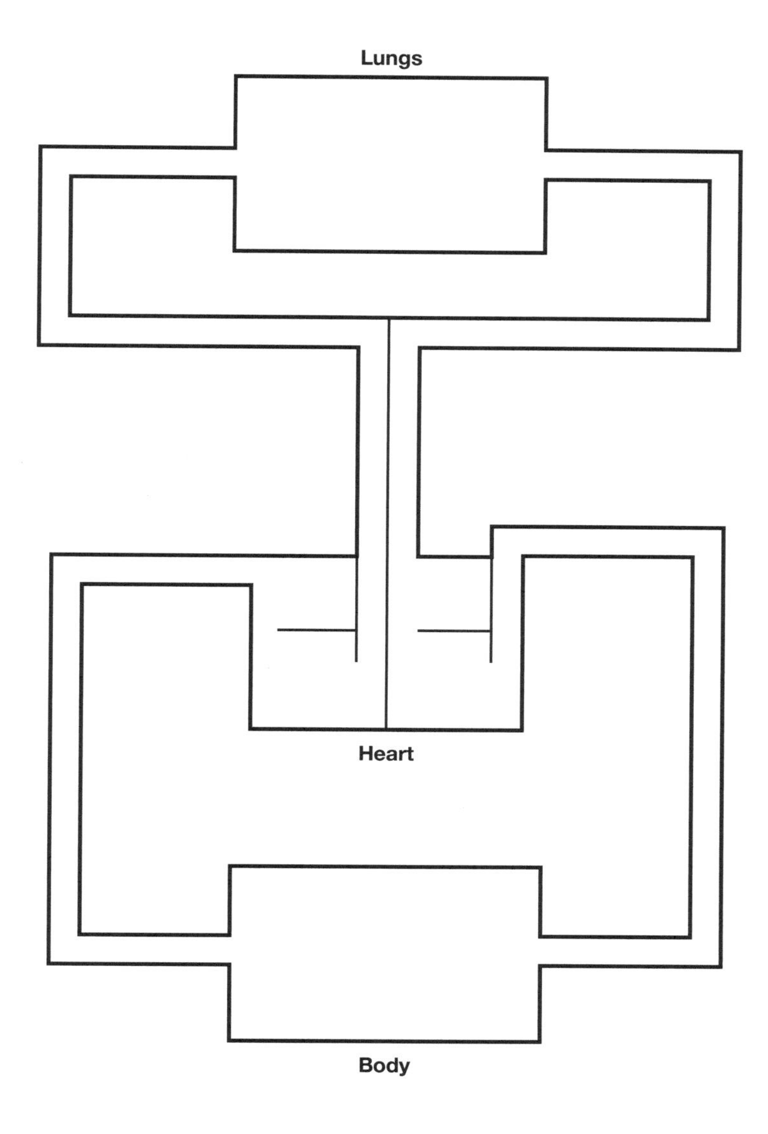

1 Colour-code the diagram to show the movement of oxygenated and deoxygenated blood.

2 Insert arrows to indicate the direction and pathway that blood takes as it moves through the circulatory system.

3 Label the chambers of the heart and the blood vessels that enter and leave it.

4 Indicate the location of valves, e.g. ⊬ ⊣

5 Add notes that outline the features and functions of the different structures.

WORKSHEET 10

Digesting dinner—digestion in humans

Use the key words listed below to complete the concept map summarising nutrition and digestion in humans. Write along the link lines between terms and phrases to show the relationships between ideas in your concept map.

amino acids	egestion	chemical digestion	carbohydrates	duodenum	rectum
bile	ileum	proteins	villi	digestive enzymes	chyme
lipids	vitamins	digestion	physical breakdown	glycogen	colon

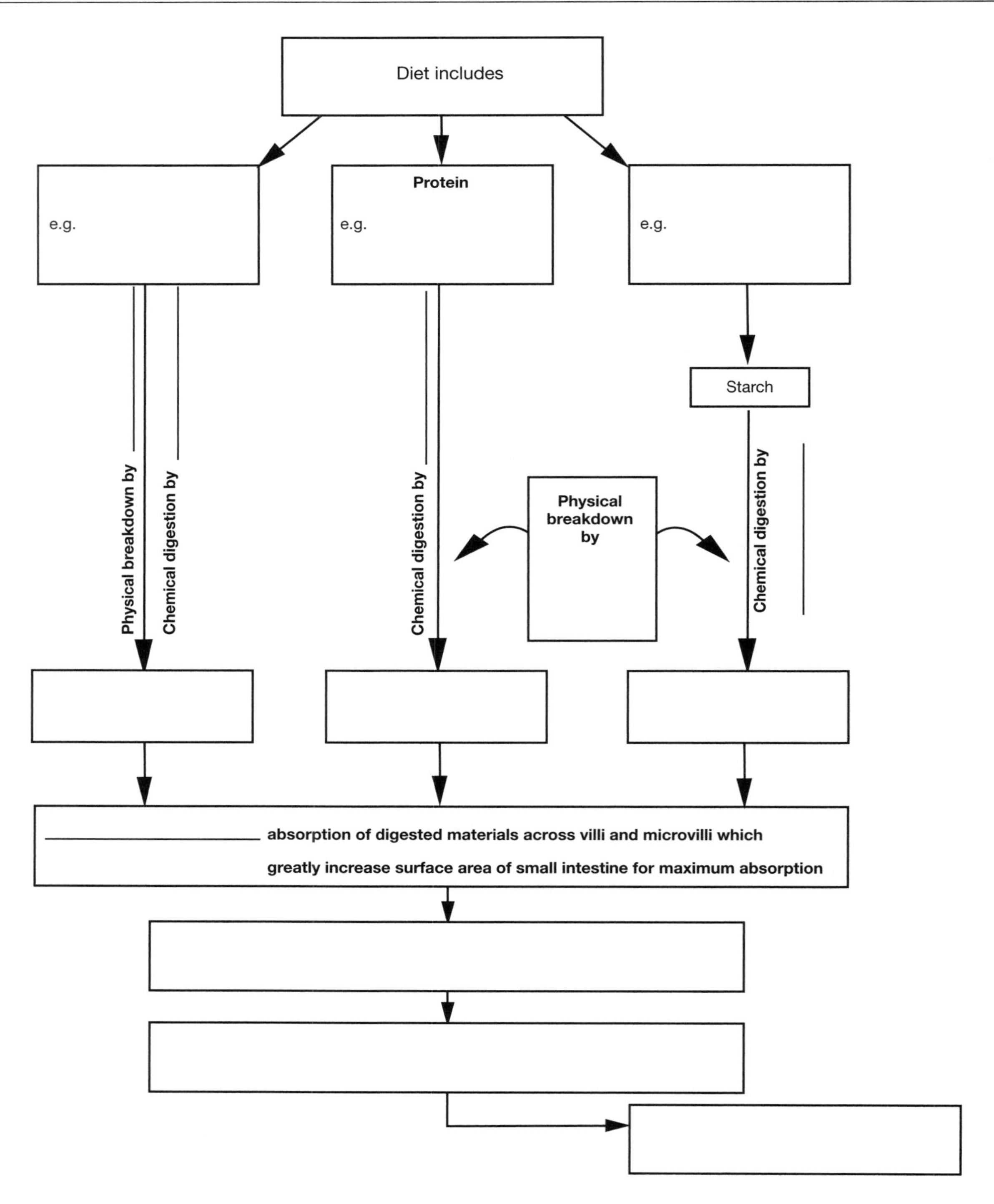

WORKSHEET 11

Gas exchange—human respiratory system

1 Select terms from the list below to complete the summary statements, outlining the key points about gaseous exchange in in humans.

alveolar sacs	bronchiole	cellular respiration	oxyhaemoglobin	trachea
ventilation	diffusion	alveoli	bronchus	

- The exchange of gases across respiratory surfaces in aerobic organisms makes oxygen available for ____________ ____________ and ensures that carbon dioxide is removed.
- Gas exchange at respiratory surfaces occurs by the process of ____________.
- In animals, the movement of air or water across the respiratory surfaces is called ____________.
- Terrestrial animals such as mammals ventilate lungs to achieve gaseous exchange. A series of respiratory passages lead from the nasal passages to the lungs, where gaseous exchange occurs at the ____________.
- The oxygen-carrying molecule in mammals is haemoglobin. When oxygen combines with this molecule in the red blood cells it forms a complex called ____________________. Carbon dioxide is carried in the blood in dissolved form.

2 Examine the diagram below, which shows parts of the respiratory system in humans. Use the remaining terms to label the flowchart that illustrates the pathway that air takes as it enters and leaves the body, allowing exchange of gases at the respiratory surface.

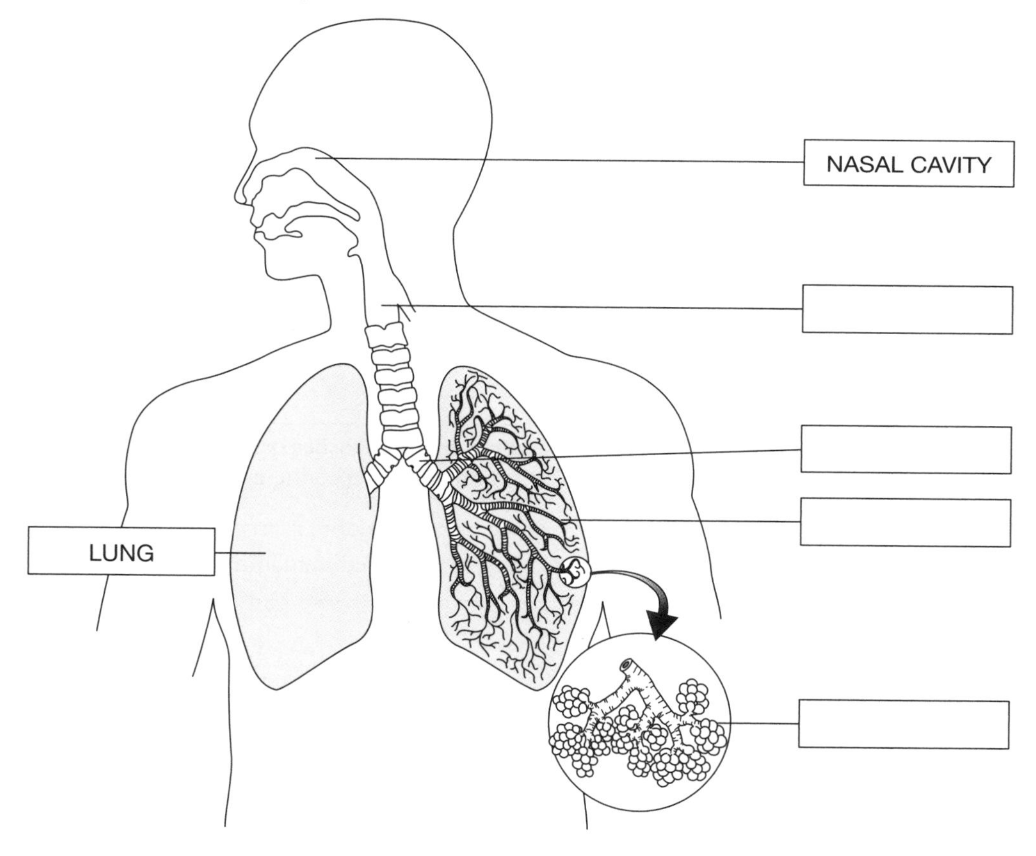

3 Describe the properties of gas exchange surfaces and explain how each property assists in the efficient diffusion of gases.

____

____

____

WORKSHEET 12

Matchmaker—removing wastes

1 Read the definitions listed in the boxes on the right-hand side of the page. Choose the correct term from the list below to match each definition. Write each term in the box corresponding to its definition.

glomerulus	dialysis	urine	loop of Henle	reabsorption	cortex	urea
kidney	excretion	ureter	nephron	urethra	bladder	

Term	Definition
	tube that carries wastes from kidney to bladder
	functional unit of the kidney
	process in which useful materials such as water, glucose, amino acids and salts are returned to the bloodstream along the length of the nephron
	network of capillaries enclosed by Bowman's capsule—the site of filtration
	tube that carries urine from bladder to exit the body
	process of removal of metabolic wastes
	artificial form of filtering metabolic wastes from the blood based on diffusion of solutes across partially permeable membrane
	organ responsible for water balance and removal of metabolic wastes
	tubule in nephron that establishes osmotic gradient responsible for water reabsorption, thereby producing concentrated urine
	nitrogenous wastes produced in mammals

2 There are three terms remaining. For each of these write a sentence summarising what is meant by the term.

Term 1: ____________________

____

Term 2: ____________________

____

Term 3: ____________________

____

PRACTICAL ACTIVITY 1

Distinguishing cells—an observational activity

INTRODUCTION

This activity provides an opportunity to design and carry out a practical investigation into the similarities and differences between cells of different kinds of organisms. You will need to be familiar with the use of the light microscope and accompanying equipment. You will also need to prepare some of your own slide specimens. If you are a little rusty on the procedures involved, your teacher will be able to arrange some refresher lessons and practice for you before you begin this activity. The following information will be a useful starting point.

PURPOSE

- To design and carry out a laboratory investigation into the structural features of cells from different kinds of organisms.
- To investigate the similarities and differences between cells from different kinds of organisms.

THE LIGHT MICROSCOPE

- The light microscope (also called the compound microscope, Figure 1.16) allows you to view highly magnified images of an object as a result of the multiplier effect of using two lenses together. These are the **eyepiece lens** and the **objective lens**. Most light microscopes have two or three objective lenses arranged on a rotating turret. The objective and eyepiece lenses have their individual magnifications marked on them, e.g. 40× or 10×. Total magnification is calculated by multiplying the magnification values of the two lenses in use.
- Beneath the microscope stage is a **mirror** or built-in light source, a **condenser** lens system to concentrate the light, and an **iris diaphragm** mechanism to regulate the amount of light passing through the object.

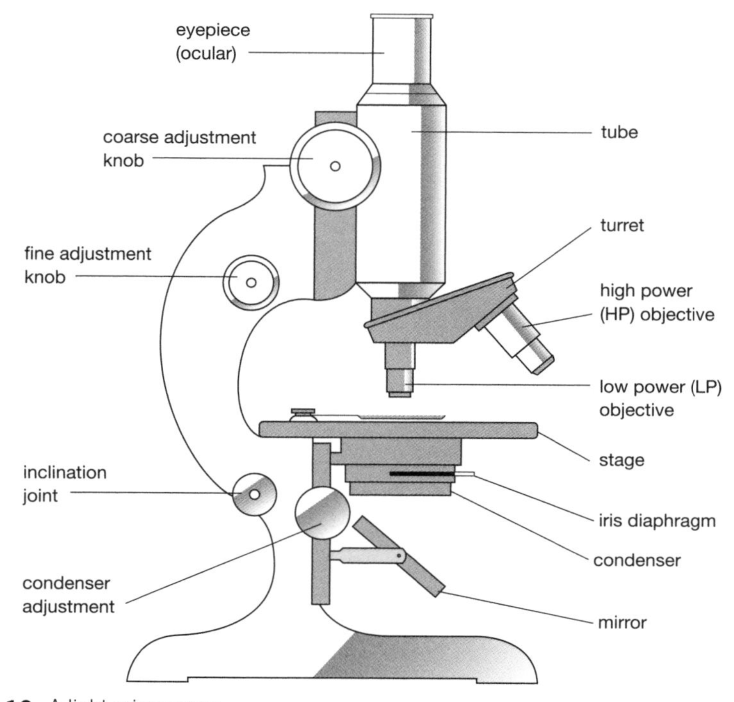

Figure 1.16 A light microscope

User-friendly microscope hints

- Look down the eyepiece lens and adjust the light source (mirror, condenser lens and iris diaphragm) so the field of view is uniformly illuminated.
- Place your prepared slide on the microscope stage and centre the object to be viewed. Use the clips to secure the slide in position.
- When setting up the microscope always view the object under low power (LP) first.
- Checking from the side, wind the coarse adjustment until the LP objective lens is as close as it can go towards the slide. (It should be no closer than 2 mm.)
- Looking down through the eyepiece lens, use the **coarse adjustment knob** to slowly move the LP objective lens away from the slide. When the object is in focus, use the **fine adjustment knob** to bring the image into even sharper focus.
- Rotate the turret to set a high power (HP) objective lens in place. Only use the fine adjustment knob when using HP.

Preparing a wet mount slide

Figure 1.17 illustrates the best technique for making a wet mount slide.

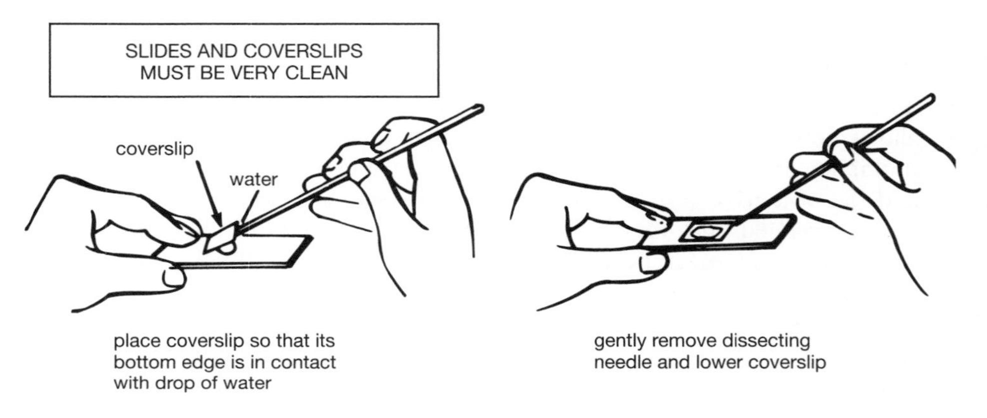

Figure 1.17 Making a wet mount slide

BIOLOGICAL DRAWINGS

The following guidelines should help you to make simple and effective biological drawings.

- Drawings should be:
  - made in grey lead pencil
  - large
  - fully labelled with the name of the specimen, the type of preparation and the magnification
  - given a size perspective so that comparison between specimen sizes can be made—draw each specimen in relation to the size of the field of view observed.

PRACTICAL ACTIVITY 1

- Lines to labels should be ruled—they should not have 'arrowheads' and should not cross over.
- Drawings of low power images do not show the detail of cells, just the 'area of cell types' (Figure 1.18).
- Drawings of images made under high power show detail of a few cells only of each type (Figure 1.19).

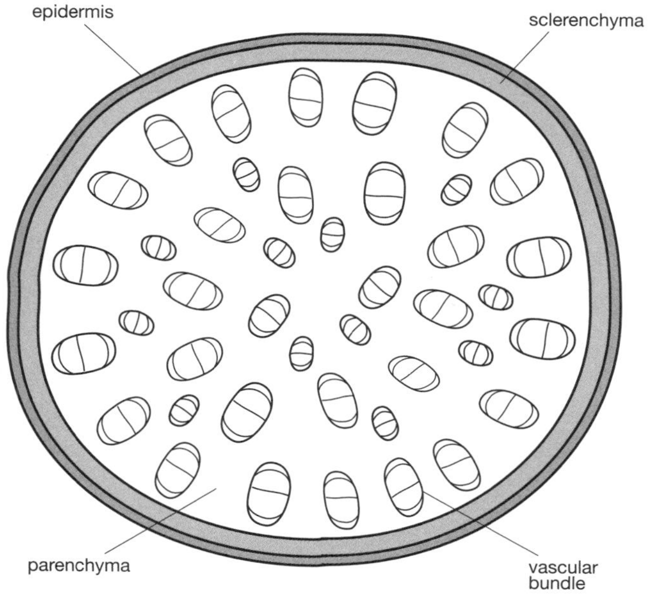

Figure 1.18 A low power view of zea maize cells (×30)

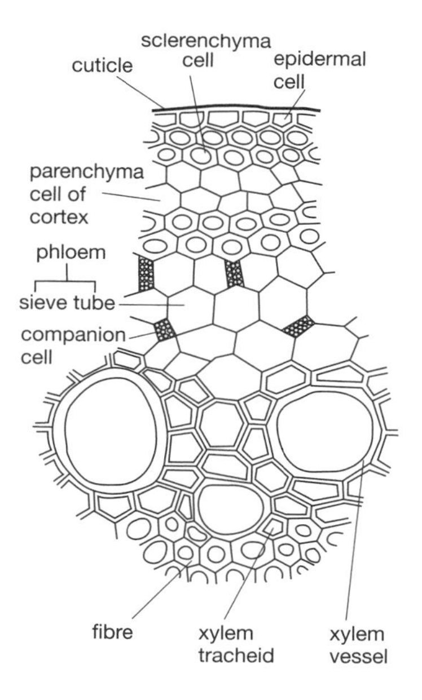

Figure 1.19 A high power drawing of zea maize cells (×600)

PROCEDURE

1. Use the materials listed to design a laboratory activity that will allow you to conduct an investigation of the structural features of cells from different kinds of organisms. You may wish to add further specimens to the suggested list—check this with your teacher.
2. Set out your procedure in a numbered, step-by-step format. Write your instructions clearly so that another student could follow them effectively.

   Your procedure should include instructions related to:
   - mounting slides
   - viewing fresh and prepared slides under the microscope
   - preparing drawings of each specimen.

Caution: Special care instructions need to be provided in relation to the use of hazardous chemicals and sharp equipment.

3. When you have completed the experimental design, have it checked by your teacher before proceeding with the laboratory work itself.

MATERIALS

- light microscope
- microscope slides
- coverslips
- onion
- elodea (pond weed)
- iodine
- white tile or cutting board
- paper towelling
- forceps
- scalpel
- selected prepared slides, e.g.:
  - protozoan
  - leaf epidermis
  - nerve cells
  - bacterium
  - white blood cells
  - cheek cells
  - cross-section of green plant stem
  - root hair tissue

PRACTICAL ACTIVITY 1 continued

EXPERIMENTAL DESIGN

Cell drawings

4 Table 1.10 includes a number of features found in eukaryotic cells. Complete the table by indicating whether or not you were able to identify the features listed for each specimen you observed.

5 Decide upon a key to indicate that particular features were identified. For example, a tick may indicate that a feature has been clearly identified, a dash might be used to indicate that a feature was not observed.

Key

Table 1.10 Summary of cell features or organelles

Cell type	Features or organelles observed										Type of organism
	Cell membrane	Cell wall	Nucleus	Cyto-plasm	Chloro-plast	Mito-chondria	Ribo-somes	Vacuoles	ER	Golgi apparatus	

1 Suggest why it might not be helpful to use a cross to indicate that a feature has not been observed in a particular specimen.

2 Outline the role of the light microscope in the study of cells.

CONCLUSION

3 Prepare a summary of your findings in this activity. Group the specimens according to common features. Include a discussion of:

- similarities between different kinds of cells
- differences between different kinds of cells.

EVALUATION

4 Outline any limitations that you encountered in this activity, and the impact they had on the investigation.

5 Suggest how these might be overcome in the future to ensure the greatest success in your experimental work.

PRACTICAL ACTIVITY 2

Shaping up—body shape versus diffusion

INTRODUCTION

Sea lettuce (*Ulva lactuca*) is a green marine alga that, as its name suggests, looks like lettuce. It grows abundantly on sheltered rocky coasts. Its structure is very simple, as it consists of just two layers of cells. When the alga is submerged in water at high tide, raw materials enter the cells directly, and wastes leave the cells and diffuse into the surrounding water.

If a small piece of raw liver is put on the bottom of a freshwater pond, it will soon attract a number of small khaki-grey planarians, commonly called flatworms. Like *Ulva*, these worms are also very thin and flat. They have few internal organs. Gas exchange occurs directly across the body surface.

Both of these aquatic organisms depend on their shape for their ability to obtain requirements and remove wastes efficiently. Very few terrestrial organisms have this 'flattened' appearance (see Figure 1.20).

PURPOSE

To investigate the relationship between the surface area to volume ratio and the diffusion rates of materials.

BACKGROUND

In this activity, the shape of organisms will be simulated by blocks of agar jelly. The jelly is a pink colour due to the presence of sodium hydroxide (a base) and phenolphthalein indicator. Phenolphthalein is colourless in acid. When the blocks are placed in an acid solution, the acid diffuses into the jelly, causing a colour change from pink to clear. The time taken for a block to totally decolourise is a measure of the rate of diffusion of acid into the jelly.

MATERIALS

- prepared sheets of agar–phenolphthalein jelly
  - 20 mm thick
  - 10 mm thick
  - 5 mm thick
- 0.1 M sulfuric acid (class supply)
- 250 mL beaker
- plastic teaspoon
- scalpel
- clear plastic ruler
- tile or large petri dish lid
- strip of paper towel
- disposable gloves
- calculator

PROCEDURE

1. Put on the disposable gloves, then accurately measure and cut a 20 mm × 20 mm block of jelly from each of the sheets provided, i.e. 20 mm, 10 mm and 5 mm thick sheets.
2. Half-fill a 250 mL beaker with sulfuric acid from the class stock.
3. Add the blocks of jelly to the acid. Watch until the first block becomes completely clear.

1 In Table 1.11 write '1st' in red pen in the top of the column for the block that became clear first.

4. Immediately remove all of the blocks from the acid, using the spoon. Quickly pat the blocks dry with paper towel. Cut them in half with the scalpel and measure, in millimetres, the depth of the clear layer in each block.

2 Record the depth of the clear layer in each block, that is, the depth to which the acid has penetrated each block.

5. Dispose of the acid and the jelly blocks as directed by your teacher.

3 **a** Calculate the surface area for each block and enter the data into Table 1.11.

b Calculate the volume of each block. Enter the data into the table.

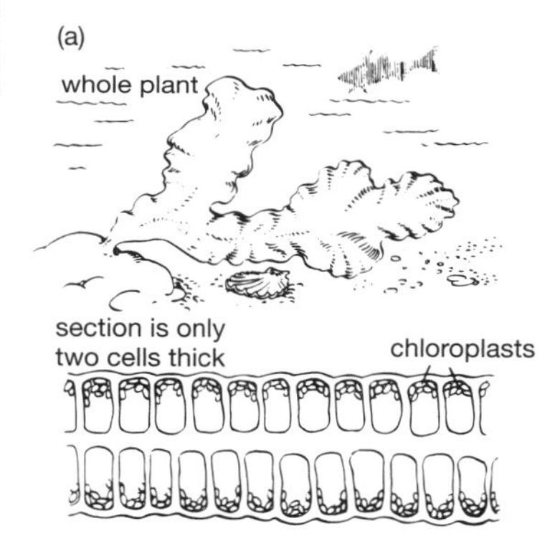

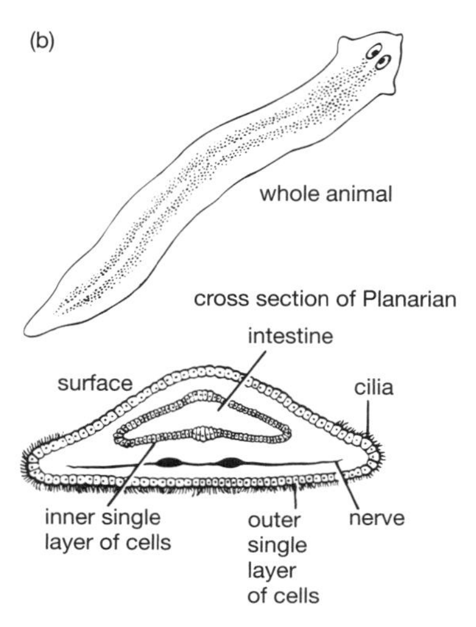

Figure 1.20 **(a)** Sea lettuce (*Ulva lactuca*) and **(b)** a planarian, commonly called a flatworm

Table 1.11 Jelly measurements			
Block number	1	2	3
Block dimensions (mm)	20 × 20 × 20	20 × 20 × 10	20 × 20 × 5
Depth of clear layer of block (mm)			
Surface area (SA, mm^2)			
Volume (V, mm^3)			
Surface area to volume ratio $\left(\frac{SA}{V}\right)$	: 1	: 1	: 1

c Use a calculator to find the surface area to volume ratio for each of the blocks. Enter the data into the table.

4 Explain what has caused the blocks to become clear. Include a discussion of both substances and processes.

____

____

____

____

5 a Which block was the first to become completely clear? ______________

b From your observations of the other two blocks, predict which would be the next to become clear. Explain why you think so.

____

____

6 a Which block has the largest surface area (SA)? ______________

b Which block has the largest volume (V)? ______________

c Which block has the largest surface area in proportion to its volume (i.e. surface area to volume ratio or SA : V)? ______________

7 Describe what happens to the SA : V ratio of a block as its size gets smaller.

____

CONCLUSIONS

8 Describe the relationship between the size and shape of a block and the rate at which acid diffuses into it.

____

____

9 Given that cells need to be able to obtain their requirements from the surrounding environment and remove wastes to the surrounding environment, suggest why cells are usually microscopic in size.

____

____

____

____

PRACTICAL ACTIVITY 3

Molecules on the move—osmosis and partially permeable membranes

INTRODUCTION

Cell membranes are partially permeable—that is, they allow certain molecules to pass through while restricting the passage of others. The movement of water across partially permeable membranes occurs by the process of **osmosis**. Potassium iodide solution is a dark yellow-brown colour. In the presence of starch the iodine solution takes on a blue-black colour.

PURPOSE

To observe and describe an example of osmosis.

MATERIALS

- dialysis (cellulose) tubing
- thistle funnel
- gas jar
- retort stand and clamp
- rubber bands
- 50 mL beaker
- iodine/potassium iodide solution
- 5% starch solution

PROCEDURE

1. Fill the gas jar to three-quarters full with water. Add iodine/potassium iodide solution until the water is quite yellow-brown.
2. Moisten the cellulose tubing and tie a knot at one end. At the other end insert the stem of the thistle funnel and fasten it firmly with the rubber band.
3. Fill the cellulose tubing with starch solution until the level rises 2–3 cm up the stem of the funnel. Dislodge any air bubbles and thoroughly rinse both the funnel stem and the bag under running water to remove any traces of starch from the outside.
4. Accurately mark the level of the starch solution on the funnel stem with a marking pen.
5. Use a retort stand and clamp to suspend the tubing in the gas jar containing the iodine and water (Figure 1.21).
6. Leave the set-up standing undisturbed for at least 20 minutes.

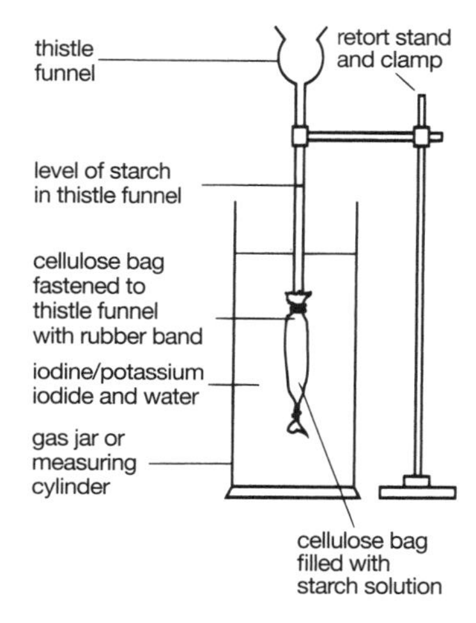

Figure 1.21 Equipment set-up for the experiment

1 **a** Describe your observations after 20 minutes.

____

____

____

b Use colour pencils to show the colour of the liquid in the gas jar and in the cellulose tubing.

2 **a** Explain what has occurred. In your explanation discuss the different kinds of molecules involved and the directions in which they have moved.

____

____

____

____

____

____

b On your diagram, label the different molecules and add arrows to show the net direction of movement of each.

3 Suggest a reason why some types of molecules have moved through the cellulose tubing while others have not.

4 **a** Check the level of starch solution in the funnel. What do you notice?

b Suggest what has occurred to account for this observation.

CONCLUSIONS

5 Define **osmosis.**

6 Using your knowledge of osmosis and your observations in this activity, suggest why some molecules are able to pass across partially permeable membranes and others are not.

PRACTICAL ACTIVITY 

Rat dissection—mammalian systems

INTRODUCTION

Cells are the building blocks of multicellular organisms. Specific cell types are organised into tissues, tissues are organised into organs, and organs into systems. Each system is composed of a number of organs and components that work together to serve a particular role within the organism.

Dissecting a rat provides an opportunity to compare the circulatory, digestive, excretory and/or respiratory systems of the rat to that of a human. Despite the difference in size, the basic structure and organisation of the two mammalian systems is similar.

PURPOSE

To dissect a rat and compare the structure and organisation of the major organs and body systems to that of a human.

DURATION

60+ minutes

MATERIALS

- rat pinned out on dissecting board
- scalpel
- dissecting scissors
- forceps
- probe
- dissecting pins
- newspaper
- ruler
- disposable gloves
- disposal bag
- disinfectant
- antiseptic handwash

PROCEDURE

1 Examine the mouth and teeth of the rat. It may be necessary to gently prise the mouth open for a better view. What does the arrangement of teeth suggest about the diet of the rat? How does this compare to a human?

2 Follow your teacher's direction (and demonstration) to open the abdomen and chest cavity of the rat. Making the initial incision is often the most difficult. At this point, it is important not to damage the organs underneath.

3 Once the skin has been peeled and pinned back, using either a photo or diagram (depending on your teacher's directions) record the initial position of each of the organs. Consider where each organ sits within the torso and the other organs nearby.

4 Identify and classify the organs associated with each of the systems you have studied—circulatory, digestive, excretory and/or respiratory systems. Make five dot-point observations at this point of the dissection. Note if there is anything unexpected or surprising about the arrangement or position of organs in the torso.

____

____

____

____

____

5 The stomach and pancreas can be viewed by gently lifting the liver with the probe.

6 Follow the pathway of the stomach to the small intestines, then large intestines. Take care not to puncture the intestines as you do so.

7 The intestinal tract can be removed by gently freeing the mesentery (membranous tissue) holding the intestines together. The mesentery contains arteries and veins that supply blood to the intestines.

8 With the intestinal tract removed, identify the caecum (a bag like structure that signals the beginning of the large intestine).

9 Identify the colon next, and finally the rectum which will contain pellet-shaped faeces.

10 Compare the length of the small intestine to the large intestine. Record the length of each using a large ruler.

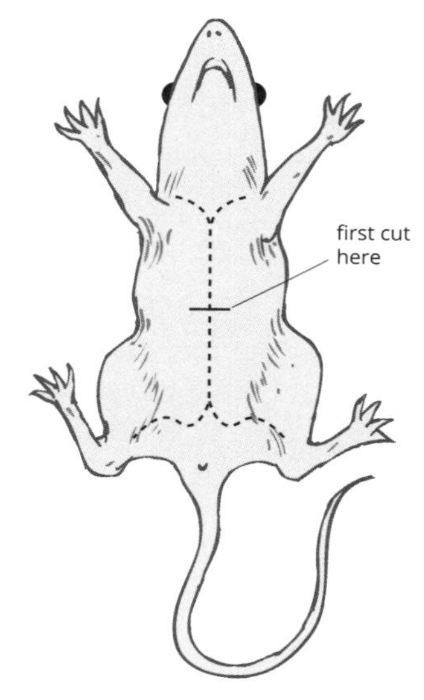

Figure 1.22 Making the incision

NOTES

- Biological material is potentially hazardous and should be handled and disposed of with care.
- Gloves and lab coat should be worn.
- Caution should be exercised when using the sharp dissecting tools. Take care to point the instruments away from yourself when cutting.

11 Identify the location of each of the kidneys. Note their relative size. Can you identify any of the other organs or components associated with the excretory system?

12 Under your teacher's directions, cut through the rib cage to expose the heart, lungs and diaphragm.

13 Upon completion of the dissection, ensure that you follow directions for the appropriate disposal of the rat and clean-up procedures.

1 Use the diagram of the rat provided to prepare a detailed and labelled sketch of the organs and components that were observed during the dissection.

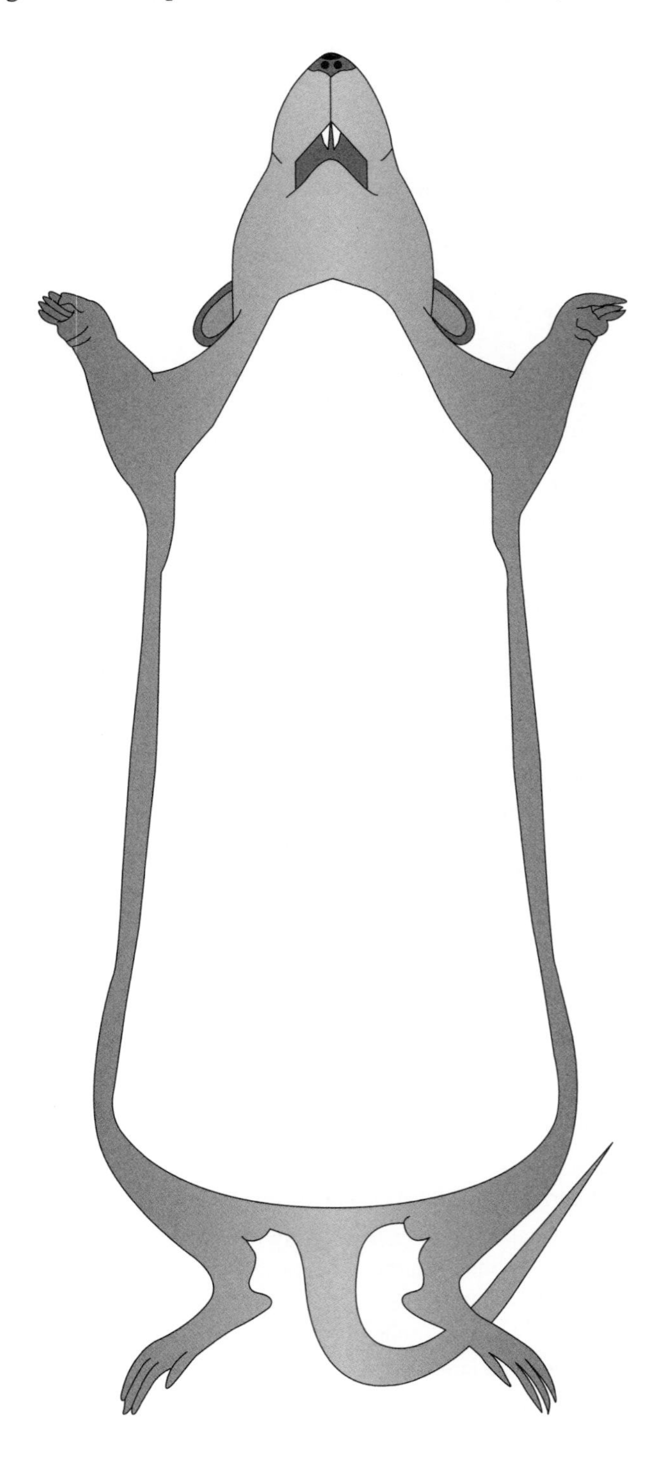

PRACTICAL ACTIVITY 4

2 Complete Table 1.12 to summarise your findings.

Table 1.12 Summary of findings during dissection of rat

Body system	Organs/components	Key observations

3 For each of the organs/components you have listed in Table 1.12, outline the role it performs and describe how the features of each organ/component make it well suited to that particular role.

4 What you can determine about the diet of a rat from its teeth?

5 Compare and contrast the teeth and diet of the rat to a human.

6 Compare the length and width of the rat's small intestine to its large intestine. How does the length of the small intestine assist its role?

7 Investigate how the digestive system of a typical carnivore compares to that of a typical herbivore. Provide an example of each in your response.

8 Humans are omnivores. How is the human digestive system different from that of herbivores or carnivores? Describe specific examples.

CONCLUSIONS

9 Describe how the tissues and organs of the digestive system are organised into a functioning system.

10 Summarise the relationship between the structure and function of the digestive system. Include two specific examples to illustrate your response.

PRACTICAL ACTIVITY 5

Tubes for transport—vascular tissue in plants

INTRODUCTION

Tissues that are specialised for transporting substances through plants over long distances are called vascular tissues. Few cells in plants are far from vascular tissue. One tissue transports water and inorganic nutrients upwards through the plant and is called **xylem**. The other tissue transports sugars (in solution) produced by photosynthesis and other manufactured products throughout the plant and is ca lled **phloem**. In stems, xylem and phloem tissue form vascular bundles, with the phloem on the outer surface of the bundle. A layer of cells called the **cambium** (a layer of cells that produces secondary tissues) runs through the vascular bundle separating the xylem and phloem.

Vascular tissue is easily visible in leaves. The parallel veins of grasses and the branching veins in most other leaves are part of the vascular network of the plant. Vascular tissue extends from the roots to the very tips of leaves, and into developing buds and fruit.

PURPOSE

- To investigate the pathway of water movement in the stem and leaves of a flowering plant.
- To examine the microscopic structure of the tissue through which water moves in a plant.
- To become familiar with the structure and function of a vascular bundle.

MATERIALS

- stick of celery that has been standing in a coloured dye solution
- undyed stick of celery
- iodine stain
- stereoscopic microscope
- high power microscope
- scalpel
- two dissecting needles
- forceps
- microscope slides and coverslips
- single-edged razor blade (new or in very good condition)
- dissecting board
- paper towel and paper tissues
- prepared slides—transverse and longitudinal sections of *Helianthus* stem

PROCEDURE

1 Collect a celery petiole (stick) that has been standing in coloured dye solution. Rinse the dye from the end and examine the petiole and leaf for evidence of dye distribution. (Try holding it up to the light.)

1 Describe the distribution of the dye.

___

___

___

2 Place the petiole on a dissecting board and, using the razor blade, cut transverse sections 1–2 mm thick in the positions shown in Figure 1.23. Arrange the sections in order on a microscope slide. (A coverslip is not needed.) Put the slide under a stereoscopic microscope and examine the cut surface of each section for the presence of dye.

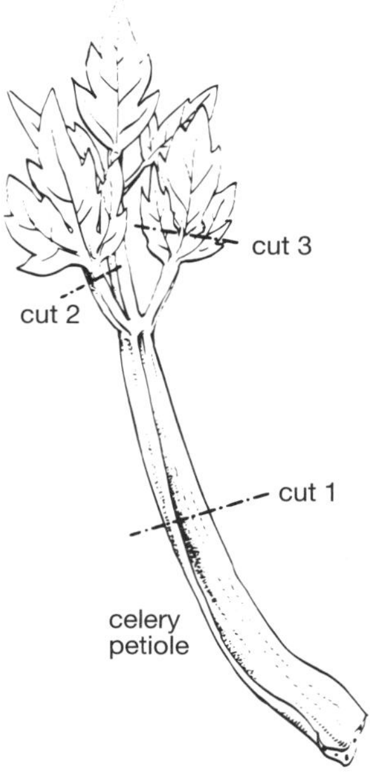

Figure 1.23 Positions for cutting celery

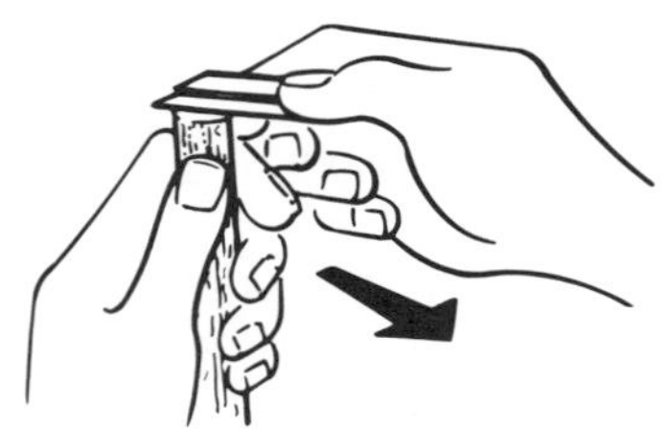

Make the slice as thin as you possibly can. Using a razor blade will yield a better result. It is also recommended that you slice only one piece at a time.

Figure 1.24 Technique for cutting sections

2 Draw diagrams of the three sections, showing the distribution of the dye.

3 Cut a section of the petiole 1 cm thick. Stand the section on its end and cut lengthways down along one of the coloured areas. Examine this section under the stereoscopic microscope.

3 Is the dye found only in definite structures within the stem? Explain.

____

____

____

4 Combining your observations of the transverse and longitudinal sections, draw a three-dimensional diagram of the petiole, showing where the dye has moved.

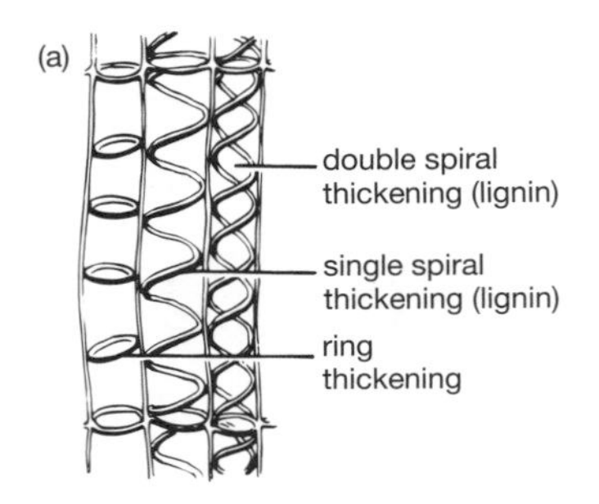

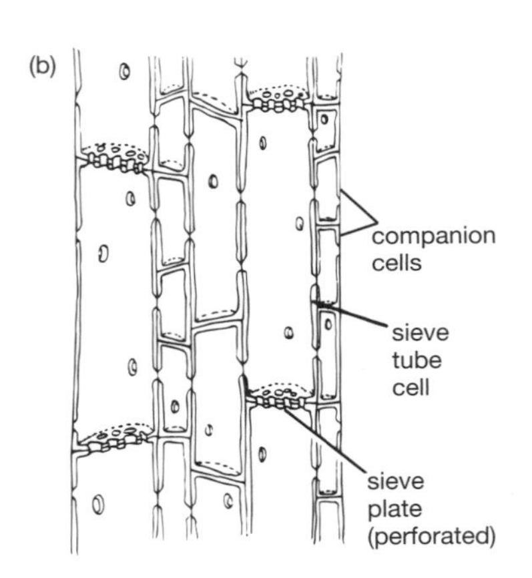

Figure 1.25 **(a)** Xylem vessel cells, **(b)** phloem sieve tube cells and companion cells from celery

5 Does the distribution of dye necessarily show where water has moved in the stem? Explain. ______________________________

____

____

4 Collect a 3 cm long piece of undyed celery petiole. Using the technique shown in Figure 1.24, cut several very thin cross-sections.
   Put the sections on a microscope slide. Select the one that looks the thinnest and mount it on another slide in a drop of iodine stain. Add a coverslip and observe under a high power microscope using the low power objective lens. Look for some thick-walled cells in about the same position as you found the dye. These are xylem vessel cells and they form part of a vascular bundle. Water moves in xylem.

5 Cut a 1 cm thick slice from the remaining undyed celery. Place it under a stereoscopic microscope and, using a scalpel, cut down through one of the vascular bundles. Use the scalpel and dissecting needles to carefully dissect out a length of the bundle. Make sure that you take only a small piece and that there are few if any cells from either side of the bundle. Transfer the bundle to a drop of iodine on a microscope slide. Thoroughly tease it apart with the needles. Place the slide on a piece of paper towel and add a coverslip. Move the coverslip from side to side while applying gentle pressure with your finger, then fold the paper tissue over the coverslip and push down on it firmly with your thumb to squash the bundle. Add some more stain at the edge of the coverslip if too much has been removed.

6 Observe the slide under the high power microscope, first using the low power objective lens, then carefully changing to high power. Identify the cell types shown in Figure 1.25.

PRACTICAL ACTIVITY 5

6 Make drawings of several cells of each type under high power magnification.

7 The walls of xylem vessel cells are thickened by a material called **lignin.** You may also observe spiral coils in the vessel cells. These too are made of lignin. What advantage would both of these features of xylem have for a plant?

____

____

7. Collect the two prepared slides of sunflower (*Helianthus*) stem. One is a transverse section, the other is a longitudinal section. In these slides, the thickening material, lignin, has stained red.
8. Examine the transverse section. You will see a number of vascular bundles. Within a vascular bundle, you will see two distinctly different tissues—phloem and xylem.

8 Draw a labelled diagram of a vascular bundle showing the arrangement of phloem and xylem tissue. Refer to a textbook if necessary.

9. Examine the longitudinal section. Locate a vascular bundle and again identify the xylem and phloem. Xylem vessels in *Helianthus* will show the same spiral thickening that you observed in celery. Move the slide so that you follow up or down a column of xylem tissue until you find a part where the ends of two vessels meet.

9 Draw several xylem vessel cells, showing how they are connected vertically to each other.

10 Phloem is made up mostly of sieve tube cells. Move the slide so that you follow up or down the phloem until you find a part where two sieve tube cells join. You may be able to see the sieve plate between them. You may also observe smaller cells in close association with the sieve tube cells. These are likely to be companion cells.

10 Draw several sieve tube cells, showing how they are connected vertically to each other. Include companion cells in your drawing if you see any.

CONCLUSION

11 Using the observations made in this activity and information from your textbook, prepare a labelled diagram showing the structure of a vascular bundle in a flowering plant. Describe the role of the following types of cells:

- xylem vessel cells
- sieve tube cells
- companion cells
- fibre cells.

UNIT 1

How do living things stay alive?

AREA OF STUDY 2

How do living systems sustain life?

Outcome 2

Explain how various adaptations enhance the survival of an individual organism, investigate the relationships between organisms that form a living community and their habitat, and analyse the impacts of factors that affect population growth.

Key knowledge

Survival through adaptations and regulation

- the structural, physiological and behavioural adaptations that enhance an organism's survival and enable life to exist in a wide range of environments
- successful adaptations as models for biomimicry to solve human challenges
- how regulation of factors is needed to maintain a relatively constant internal environment, explained by the stimulus-response model and the use of homeostatic mechanisms including feedback loops
- factors regulated by homeostatic mechanisms in humans, including temperature, blood glucose and water balance
- malfunctions in homeostatic mechanisms that result in diseases, including Type 1 diabetes and hyperthyroidism in humans.

Organising biodiversity

- classification of biodiversity, past and present, into taxonomic groups based on shared morphological and molecular characteristics, and naming using binomial nomenclature
- strategies for managing Earth's biodiversity to support the conservation of species and as a reservoir for the bio-prospecting of new food sources and medicinal drugs.

Relationships between organisms within an ecosystem

- the beneficial, harmful and benign relationships between species including amensalism, commensalism, mutualism, parasitism and predation
- interdependencies between species as represented by food webs, including impact of changes to keystone species
- the distribution, density and size of a population of a particular species within an ecosystem and the impacts of factors including available resources, predation, competition, disease, chance environmental events, births, deaths and migration.

KEY KNOWLEDGE

Adaptations

Adaptations are the characteristics of an organism that assist it to survive and reproduce in its environment. Adaptations are inherited.

An organism's **habitat** is the place where it lives. For example, the habitat of a yellow-footed rock wallaby is the rocky cliffs and outcrops in the Flinders Ranges. The habitat of *Eucalyptus pauciflora* (snow gum) is the high country of the Great Dividing Range.

The **environment** of an organism is made up of the biotic and abiotic factors in its habitat that have an effect on it at some time in its life.

Abiotic factors are the non-living factors in an organism's environment—its physical surroundings.

Biotic factors are the living organisms in an organism's habitat. Humans are inspired to solve problems by copying or mimicking nature's designs. This is called **biomimicry**.

TYPES OF ADAPTATIONS

1 **Structural**—physical features or structures of an organism
Example:
   - Mangroves have specialised aerial roots for oxygen uptake at low tides; they disperse buoyant seeds that have germinated while still attached to the parent plant.

2 **Physiological**—the way in which an organism's body functions
Example:
   - The flowering response of the snow daisy occurs in summer; it can survive low winter temperatures.

3 **Behavioural**—the way in which an organism acts or behaves
Example:
   - Some animals hibernate during cold periods.

The adaptations that organisms have affect their ability to survive in particular environments. In turn, their **distribution** is determined by the presence or absence of features that would make them well suited to a particular environment.

The environment of an organism must provide it with the things it needs—its **requirements**. Requirements include nutrients such as oxygen and water, as well as shelter. If a requirement is in short supply it can affect the survival and reproduction of an organism. This is called a **limiting factor**. For example, if the magnesium concentration in soil is too low to meet the needs of a plant (in this case, the manufacture of chlorophyll) then the plant may not survive. Magnesium is a limiting factor, even if all of the other requirements are met.

All organisms have a **tolerance range** within which they can survive. When conditions move beyond these limits the organism cannot survive. For example, a particular reptile with temperature tolerance limits of 0° to 35°C will survive when this temperature range is met. However, the reptile will die if it is subjected to temperatures outside this range.

Organisms have tolerance limits for a range of factors.

AQUATIC PLANTS

Aquatic plants (hydrophytes) are plants that live either partially or fully submerged in water. This presents problems in acquiring some nutrients; e.g. light and oxygen can be limiting factors. Hydrophytes have adaptations that assist them in overcoming such problems (see Table 1.13).

Mangroves are plants found in the warm tidal waters of much of the Australian coastline. They must cope with a wide range of often harsh environmental factors including excessive exposure to salt and inundation of their roots by water. Pneumatophores (aerial roots) are a structural adaptation that enhances oxygen uptake (see Figure 1.26 on page 49).

Table 1.13 Adaptations of aquatic plants (hydrophytes)

Adaptation	Example
• Leaves flat, few stomata, thin cuticle (submerged plants)	Marine sea grass, fish tank plants
• Emergent roots that protrude above the water	Cumbungi, reeds
• Roots under water, leaves above • Have air-filled spaces to circulate air	Rice
• Floating leaves with stomata on upper surface of leaves	Water lily
• Free floating plants feature air-filled spaces and thick cuticle	Duckweed

KEY KNOWLEDGE

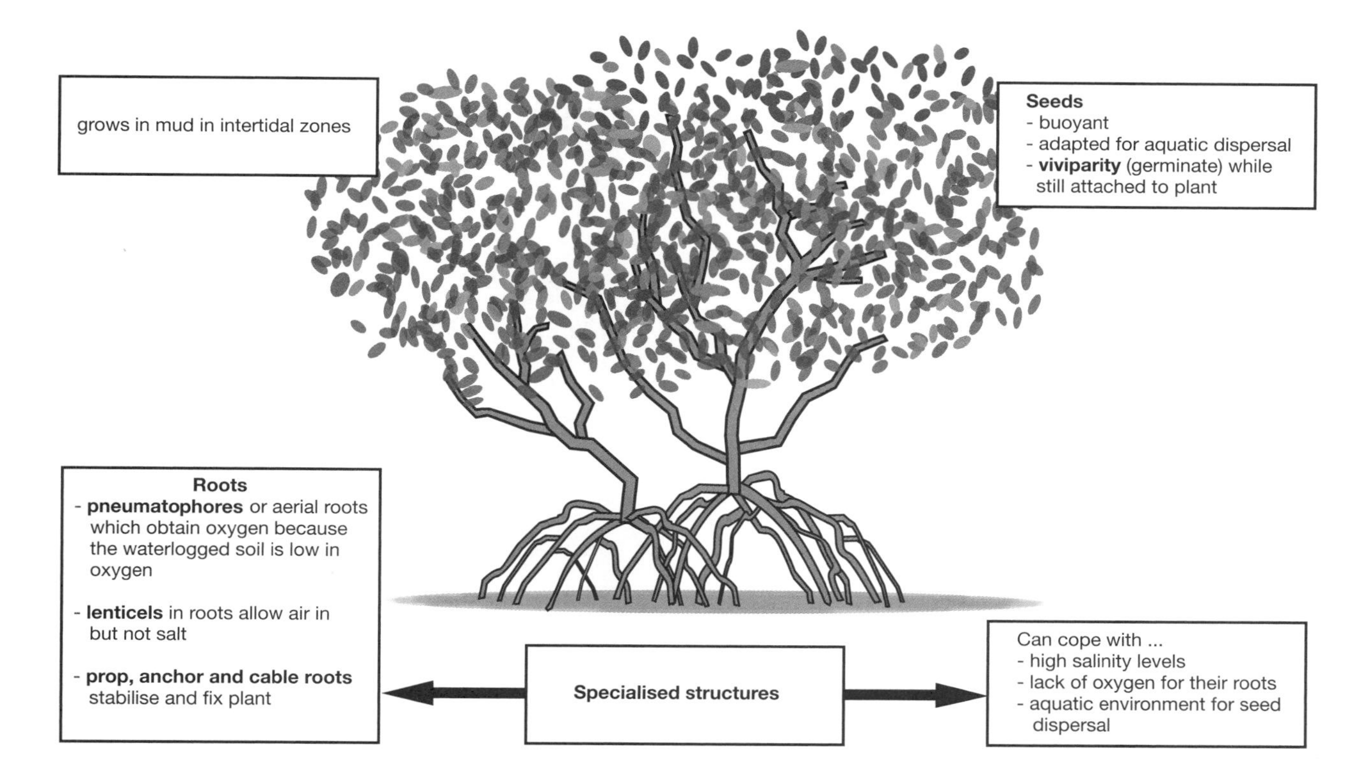

Figure 1.26 Specialised structures of mangroves that have enabled them to adapt

ARID ENVIRONMENTS

Plants in arid environments

Xerophytes are plants that are adapted to hot, dry environments.

- They have adaptations that reduce water loss.
- They have an increased tolerance to dry conditions.
- Adaptations include:
  - thick cuticle—reduces evaporation of water from leaf surface
  - hairs covering leaves—increases humidity around stomata, thereby decreasing the water vapour gradient and reducing the diffusion of water vapour from the stomata to the external air
  - sunken stomata—creates pockets of humid air around stomata, decreasing the water vapour gradient and reducing the diffusion of water vapour from the stomata to the external air
  - fewer stomata from which to lose water
  - reduced leaves—decreased surface area to volume ratio, resulting in smaller surface across which to lose water by evaporation
  - leaves facing away from the sun—reduces temperature of leaves and thereby reducing evaporation.
- Xerophytes are of two types:
  - fleshy succulents (fleshy thick-stemmed), e.g. cacti
  - sclerophylls (hard-leaved), e.g. eucalypts.

Cacti obtain and retain more water than non-succulent plants. They can have:

- downward pointing spines to direct condensed water vapour downwards to drip on roots; deter herbivores
- no leaves (reducing surface area of plant to conserve water)
- specialised water-storage cells in stem
- a thick cell epidermis to reduce evaporation
- a thin layer of cells for photosynthesis
- globular or rod-shaped leaves (decreasing surface to volume ratio); are covered with white hairs or wax.

Halophytes are plants that are adapted to high levels of salt. They are able to survive because they have mechanisms for removing excess salt. Plants may remove salt by:

- excretion of salt through salt glands
- shedding leaves that have a high salt content.

Adaptations to fire

Some Australian plants are able to survive the extreme temperatures that accompany bushfire.

- **Lignotuber:** swelling at the base of the stem or trunk that allows regeneration even after the shoot has perished, e.g. mallee eucalypts
- **Epicormic bud:** bud tissue that lies beneath the bark of some trees from which new plant tissue grows after fire.

KEY KNOWLEDGE

Animals in arid environments

The desert is a harsh environment with very little rainfall and extreme temperatures. Desert animal life is not abundant.

Animals that live in the desert have adaptations to cope with the lack of water, the extreme temperatures, and the shortage of food.

Adaptations can be structural, physiological or behavioural. Some of the adaptations shown by land animals to the arid environment are listed in Table 1.14.

Figure 1.27 Australian hopping mouse

Figure 1.28 Thorny devil

Table 1.14 Adaptations of animals to arid environments

	Adaptation		
	Structural	**Physiological**	**Behavioural**
Low water availability	Relatively round body shape reduces surface area to volume ratio and thus reduces water loss, e.g. water-holding frog *Cyclorana*	Tolerate high body temperatures Do not pant or sweat Do not drink—get sufficient water from food and body metabolism Reptiles and birds excrete uric acid Accelerated life cycle during wet seasons Hibernation Mammals produce concentrated urine	Reduced activity Nocturnal Lick fur Spend time in shade
High temperature	Small body size Body covering of thick coat of insulating fur, exoskeleton or shell Grooves in skin to collect water	Excrete almost-dry faeces Rich network of capillaries in mouth and nose increases heat loss Hibernation	Change body posture and orientation to maximise heat loss Nocturnal activity—avoid the heat of day Live in burrows where temperatures are lower

DETECTING, RESPONDING AND HOMEOSTASIS

Detecting and responding to change is critical to the survival of organisms. Plants and animals have different mechanisms for meeting these demands.

Regulation of the internal environment in multicellular animals is more complex than in plants. It relies on the integration and coordination of both the **central nervous** and **endocrine** systems to maintain internal conditions within a relatively narrow range (see Figure 1.29). This ability to maintain a relatively stable internal environment is called **homeostasis**.

The **internal environment** of multicellular organisms is the extracellular fluid—the fluid surrounding the cells including the blood plasma. The **external environment** is the medium in which an organism lives.

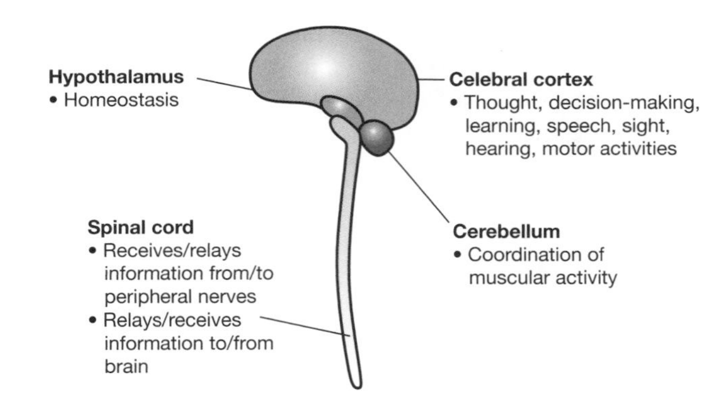

Figure 1.29 The central nervous system and selected endocrine glands

KEY KNOWLEDGE

Multicellular organisms may display homeostatic control in relation to many aspects of their internal environment, including:

- core body temperature
- blood concentrations of glucose; hormones, (e.g. insulin), carbon dioxide, inorganic ions
- oxygen levels
- pH of blood
- blood pressure
- solute concentration (water balance).

Homeostasis in vertebrates is achieved through the integration of the **nervous** and **endocrine** systems. Together they regulate the activities of other body systems. Maintaining internal conditions within narrow limits relies on feedback loops called **negative feedback mechanisms**.

The nervous system

The mammalian nervous system is composed of

- the central nervous system (CNS)—brain and spinal cord
- the peripheral nerves—nerves that relay information to and from the CNS.

Responses coordinated by the nervous system may be voluntary (under conscious control) or involuntary. Involuntary activities are under the control of the **autonomic nervous system**, which regulates unconscious activities such as digestion and metabolism, as well as life-sustaining functions such as heartbeat and breathing.

The functional unit of the nervous system is the nerve cell (neuron). See Figure 1.30.

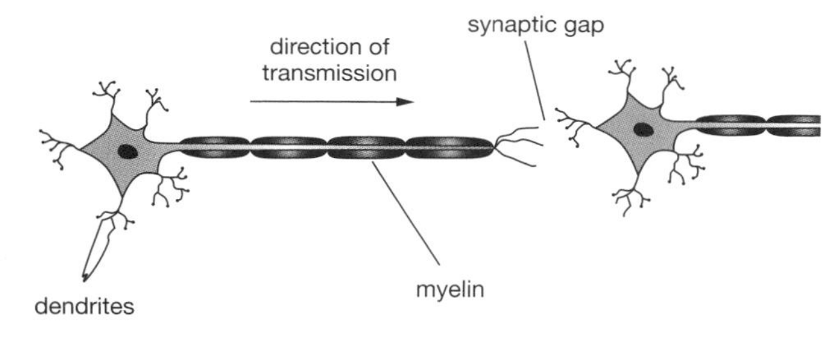

Figure 1.30 A neuron

Information is conducted along a nerve cell as an electric impulse, or **action potential**. The magnitude of an action potential does not vary—when a nerve cell is electrically stimulated an action potential either occurs or does not occur; that is, the stimulus is sufficient to generate an action potential or not.

Communication between nerve cells occurs by chemical transmission (**neurotransmitter**) across the **synaptic gap**.

Reflex responses

A reflex response is the simplest kind of nerve pathway (see Figure 1.31). Sensory neurons are stimulated, resulting in a rapid and automatic response. Such responses come under the **sympathetic division** of the autonomic nervous system. Reflex responses generally protect the body from further harm by immediately removing the affected part of the body from the stimulus.

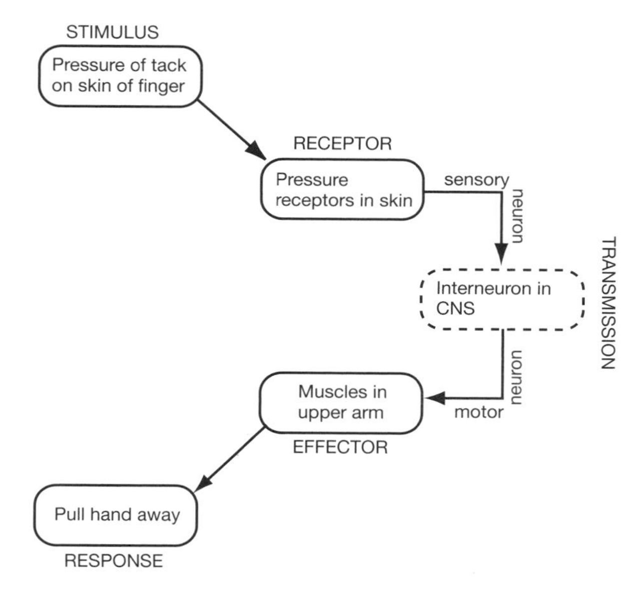

Figure 1.31 A reflex response

The endocrine system

The endocrine system is a system of 'ductless' glands that produce hormones involved in the regulation of various body functions (See Figure 1.32). Hormones:

- travel from the glands that produce them to target tissue where they exert their effect
- travel via the bloodstream
- are specific, initiating a response only in target tissue
- are effective in low concentrations
- elicit responses that are relatively slow and long-lasting compared to nervous responses.

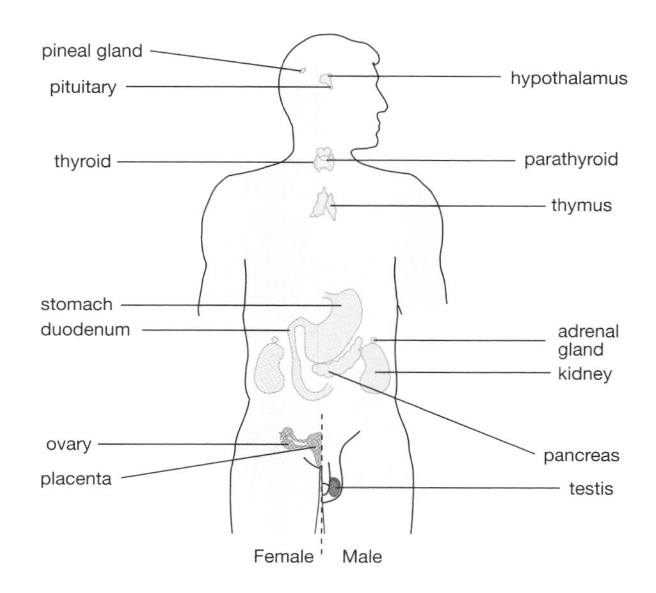

Figure 1.32 The endocrine system

KEY KNOWLEDGE

FEEDBACK LOOPS

Disturbance detectors alert the body to changes in the internal or external environment, initiating appropriate responses. When factors in the internal environment move beyond the 'normal range' **misalignment detectors** come into play and the body mounts a more vigorous response to correct the situation.

Negative feedback

Negative feedback is an important homeostatic mechanism. It is a stimulus–response mechanism in which the response reduces the magnitude of the original stimulus. This returns the internal environment to its original state.

Negative feedback operates to maintain various factors of the internal environment in multicellular animals, such as blood glucose regulation, temperature in endothermic animals and water balance.

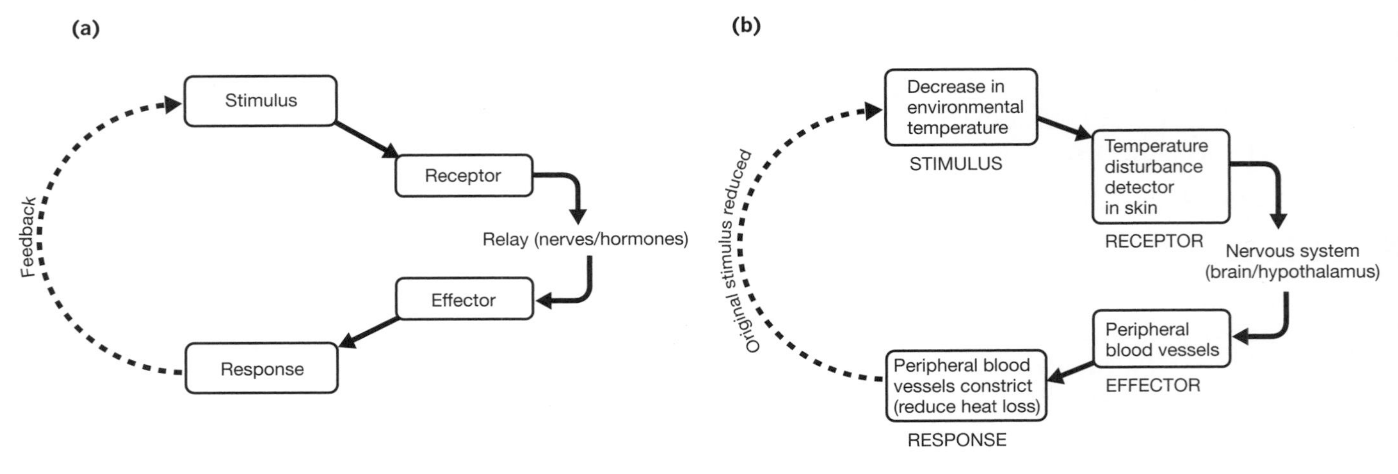

Figure 1.33 **(a)** Negative feedback model. **(b)** Negative feedback and temperature control.

BLOOD GLUCOSE REGULATION

Blood glucose levels are regulated by an interplay of the hormones **insulin** and **glucagon**. Insulin decreases blood glucose level when it is high. Glucagon increases blood glucose level when it is low. (see Figure 1.34).

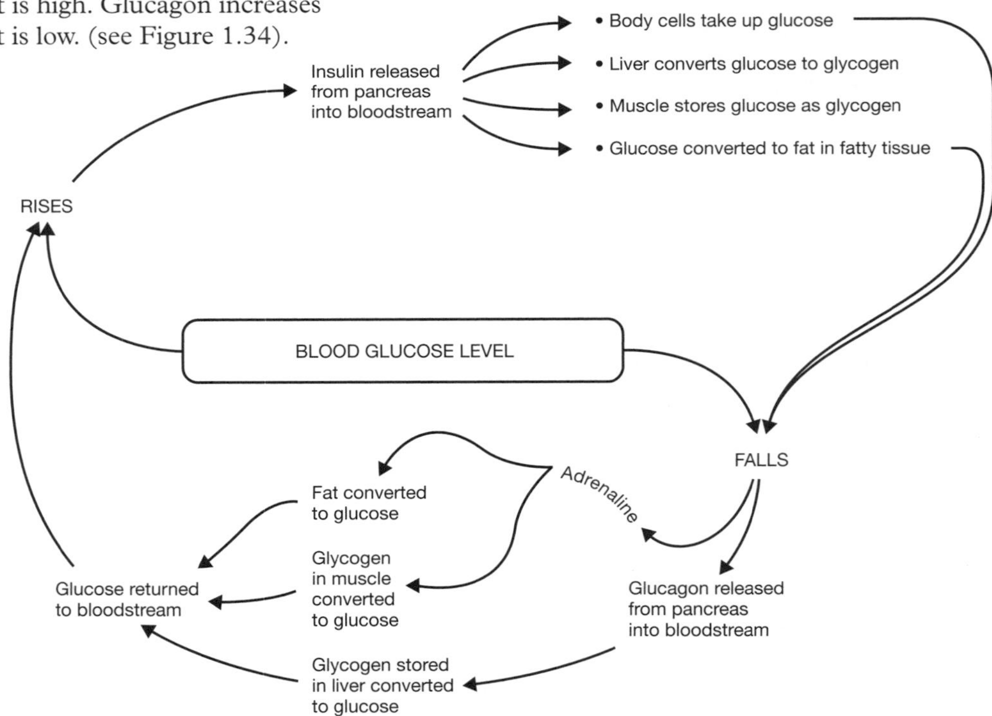

Figure 1.34 Concept map—blood glucose level control

KEY KNOWLEDGE

Temperature regulation

The body temperature of **ectotherms** is dependent on their environment, but **endotherms** generate their own body heat through metabolic processes, and tend to maintain an internal body temperature that is above that of the environment. **Heterotrophs** sometimes operate as endotherms and sometimes as ectotherms.

Multicellular animals display different kinds of adaptations with respect to temperature control. These may be structural, behavioural or physiological (see Table 1.15).

Temperature **disturbance detectors** in the skin detect changes in the external environment. The body responds in ways that ensure no change to the core body temperature. When these responses are not sufficient to maintain core body temperature within the optimal range, **misalignment detectors** recognise the change to core body temperature and a more vigorous response is put in place to return the body temperature to normal.

Table 1.15 Examples of adaptations to temperature regulation

Type of adaptation	Example	Description
Structural	Fur, feathers	Provide a layer of insulation, reducing the loss of heat
Behavioural	Retreating to a burrow in hot conditions	Reduces exposure to excessive heat, reducing heat gain
Behavioural	Huddling Panting Licking fur	Reduces surface area of group that is exposed to environment, thereby reducing heat loss by individuals
Physiological	Sweating	Evaporative cooling—heat energy from the body is lost as water evaporates from body surfaces, thereby having a cooling effect
Physiological	Dilation of peripheral blood vessels in hot conditions	Increases surface area across which heat can be lost to environment
Physiological	Constriction of peripheral blood vessels in cold conditions	Reduces surface area across which heat can be lost to environment

Water balance

Maintaining water balance presents different challenges for aquatic and terrestrial organisms. Aquatic organisms face challenges in relation to internal solute concentrations and water balance. This varies enormously between salt water and freshwater environments. Solute concentration in **osmoconformers** is the same as the solute concentration of the external environment in which they live. **Osmoregulators** control their body solute concentrations (Table 1.16).

Terrestrial animals face continual water stress. They have different kinds of adaptations to achieve water balance. Water is lost through the excretion of harmful nitrogenous wastes that are produced during metabolism. It is also lost from the respiratory surfaces, from skin and in faeces. Water loss can be reduced, depending on the form in which the nitrogenous wastes are removed from the body. This is specific to different kinds of organisms—the form of nitrogenous waste produced is dependent on the availability of water.

The nitrogenous waste produced by the cells of mammals is called **urea**. Urea is toxic to cells. It is soluble in water and removed at the kidneys in the urine.

Table 1.16 Body solute concentration and water balance

Osmoregulator	Body solute concentration	Maintain solute concentration by
Freshwater fish	Higher than external environment	Rarely drink; Actively take up salts; Large volume dilute urine
Saltwater fish	Lower than external environment	Drink sea water; Actively excrete salts; Small volume concentrated urine

KEY KNOWLEDGE

Classifying organisms

PURPOSE OF CLASSIFICATION

- Communicate biological knowledge effectively among scientists and naturalists.
- Identify harmful or dangerous organisms.
- Recognise potentially beneficial organisms, e.g. for food or sources of drugs.
- Understand relationships between various organisms, e.g. to control pests and diseases.
- Be able to cope with the vast diversity (biodiversity) of organisms on the planet and understand interactions between them and humans, particularly if species are endangered.

PRINCIPLES OF CLASSIFICATION

Classification involves sorting similar organisms into groups. Sorting can be based on similarities in:

- external characteristics
- mode of reproduction
- internal anatomy
- physiology
- genetic material.

Naming of biological groups is referred to as **taxonomy**. Groups can be large or small, and represent different levels of biological classification (in the form of a **hierarchy**). Groups at the top contain many organisms that share a few major similarities, while those at the bottom contain fewer organisms that share many common characteristics (see Figure 1.35).

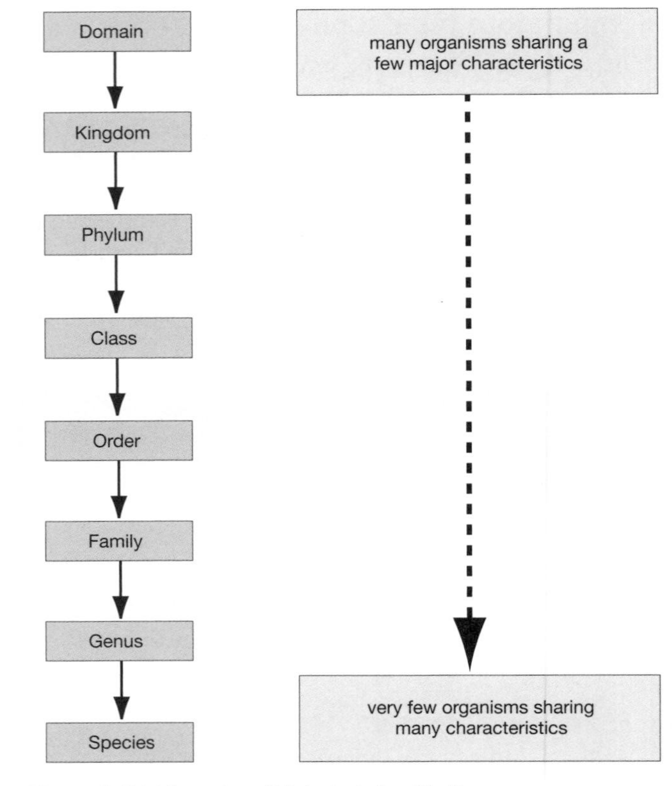

Figure 1.35 Hierarchy of biological classification

Organisms that belong to the same class must also belong to the same **domain**, **kingdom** and **phylum**. At the bottom of the hierarchy is the **species** level (see Figure 1.35).

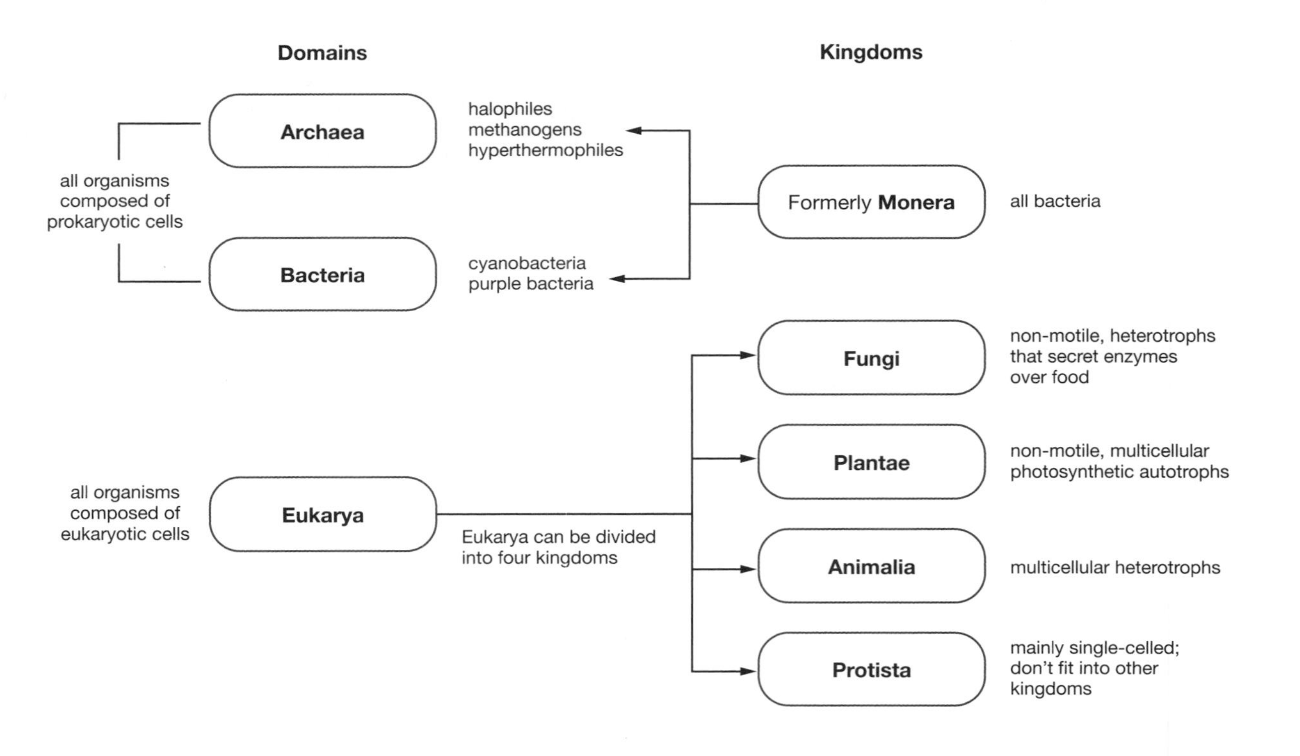

Figure 1.36 Relationship between the three-domain and five-kingdom classification systems

A species is a group of similar individuals that are able to reproduce in their natural environment to produce fertile offspring.

The naming of species is based on a **binomial system** developed by Carl von Linné, also known as the **Linnaeus system** of classification.

Each organism is given two Latinised words for its scientific name.

The first is the generic name (genus name).

The second is the specific descriptive name.

For example, the red kangaroo (common name) has the scientific name *Macropus rufus*.

This naming system avoids ambiguity and clearly indicates which organism is being referred to, no matter what language you speak.

CONSTRUCTING TAXONOMIC GROUPS

Classification systems have varied over the years, mainly due to our ever-growing knowledge of organisms and the advances in technology that allow us to study them in more detail (e.g. DNA technology). Organisms have been classified into five kingdoms, but recently a further division into domains has occurred.

Classification keys allow organisms to be identified based on observable features. Dichotomous keys provide an alternative choice of features that leads to accurate identification.

Managing biodiversity

The last couple of hundred years has seen a dramatic decrease in biodiversity on Earth. This has been largely due to human activity, either by direct or indirect means. Today, strategies are in place to maintain biodiversity and to reduce the rate of biodiversity loss.

Conservation reserves

- These are areas set aside under government protection.
- Habitats and communities, including the **protected species** they support, can be monitored.
- They don't have to be enormous; some species survive extremely well in remnant strips of vegetation along roads.
- These strips also act as **corridors** or links to larger reserves.

Small habitats

- These have small populations that are more vulnerable to disturbance.
- Experience inbreeding, which leads to low genetic variety and therefore reduced ability to adapt to change.
- They have a larger edge relative to their area than large reserves. More individuals are exposed to **edge effects**—greater exposure to the weather, predators, etc.

Some conservation bodies

- World Wide Fund for Nature (WWF)
- World Heritage List

Table 1.17 Reasons for species conservation

Aesthetic	Ecological	Practical
Simple pleasure of enjoying the living record of biodiversity	All species interact with one another, including us. All organisms are linked and the loss of one could affect many others.	Plants provide us with food, shelter, fuel, medicines, etc. Animals provide us with food, clothing, labour, companionship etc.

Components of ecosystems

COMMUNITIES OF LIVING ORGANISMS

A **community** is a group of different species living together and interacting with one another in a particular **habitat**, the physical place where they live. An **ecosystem** is a system of organisms interacting with one another and with their non-living surroundings.

A microhabitat is a small living space within a larger habitat.

- **Biotic factors**: living organisms in the environment.
- **Abiotic factors**: non-living or physical factors in the environment (Table 1.18 on page 56).

A **self-sustaining ecosystem** does not require any external input to preserve the species within it. A lake aquatic system is self-sustaining because all the species within the community can survive and reproduce without interaction with factors outside the lake. A cliff-side nesting ground of gulls is not self-sustaining because the gulls need to go out to sea to fish.

ECOLOGICAL GROUPINGS

There are three main ways of naming an ecosystem:

1. Focus on major abiotic factors for a label, e.g. marine, freshwater and terrestrial.
2. Identify the dominant species or most abundant species of the system, e.g. oyster community or eucalyptus forest.
3. Describe by the plant community of the system. The description is made up of a combination of the tallest or dominant plant and the percentage sunlight coverage of the canopy, e.g. closed-forest.

KEY KNOWLEDGE

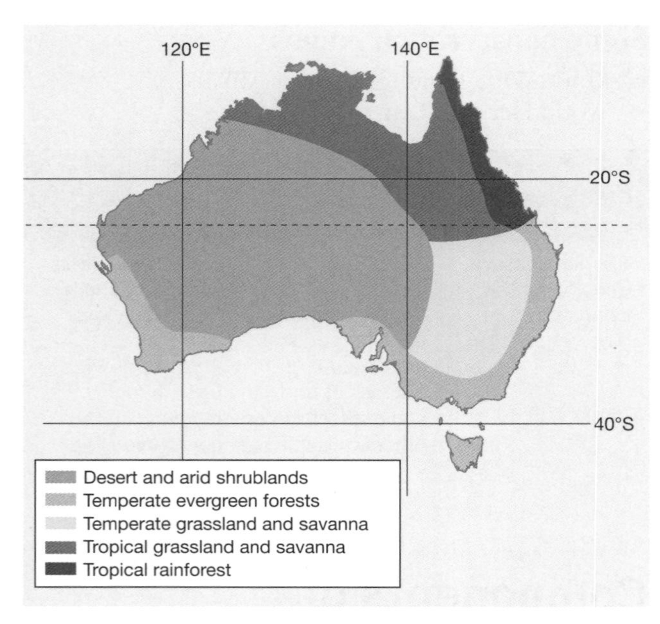

Figure 1.37 Distribution of major biomes of Australia

A **biome** is a general description of an ecosystem defined by its climate or specific characteristics, e.g. alpine, coral reef (see Figure 1.37).

The Earth is a **biosphere** that contains all the ecosystems in the world.

ECOLOGICAL NICHE

All organisms in an ecosystem interact with other organisms and with their non-living surroundings. These relationships are important in maintaining the stability of the ecosystem. The role that a particular species occupies in an ecosystem is called its **ecological niche**. For example, the niche of plants in an ecosystem is that of producer—through photosynthesis they manufacture organic compounds for their own growth. In so doing they provide an energy source for consumers. Bacteria occupy the niche of decomposer, recycling materials from organisms that have died so they become available to be used again.

Australian habitats

Table 1.18 Abiotic characteristics of habitats

Terrestrial			Aquatic	
Tropical (north)	**Temperate (south)**	**Semi-arid to arid desert**	**Freshwater**	**Marine**
• High rainfall • Warm • Rainforests	• Cool • High altitudes • Winter snow	• Low rainfall • Desert-like environment • Hot	Relatively low water salt concentration; inland lakes, rivers, streams	Relatively high water salt concentrations; sea/ocean

AQUATIC ENVIRONMENTS

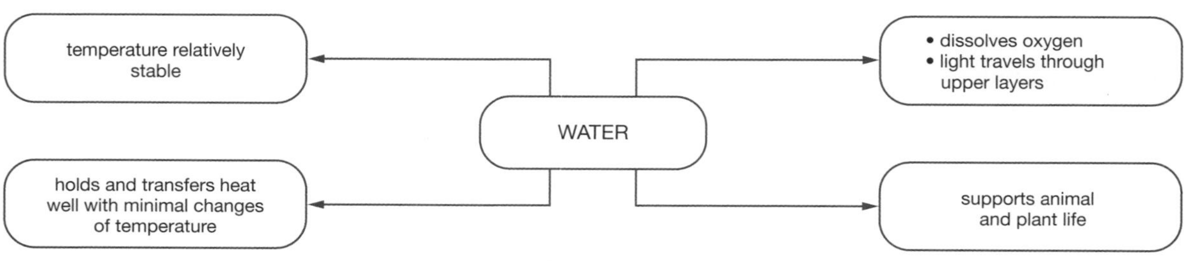

Figure 1.38 Advantages that come from living in aquatic environments

Relationships between organisms

Organisms living together in an environment constantly interact with and influence each other. These interactions can be benign, beneficial or harmful to the organisms.

FEEDING RELATIONSHIPS

Predator–prey food chains are linear sequences of 'who eats who'. Each level of feeding within the food chain is called a **trophic level** (see Figure 1.39).

Parasite–host food chains:

- small organism, the **parasite**, living on or inside a larger organism, the **host**
- the parasite takes nutrients and resources directly from the body of its host
- has complex life cycle, often involved in several different food chains at different stages of development.

Food webs show how various organisms are a part of many linking food chains within a community. A particular organism can be at multiple **trophic levels** within a food web. Ecosystems and food webs include **keystone species**. Keystone species play a critical role in maintaining the integrity of an ecosystem. Their removal destabilises the ecosystem (see Figure 1.40).

The direction of arrows indicates the flow of energy along a food chain. Removing a species from a food web affects other organisms in the food web.

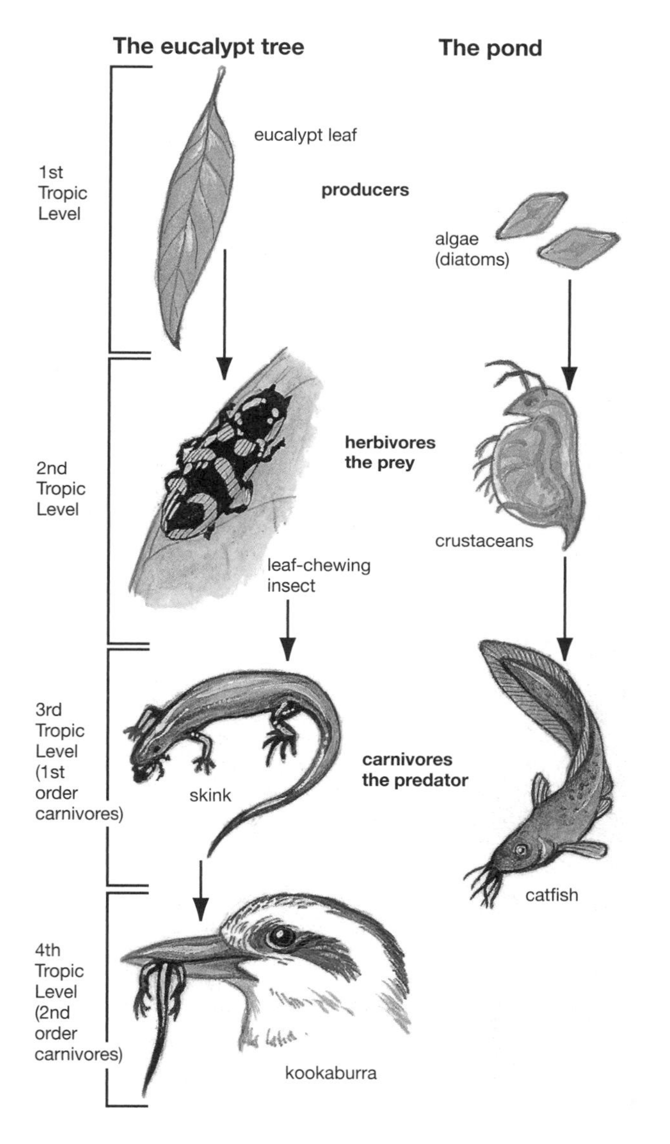

Figure 1.39 Two simple food chains, one in the eucalypt tree and one in the pond. These include examples of predator–prey food chains.

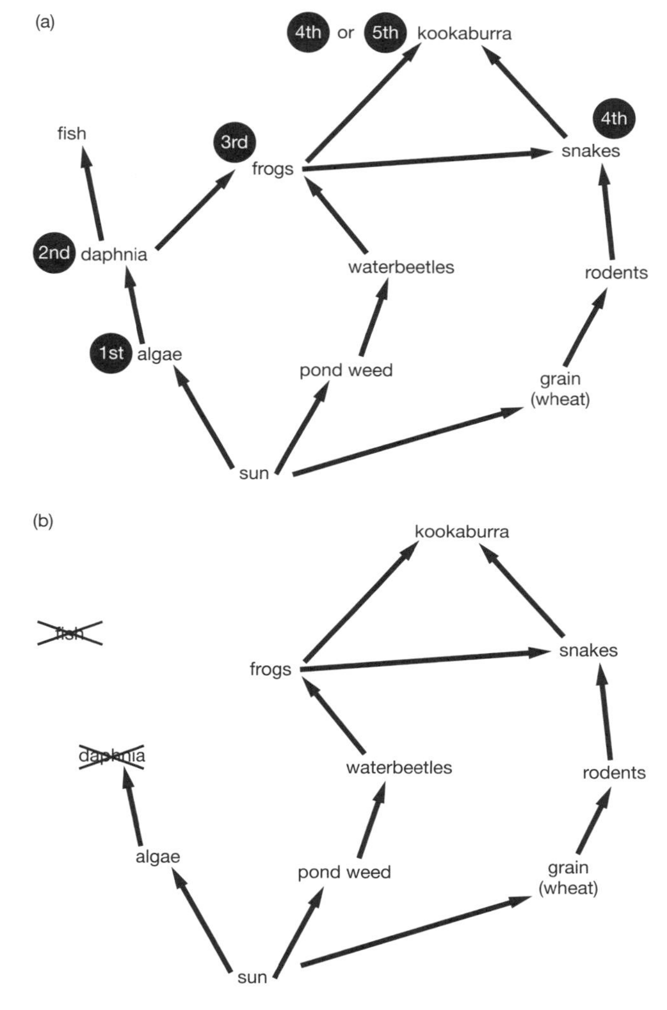

Figure 1.40 **(a)** A hypothetical food web. The kookaburra is at both 4th and 5th trophic levels, i.e. it is both a 4th and a 5th order consumer. **(b)** The domino effect on trophic levels. When daphnia is removed from the food web, frogs lose a source of food but survive, while fish lose their food source and die out. Complex webs are more stable because organisms are involved in more than one food chain.

KEY KNOWLEDGE

Table 1.19 Components of food chains

Type	Acquires energy through	Example
Producer/autotroph	Photosynthesis	All green plants
Consumer/heterotroph	Feeds on other organisms	All animals
• herbivore	Feeds on plant material	Kangaroo
• carnivore	Feeds on other animals	Killer whale
• scavenger	Feeds on dead animals	Tasmanian devil
• detritivore	Feeds on decomposing and waste material	Worm
• omnivore	Feeds on both plant and animal matter	Bear
Parasite	Takes nutrients from other organisms often harming the host	Tapeworm, mistletoe, flea
Decomposer	Breaks down dead matter	Bacteria

SYMBIOSIS

Symbiosis is a relationship in which two organisms live in close association with each other and in which at least one organism benefits from the relationship (Table 1.20).

When organisms have the same survival requirements, they must compete for the limited resources.

Competition

Interspecific competition: organisms of different species compete for the same resources, e.g. various bird species in a forest competing for nest sites.

Intraspecific competition: different individuals of the same species compete for resources. e.g. male koalas fighting over mating rights with females.

Figure 1.41 The ivy vine growing on the tree trunk is an epiphyte. They are supported by the tree but do not obtain food from it, and they do not affect the health of the tree.

Table 1.20 Types of symbiosis

Type	Species A	Species B	Examples
Amensalism	No effect	Harmed	Human activity of deforestation is detrimental to the species of plants and animals that inhabit the forest, however there is no biological benefit to the humans
Mutualism	Benefits	Benefits	Alga and fungus living together as lichen Plant roots and soil fungi co-exist, exchanging sugars and phosphorus in a relationship specifically called mycorrhiza
Commensalism	Benefits	No effect	Perching plants, epiphytes, use a tree as a surface to live on for good access to sunlight Remora living on the side of a shark, eating food scraps from shark kills
Parasitism	Benefits	Harmed	Heartworm feeding on the blood of a dog Mistletoe absorbing nutrients from a host tree

Population dynamics

FACTORS AFFECTING ABUNDANCE AND DISTRIBUTION

- **Population:** number of individuals of the same species living in a particular area.
- **Distribution:** geographic range over which the individuals in the population live.
- **Abundance:** actual number of individuals in the population.

The distribution and abundance of species is related to the availability of their requirments. This includes food, water, shelter, mate and suitable environmental conditions. Factors such as competition for resources, disease and chance environmental events also impact on species.

Biological control is the use of a natural predator or parasite to limit the population of a pest species. For example, prickly pear is successfully controlled by the moth *Cactoblastis cactorum*. The cane toad was introduced to control cane beetles but became a pest species itself.

DETERMINING POPULATION SIZES

Abundance = birth + **immigration**
(individuals moving into existing population)
– death – **emigration**
(individuals moving out of the population)

CARRYING CAPACITY

The **carrying capacity** of an ecosystem is the number of organisms of a particular species that the ecosystem can sustain (Figure 1.42).

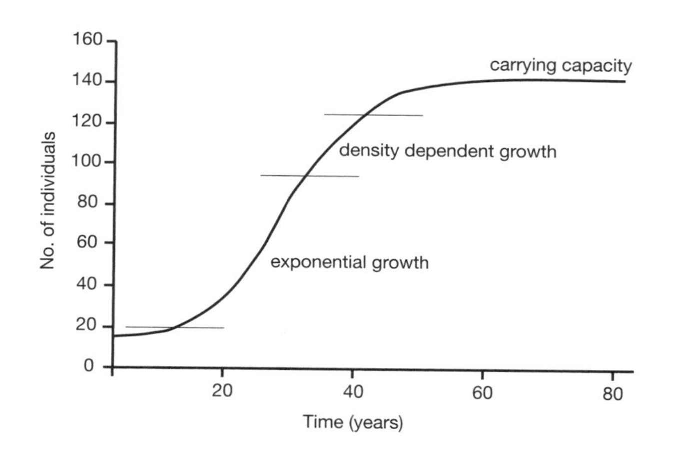

Figure 1.42 Population growth curve

- **Limiting factors** such as the presence of predators restrict populations of organisms from exponential growth, thereby keeping populations in check.
- **Population explosions** (exponential growth) occur when an ecosystem doesn't have sufficient factors to limit the population growth. For example, the crown-of-thorns sea star in the Great Barrier Reef has abundant food resources, high reproductive success but few predators.
- When factors such as birth rate and immigration are in balance with death rate and emigration, populations of organisms are maintained at a constant level.

Table 1.21 Factors that determine distribution and abundance of organisms

	Abiotic characteristics of environment	Biotic characteristics of organism	Biotic interactions between organisms
Explanation	The physical limitations of the environment	The physical, functional and behavioural adaptations of the organism	How all the species in a community affect and influence each other
Example	The availability of water in a desert	Koalas' ability to digest leaves that other herbivores cannot digest	Prey populations will explode without predators to keep them in check

Techniques of monitoring and maintaining ecosystems

QUADRATS AND TRANSECTS

A **quadrat** is an area marked out with a frame for the purpose of gathering data related to populations of organisms in a given area.

- It is usually 1 m^2 but can be adapted to suit the specific ecosystem.
- A number of quadrats placed randomly around the habitat can provide a useful estimate of the presence, abundance and density of different species within the area.

A **transect** is a line marked out randomly through a habitat.

- Every organism on the line at regular intervals or within the transect is recorded.
- Variations in community composition throughout the habitat can be assessed.
- **Line transects** are time-efficient and can minimise disturbance to the environment. However, species of low abundance can be missed.
- **Belt transects** extend out a specific distance to either side of the line. They are time-intensive but can provide more accurate estimates of community populations.

Permanent quadrats and transects can be used to measure, estimate and predict changes in the diversity and abundance of populations over time.

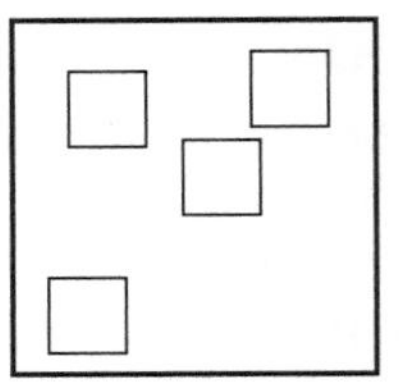

quadrat sampling

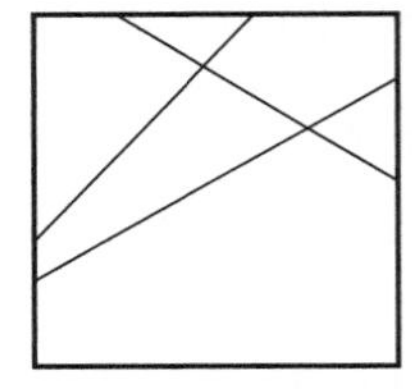

line transect sampling

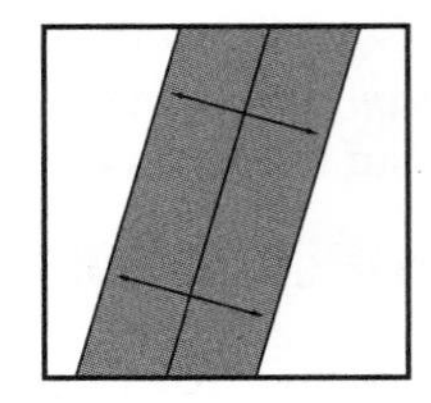

belt transect sampling

Figure 1.43 Sampling methods

Monitoring environmental factors

Environmental factors affect the ability of organisms to function at an optimal level. Various tools and techniques are used to monitor environmental factors, as shown in Table 1.22. The use of such tools and techniques is important in the management of plants, animals and environmental resources.

Table 1.22 Techniques to monitor environmental change

Factor	Technique for monitoring factor	Notes
pH	pH probe measures degree of acidity/alkalinity in soil or water	Different species of plants have particular pH requirements in order to grow efficiently. Australian inland waters have a pH range of 6 to 9. Aquatic organisms tolerate a wide range of pH, but will be adversely affected if pH goes beyond this range.
Light	A light meter measures the intensity of light at different levels of penetration in a habitat	The intensity of light is an important factor affecting the distribution of producer organisms (plants) in a given habitat. This, in turn, affects the abundance and distribution of animals that feed either directly or indirectly on the plants.
Oxygen	Probes are available to monitor oxygen concentration	Oxygen is a requirement for organisms; when oxygen availability is reduced below the tolerance limit for organisms, cellular respiration cannot occur at a rate sufficient to provide energy to cells and the organism dies.
Carbon dioxide	Probes are available to monitor carbon dioxide concentration	Plants require carbon dioxide for photosynthesis; high levels of this gas are toxic to animals.

WORKSHEET 13

Crossword—environmental factors and adaptions

Complete the crossword puzzle to help you check your knowledge and understanding of key terms and processes related to the adaptions of organisms to their environments.

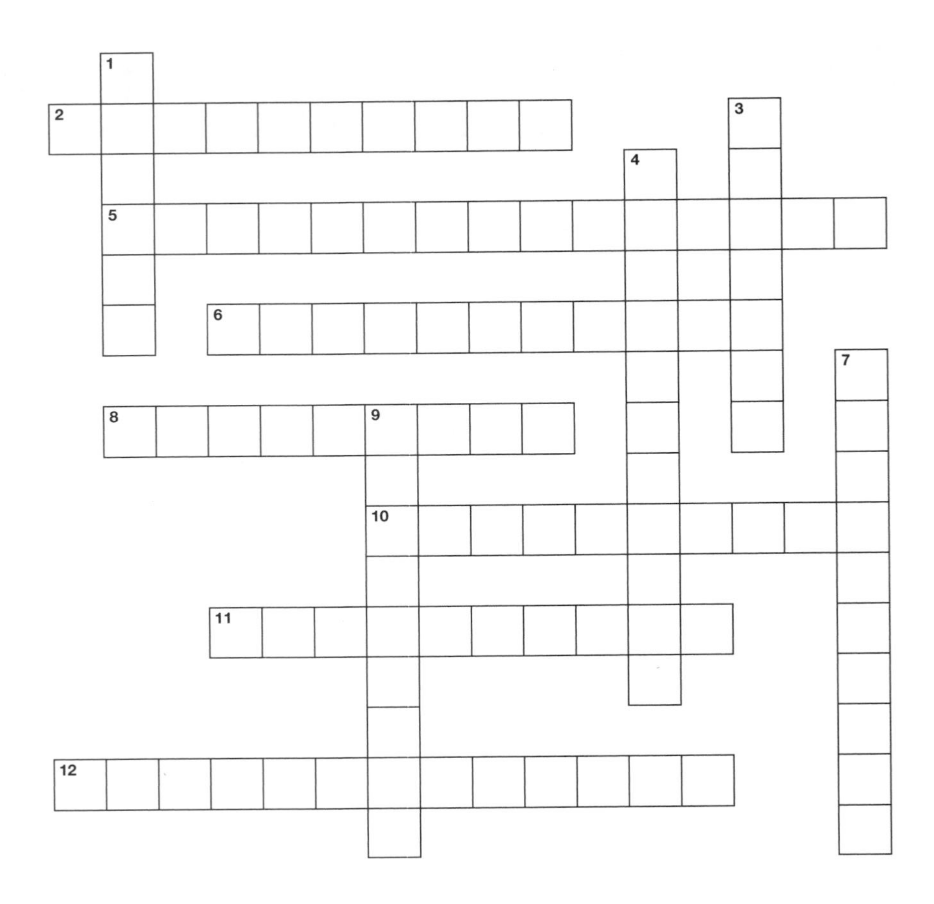

Across

2 The approach in which humans copy adaptions of organisms in nature to solve problems. [10]

5 Range of conditions within which an organism can survive. [15]

6 Surroundings of an organism—includes living and non-living. [11]

8 Type of plant adapted to hot, dry environments. [9]

10 Underground stem that forms a swelling at the base of a tree and allows regrowth after fire. [10]

11 Feature that makes an organism well suited to its environment and/or lifestyle. [10]

12 Aerial root that allows uptake of oxygen in plants whose roots are submerged in water. [13]

Down

1 Describes the living factors in an organism's environment. [6]

3 Describes the non-living factors in an organism's environment. [7]

4 Long term torpor usually triggered by the onset of winter in some animal species. [11]

7 Type of plant that is able to withstand immersion of some parts in water. [10]

9 Type of plant that is tolerant to high levels of salt. [9]

WORKSHEET 14

Amazing adaptations—features for survival

Organisms face many challenges in their respective environments. Features that help them to survive such challenges are called **adaptations**. These can be structural, an anatomical feature; behavioural, related to the way an organism acts; or physiological, related to processes in the body.

Consider the adaptations of the plants and animals shown that help them survive in their particular environments. In each case:

- outline the challenge faced by the organism
- describe how the feature offers survival value
- identify the adaptation as structural, behavioural or physiological.

GOANNA BASKING IN SUN

Challenge: ______________________________

Adaptation: ______________________________

____

____

____

____

Adaptation: Structural Behavioural Physiological

MANGROVE WITH PNEUMATOPHORES (AERIAL ROOTS)

Challenge: ______________________________

Adaptation: ______________________________

____

____

____

____

Adaptation: Structural Behavioural Physiological

SUGAR GLIDER WITH OUTSTRETCHED MEMBRANES

Challenge: ______________________________

Adaptation: ______________________________

____

____

____

____

Adaptation: Structural Behavioural Physiological

STONE PLANT—SUCCULENT LEAVES AND UNDERGROUND GROWTH

Challenge: ______________________________

Adaptation: ______________________________

____

____

____

____

____

____

____

Adaptation: Structural Behavioural Physiological

PELICANS—SALT GLANDS AT BASE OF BEAK

Challenge: ______________________________

Adaptation: ______________________________

____

____

____

____

____

____

____

Adaptation: Structural Behavioural Physiological

MARRAM GRASS—LEAVES ROLL IN DRY CONDITIONS

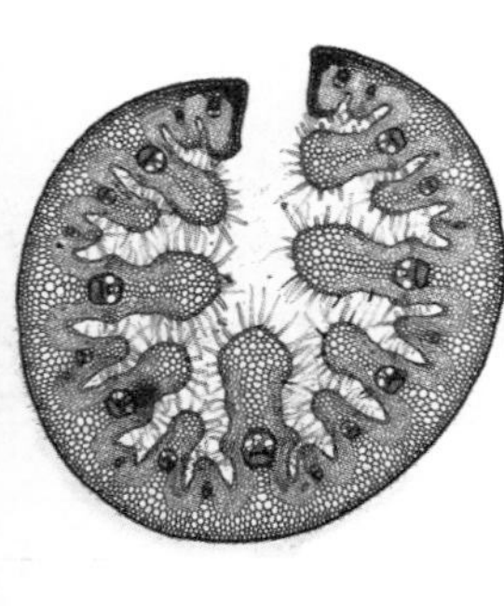

Challenge: ______________________________

Adaptation: ______________________________

____

____

____

____

____

____

____

Adaptation: Structural Behavioural Physiological

WORKSHEET 15

Routine regulation—regulatory mechanisms in animals

1 Select terms from the list below to complete the summary statements outlining the key points in relation to regulatory mechanisms in animals.

synapse	transmission	target cells	cerebral cortex	nervous	cerebellum	
action potential	autonomic	spinal cord	negative feedback	hormones	homeostasis	myelin
brainstem	pituitary gland	neuron	endocrine	hypothalamus	dendrites	peripheral

- The ability of some multicellular organisms to maintain a relatively stable internal environment is called ______________.
- The **regulatory mechanisms** that maintain internal conditions within relatively narrow limits include **communication** between different cells and tissues of the body. This communication is achieved by the integration and coordination of the ______________ system and the ______________ system.
- The functional unit of the nervous system is the ______________. Conduction of information along nerve cells occurs by electric impulse, also called an ______________ ______________.
- In contrast, ______________ secreted by endocrine glands reach their _______ _______ via the bloodstream.
- The nervous system is composed of the **central nervous system** and the ______________ nerves that relay information to and from the central nervous system, enabling the body to respond appropriately to various stimuli.
- The nervous system controls both voluntary and involuntary activities in the body. Involuntary activities are regulated by the ______________ nervous system and include life-sustaining functions such as heart rate and breathing rate, as well as other processes such as cell metabolism and digestion.
- Hormones produced by endocrine glands regulate a variety of body processes including growth, metabolism, blood glucose levels and reproductive cycles.
- Some responses by the body operate to reduce the magnitude of the original stimulus. This is called a ______________ ______________ system. Such mechanisms may involve both nervous and endocrine systems.

2 You will see that there are ten terms remaining. Use the terms to complete the summary information for the central nervous system, endocrine glands and nerve cell shown on page 66. Label the structures indicated and outline their respective roles.

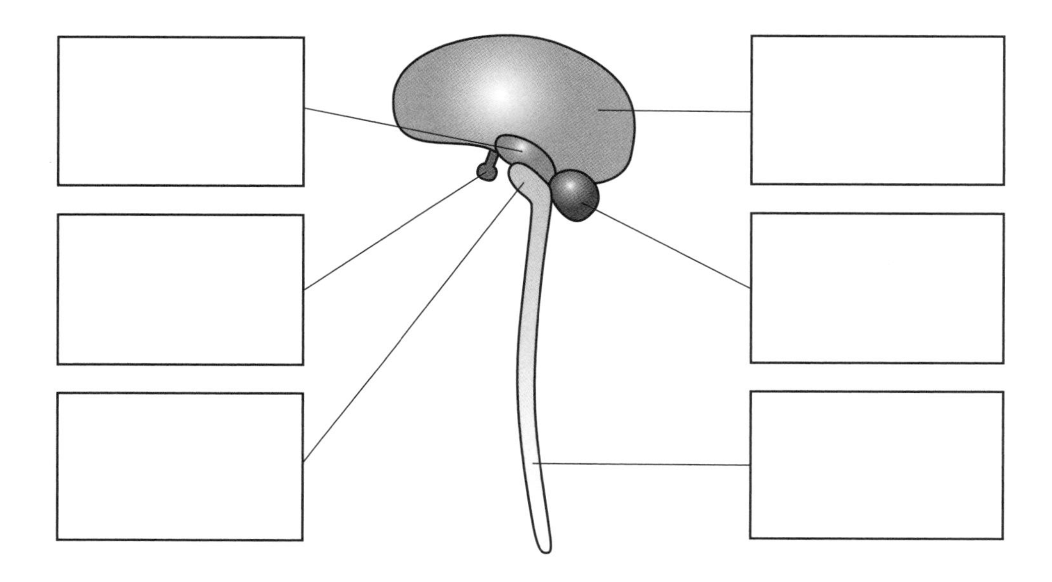

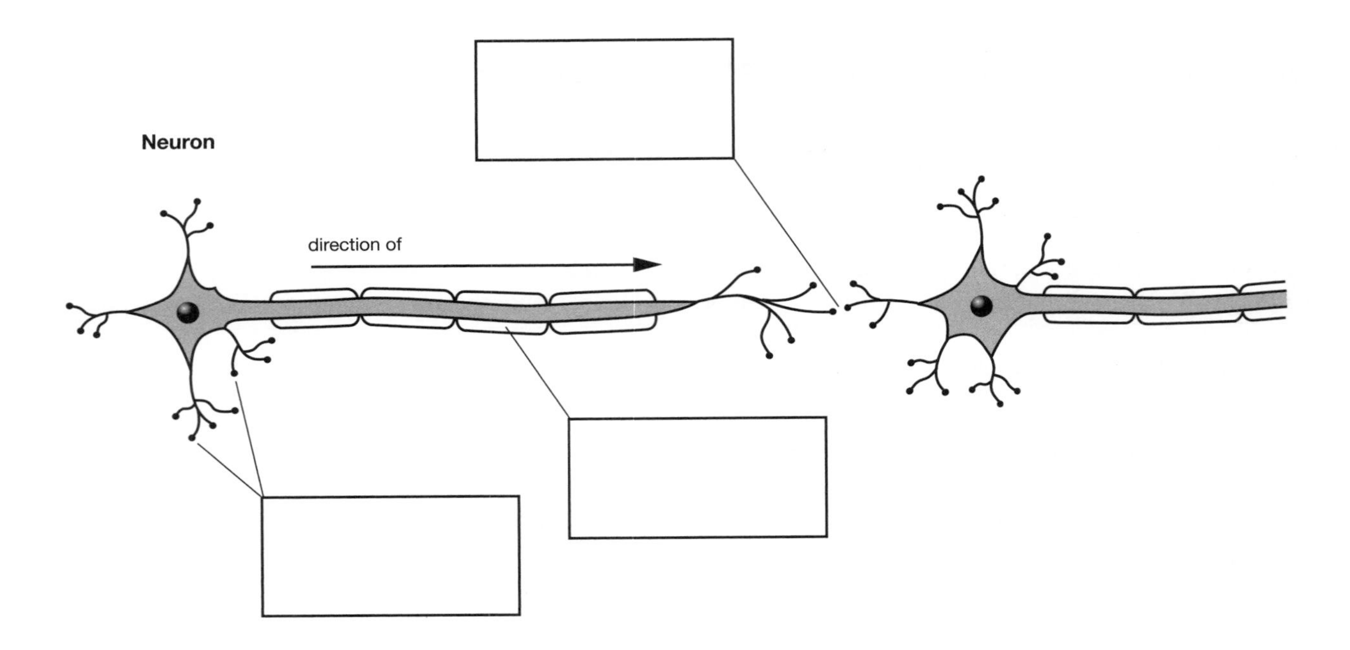
Neuron
direction of

WORKSHEET 16

Integrated impulses—a network of nerves

A **stimulus–response model** is a simple means of representing the pathway taken by nerve impulses from the input of information, its processing through the central nervous system, to the final output in terms of an appropriate response.

1 Consider each of the stimuli listed below. Using a pencil, complete the stimulus–response model by entering the **receptor**, kinds of **nerves** involved in transmission, **effector** and **response** for each stimulus. You may include more than one effector and response in some instances. An example has been completed for you (Figure 1.44).

Example: You prick your finger on a tack.

Stimulus

- A bright light shines into your eyes.
- You hear a sudden loud noise.
- You stand on a sharp object.
- You are hungry and smell dinner cooking.

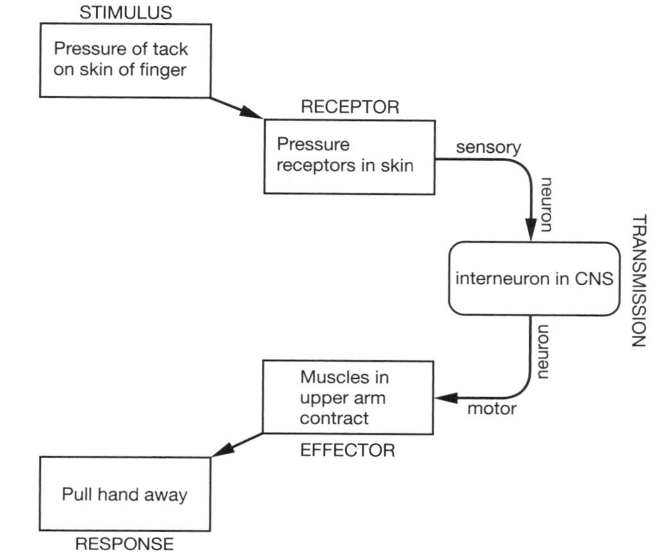

Figure 1.44 Stimulus–response model

2 Some stimulus–response mechanisms are very rapid and occur automatically. This is called a **reflex** response. Use the following terms to describe what happens in a reflex response.

sympathetic division	stimulus	effector
motor neuron	interneuron	response
sensory neuron	central nervous system	

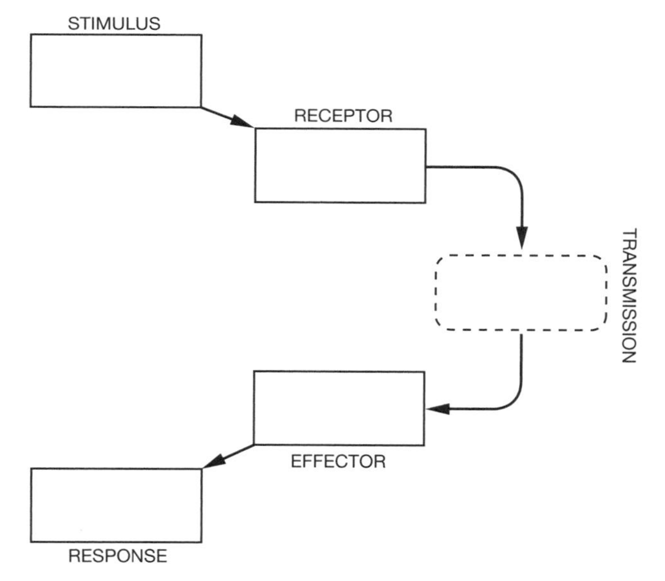

3 Outline the importance of reflex responses to the body.

WORKSHEET 17

Crossword—homeostasis

Complete the crossword puzzle to help you check your knowledge and understanding of key terms and processes related to homeostasis.

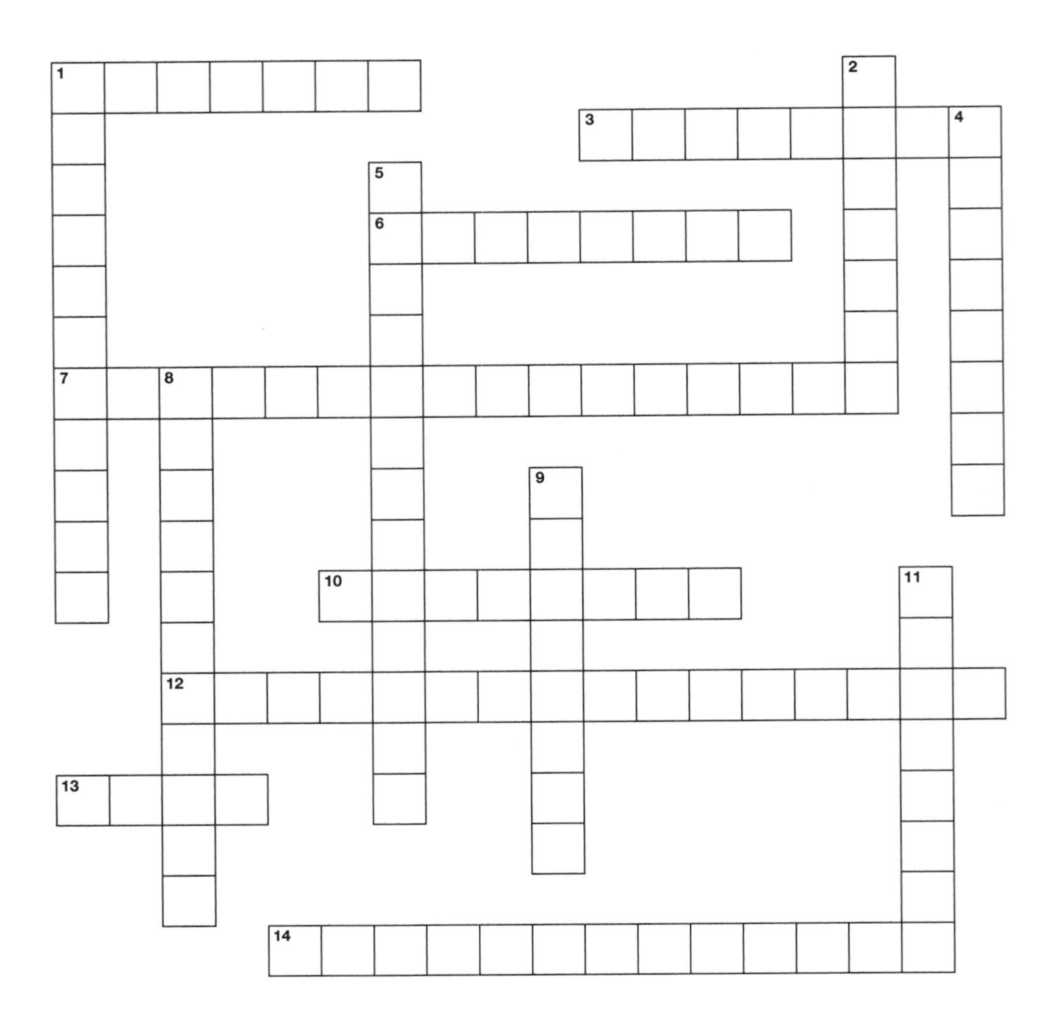

Across

1 Signal molecules that travel through the vascular tissue to target cells where they have their effect. [7]

3 Behavioural or physiological change in an organism resulting from a stimulus. [8]

6 Factor in internal or external environment that causes a response in an organism. [8]

7 Describes the body's homeostatic control of body temperature. [16]

10 Hormone that acts to increase blood glucose level when it is low. [8]

12 A homeostatic mechanism in which the body's response reduces the original stimulus. [16]

13 Form in which nitrogenous wastes are removed from the body at the kidneys. [4]

14 Describes the environment within the cell. [13]

Down

1 Maintenance of relatively stable internal conditions despite changes in the external environment. [11]

2 Hormone produced by the pancreas that reduces blood glucose level. [7]

4 Muscle or gland that responds to a particular stimulus. [8]

5 Organism whose body fluids are maintained at particular concentrations despite different concentrations in their surroundings. [13]

8 This aspect of an organism's surroundings can be intercellular, internal or external. [11]

9 Disease characterised by insulin deficiency. [8]

11 Specialised structure that detects a stimulus. [8]

WORKSHEET 18

Human thermostat—temperature regulation

Negative feedback systems are important homeostatic mechanisms that ensure the internal environment remains within narrow limits. A negative feedback model is set out as a guide.

Example: It's a warm day, you're playing sport and forgot your water bottle.

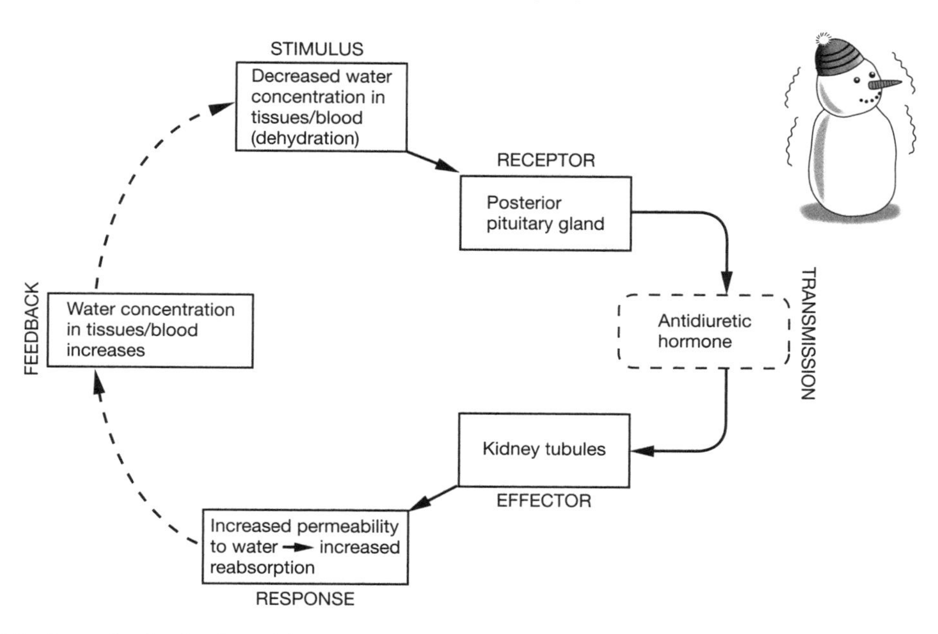

Figure 1.45 A negative feedback model

1 Use a pencil to complete the negative feedback model below. List the receptor, means of transmission, effector, response and feedback for the different stimuli listed. You may include more than one effector and response.

Stimulus

- It snows—you are outside and unprepared.
- You are outside on a very hot summer day.

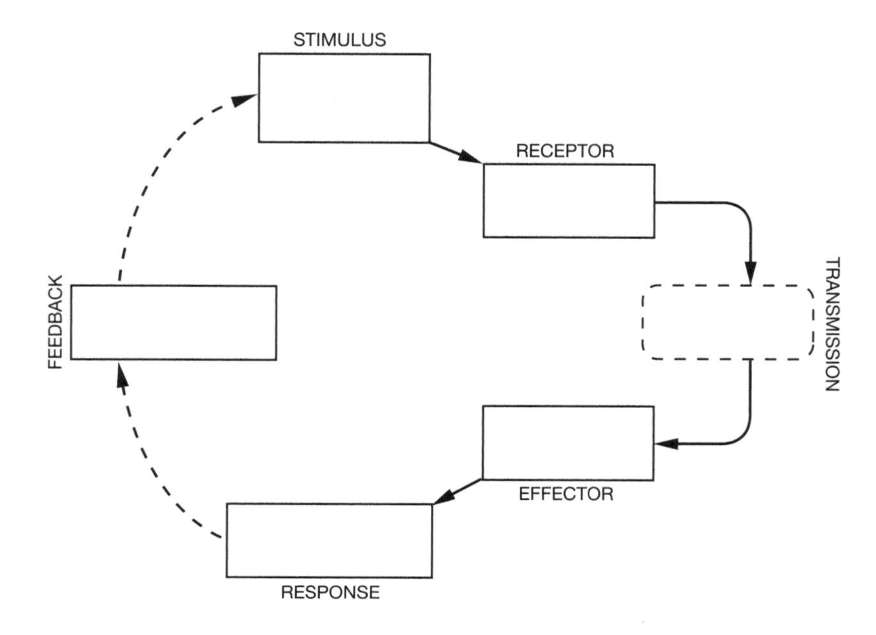

2 Outline the difference between a stimulus–response model and a negative feedback model.

3 Summarise the importance of negative feedback systems to the body.

WORKSHEET 19

Classy classification—identifying individuals

1 Use the key words listed and your knowledge of classification to complete the summary notes and table below.

order	bacteria	biodiversity	class	Plantae	Animalia	phylum
genus	family	Protista	Fungi	taxonomy	species	Archaea

- The enormous variety of living organisms on Earth is described as ______________________.
- Scientists group or classify organisms according to features they possess. This practice is called ____________.
- There are different levels of classification. The largest single group of living things is the kingdom. The smallest taxonomic group is a ____________.
- There are three domains and four kingdoms.

Domain	Kingdom	Features of organisms in this taxonomic group	Examples of organisms

- The eight levels of classification are:
  Domain, ______________________, ______________________, ______________________,
  ______________________, ______________________, ______________________, species
- A species is defined as ______________________
  ____
  ____
- By convention, species are named using the binomial system—this means:
  ____
  ____
- Outline three reasons why scientists classify organisms.
  Reason 1: ______________________
  ____
  Reason 2: ______________________
  ____
  Reason 3: ______________________
  ____

2 Classification keys are used to identify organisms, placing them into taxonomic groups with other organisms that share similar features. Consider the animals listed below. Use and extend the key provided until you have classified the red kangaroo into a group containing only this organism.

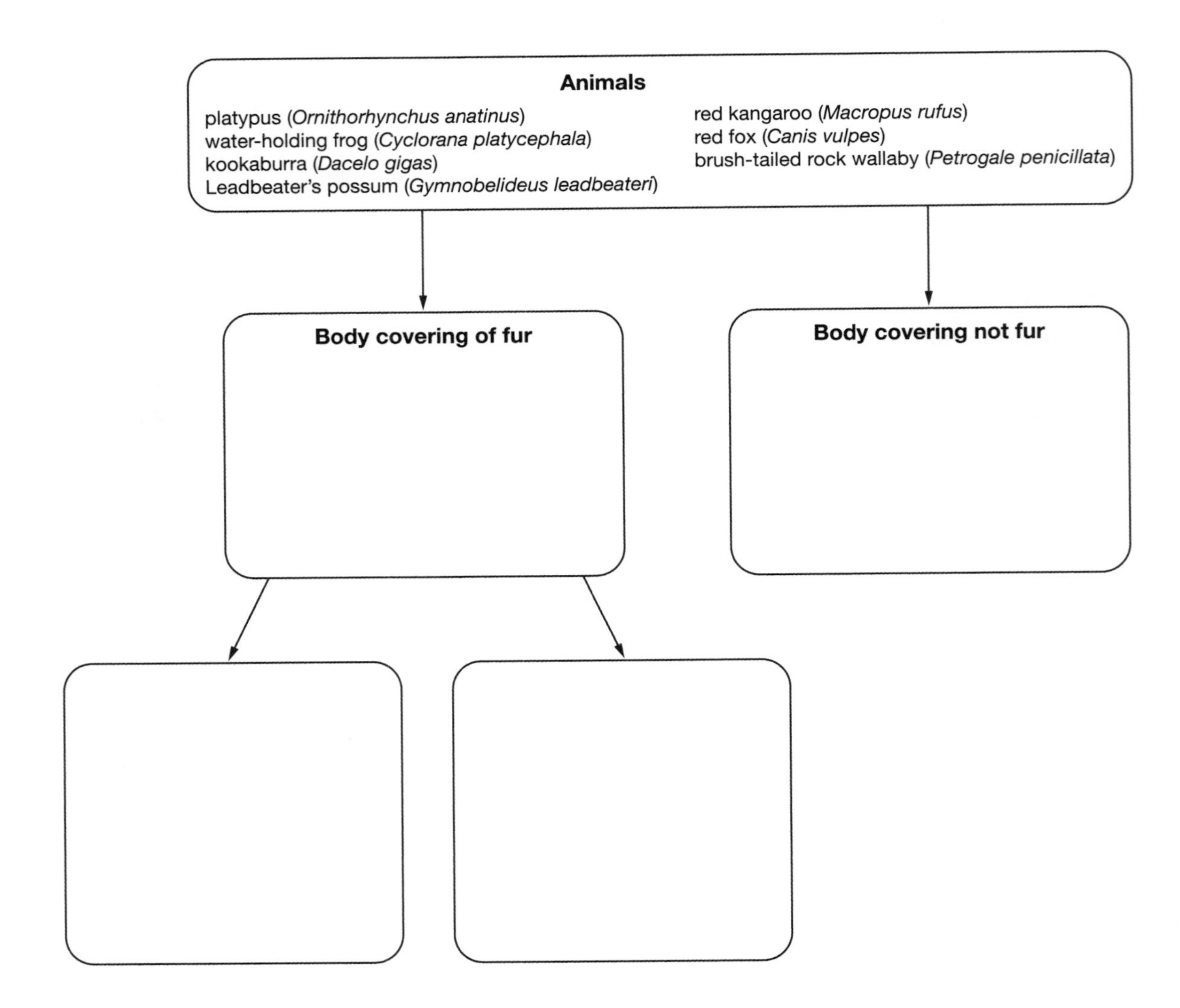

WORKSHEET 20

Counting the cost—an ecological footprint

In recent years there has been increasing awareness that humans, as a species, are living beyond our ecological means; that is, we are using our resources at a greater rate than they can be supplied by Earth. In the process we are fast-tracking the biological clock of our own existence.

The measure of the amount of resources needed to support ourselves and the lifestyles we live is called our **ecological footprint**. The information below provides a comparison of the ecological footprint of some of the world's richest and poorest nations.

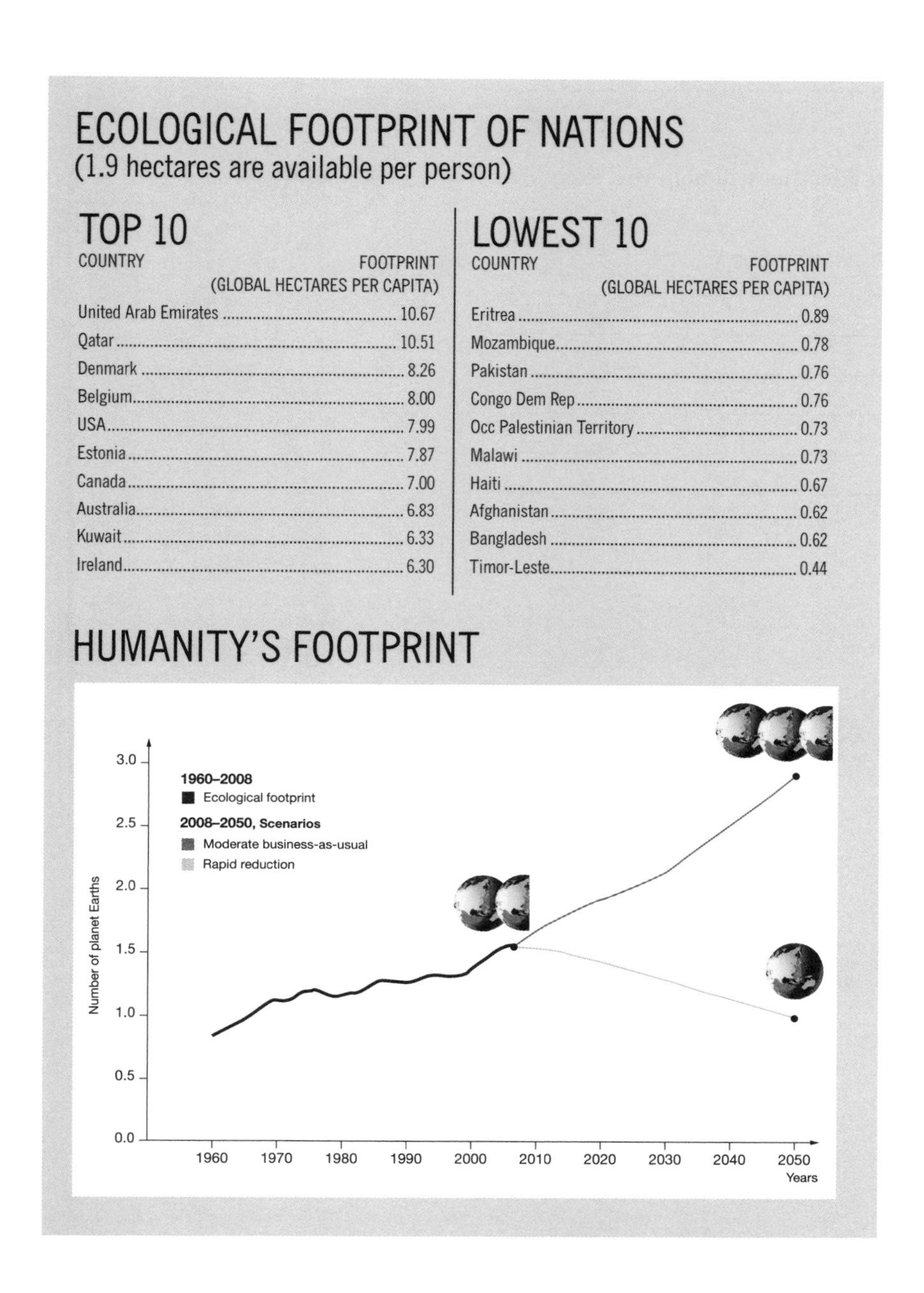

ECOLOGICAL FOOTPRINT OF NATIONS
(1.9 hectares are available per person)

TOP 10

COUNTRY	FOOTPRINT (GLOBAL HECTARES PER CAPITA)
United Arab Emirates	10.67
Qatar	10.51
Denmark	8.26
Belgium	8.00
USA	7.99
Estonia	7.87
Canada	7.00
Australia	6.83
Kuwait	6.33
Ireland	6.30

LOWEST 10

COUNTRY	FOOTPRINT (GLOBAL HECTARES PER CAPITA)
Eritrea	0.89
Mozambique	0.78
Pakistan	0.76
Congo Dem Rep	0.76
Occ Palestinian Territory	0.73
Malawi	0.73
Haiti	0.67
Afghanistan	0.62
Bangladesh	0.62
Timor-Leste	0.44

HUMANITY'S FOOTPRINT

On average, each Australian has a footprint of about 7.8 hectares. If everyone in the world had our ecological footprint, we would need another three planets to keep us alive.

1 Visit the EPA website (www.epa.vic.gov.au/ecologicalfootprint/calculators/personal/introduction.asp) and follow the prompts to calculate your own ecological footprint. Enter the information in the footprint below.

2 Think about the resources that are used to provide you with the lifestyle you enjoy. Identify those you think make the biggest contributions to your ecological footprint.

____

____

____

____

____

____

3 Write a prescription for yourself to follow that will help you to reduce your ecological footprint.

____

____

____

____

____

____

____

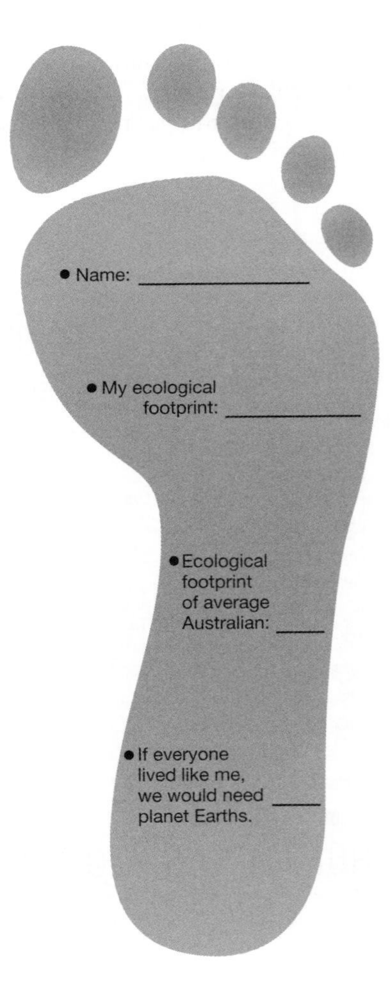

WORKSHEET 21

Diminishing diversity—saving species

The impact of human activity on the natural resources and biodiversity of planet Earth has been devastating over the last 240 years. Growing human populations, together with land clearing, farming practices, urbanisation and industrialisation, have led to alarming statistics in relation to habitat and species loss on our planet.

In Australia alone:

- 30 species of mammals and 24 species of birds have become extinct
- more than 400 species of animals are currently listed as threatened
- more than 1200 plant species are currently listed as threatened.

Investigate an Australian species of plant or animal that is listed as threatened.

Visit the **Species profile and Threats database** at the website of the **Department of the Environment** and follow the prompts.

1 Identify the species you have selected. ______________________________

2 Write down the status of this species and explain why it has this status.
(Choose from **vulnerable**, **endangered**, **critically endangered**, **extinct in the wild**.)

____

____

3 Identify and describe the human activities that have posed a threat to this species.

____

____

4 Describe the measures that are currently in place to address the threats for the species you have chosen.

____

____

5 Outline why this species is important.

____

____

____

6 Explain why conservation of species and our environment is an important issue for us to address.

____

____

____

WORKSHEET 22

Crossword—ecosystems

Complete the crossword to help you check your knowledge and understanding of key terms and processes related to ecosystems.

Across

4 A system composed of living organisms that interact with one another and with their non-living surroundings. [9]

5 The total quantity or weight of organisms in a particular area. [7]

7 The global ecosystem, including the collective ecosystems of Earth, in which organisms live. [9]

10 Arrival of organisms into a population. [11]

13 Describes the living components within an ecosystem. [6]

14 A factor in an organism's surroundings that may be in short supply, reducing its chances of survival. [14]

15 Line along which quadrats are placed in an ecosystem for the purpose of measuring aspects of the biological community. [8]

16 A group of different kinds of organisms living in an ecosystem and interacting with one another. [9]

Down

1 A small local area in which an organism lives that is contained within a larger area. [12]

2 Sample area of land in an ecosystem marked out for the purposes of describing aspects of a biological community. [7]

3 Role of species in an ecosystem. [5]

6 Describes the capacity of an ecosystem to be maintained without relaying on external inputs. [14]

8 The place where an organism lives. [7]

9 Movement of organisms out of a population. [10]

11 Group of organisms of the same species living together in a specific area. [10]

12 Describes the non-living components of an ecosystem. [7]

WORKSHEET 23

Classic communities—living in an ecosystem in an ecosystem

1 Ecosystems are characterised by the integration of various biotic and abiotic factors. Use the spaces provided to:

- name each organism
- describe its habitat in the ecosystem
- outline its niche.

- kookaburra
- upper tree canopy, tree hollows
- predator—eats small mammals and reptiles

2 Choose an appropriate name for this ecosystem. Describe the criterion you used to decide on this name.

3 List three abiotic factors in this ecosystem.

4 Make a list of other organisms you would expect to form part of this ecosystem community.

5 Browse through the Internet, magazines or texts to find and select one other kind of ecosystem for comparison. The list below may give you some ideas. Then answer the following questions for this ecosystem.

grassland ecosystem	semi-arid ecosystem	pond ecosystem
reef ecosystem	woodland ecosystem	desert ecosystem
mangrove ecosystem	river ecosystem	alpine ecosystem

6 Name of ecosystem:

7 Description of ecosystem:

8 Abiotic factors:

9 List five organisms you would expect to find in the ecosystem and describe the niche for each:

WORKSHEET 24

Matchmaker—web of interactions

1 Read the definitions listed in the boxes on the right of the page. Choose the correct term from the list below to match each definition and write this term in the corresponding box.

parasitism	trophic level	consumer	commensalism	food chain	herbivore
scavenger	symbiosis	food web	mutualism	detritivore	keystone species
carnivore	decomposer	producer	predator	amensalism	

Term	Definition
	a species that has a critical role in maintaining the integrity of an ecosystem
	linear feeding relationship between organisms in an ecosystem
	organism that uses photosynthesis to produce its own organic compounds
	organism that breaks down the dead remains of other organisms
	relationship in which one organism benefits at the expense of its host
	flesh-eating organism
	feeding level of an organism
	animal that hunts and kills other animals for food
	consumer that feeds on and breaks down decaying matter
	interrelationship of food chains
	organism that feeds only on plant matter
	organism that acquires its organic compounds by feeding on other organisms

2 Five terms remain. For each of these write a sentence summarising what is meant by the term.

Term 1: ______________________________

Term 2: ______________________________

Term 3: ______________________________

Term 4: ______________________________

Term 5: ______________________________

PRACTICAL ACTIVITY 

A question of balance—blood glucose regulation

PURPOSE

- To consider the hormones and negative feedback systems that are in place to control blood glucose levels.
- To explore the effects on blood glucose levels and the individual in the case of hormone deficiency, such as occurs in diabetes.

PART A NORMAL BLOOD GLUCOSE REGULATION

BACKGROUND INFORMATION

In 1868 at the University of Freiburg in Germany, Paul Langerhans, a professor of pathology, was examining pancreas sections under the microscope. At that time, it was known that the pancreas secreted digestive enzymes that were carried in ducts to the duodenum. Langerhans observed several small areas of cells that looked quite different from the other pancreas cells. These clusters of cells appeared to have no ducts associated with them and they were well supplied with blood vessels. They become known as 'islets of Langerhans'. Scientists were interested to learn what the function of these clusters of cells was. A number of observations were made:

- Animals from which the pancreas had been removed developed symptoms similar to those shown by diabetics, that is, they excreted large amounts of glucose in their urine.
- Tying off the pancreatic duct that carried the digestive enzymes to the duodenum caused the pancreas to partially degenerate, but the islet cells were not affected and the animals did not develop diabetes.

By 1912, scientists were almost certain that the islet cells produced the substance that prevented the onset of diabetes. They named the substance insulin, from the Latin *insula*, meaning islands.

Today we know that the pancreas is involved in the production of two important hormones that together control the levels of glucose in the bloodstream. These hormones are **insulin** and **glucagon**.

Insulin

Insulin is produced in the beta (β) cells of the islets of Langerhans of the pancreas in response to rising blood glucose levels, and travels in the bloodstream. It enhances the rate at which cells take up glucose from the blood. There are receptor sites on cell membranes that bind to insulin, altering the permeability of the plasma membranes to glucose and altering the rate of activity of the enzyme systems within the cell. In the liver, for example, glucose is converted to glycogen, fat and carbon dioxide.

Glucagon

Glucagon is produced in the islets of Langerhans by cells called the alpha (α) cells. It is one of a number of hormones that act to increase the level of blood glucose if the level in the blood falls. Glucagon molecules bind to receptor sites on the liver cell membranes and stimulate the breakdown of stored glycogen to glucose, which is then released into the bloodstream to increase blood glucose levels.

PRACTICAL ACTIVITY 6

QUESTIONS

1 **a** Insulin and glucagon are hormones. Define the term 'hormone'.

b Hormones travel throughout the body in the bloodstream but they only provoke a response in the target tissue. Suggest why only target cells respond to these hormones and not other cells that might be exposed to the hormones.

2 Name the target tissue or cells upon which these hormones have their effect and describe their effect in each case.

Insulin:

Glucagon:

Consider the graphs in Figure 1.46 showing the relationship between blood glucose level and insulin levels.

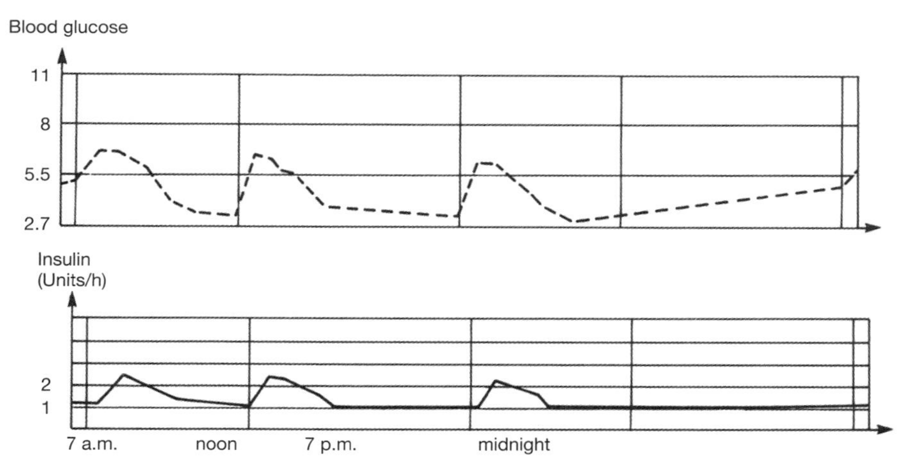

Figure 1.46 Relationship between blood glucose and insulin levels

3 **a** Describe the relationship between blood glucose level and insulin level.

b Describe when in the day your pancreas is likely to be releasing insulin into the bloodstream. Explain your reasoning.

c When is glucagon most likely to be released? Explain.

4 **a** Define the term 'negative feedback system'.

____

____

____

b Use your knowledge and understanding of negative feedback systems and the homeostatic mechanisms involved in the control of blood glucose levels to complete the negative feedback models below.

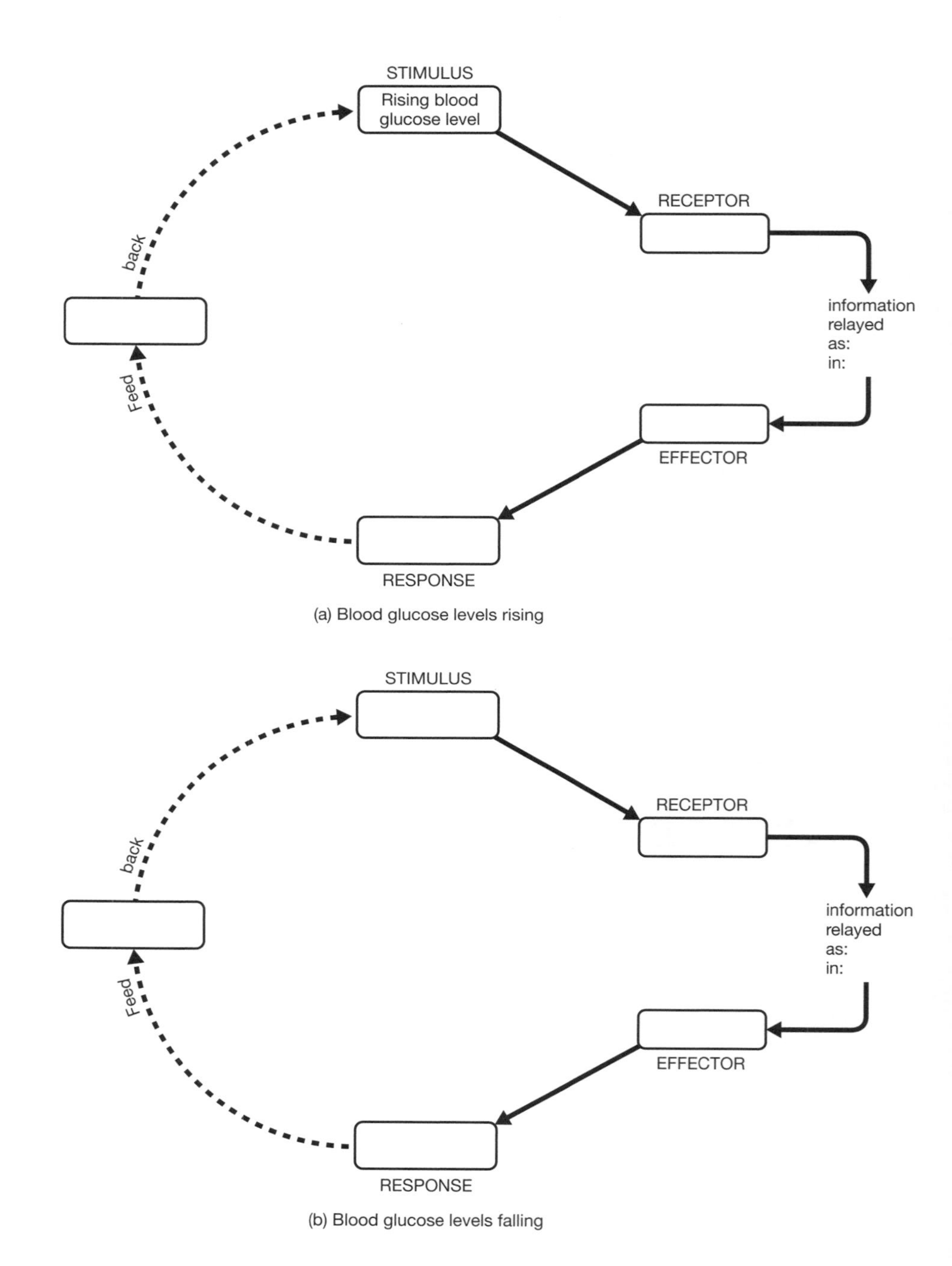

(a) Blood glucose levels rising

(b) Blood glucose levels falling

PRACTICAL ACTIVITY 6

PART B INSUFFICIENT INSULIN

BACKGROUND INFORMATION

Diabetes mellitus is a disorder of the body's blood glucose regulatory mechanism. In everyone, diabetics and non-diabetics alike, the digestion of carbohydrates results in a rise in the levels of glucose in the blood. In a non-diabetic, this causes an increase in the level of insulin, which in turn leads to a reduction in blood glucose level. In diabetics, this either does not occur or occurs at a greatly reduced rate, so that levels of glucose in the blood remain so high as to be outside the normal tolerance range to maintain a healthy individual.

There are different forms of diabetes with different causes, but they are all characterised by high levels of blood glucose. The treatment for patients depends on the particular form of diabetes. Type I diabetes is a form of the disease in which the beta cells of the pancreas have deteriorated to the point where they no longer produce insulin or sufficient insulin to adequately reduce high blood glucose levels. Type I diabetes is also called insulin-dependent diabetes because sufferers must administer regular injections of insulin during the day to replace the insulin that is no longer produced by the pancreas. Juvenile diabetes is a form of the disease that occurs in young people. Symptoms usually occur suddenly and treatment involves lifelong insulin injections. In Australia, there are over 100 000 Type I diabetes patients, the vast majority of them diagnosed as children.

QUESTIONS

5 Explain why diabetes results in excessive blood glucose levels.

____

____

6 Symptoms of excessively high blood glucose levels include:

- excessive urination
- increased thirst
- tiredness
- weight loss.

Use your knowledge and understanding of the role of glucose in the body and the osmotic effect of high levels of glucose in kidney filtrate to explain why each of these symptoms occurs.

____

____

____

____

Diabetes patients must check their blood glucose levels several times each day before administering an insulin shot. Blood glucose levels are measured in millimoles of glucose per litre of blood (mmol/L) using a portable blood glucose monitor. The patient takes a small sample of blood, usually from a finger, using an automatic finger-prick device that retains the sample in a small tube. The tube is placed into the blood glucose monitor where it is quickly analysed. In non-diabetics, the normal blood glucose level is around 5 mmol/L. Soon after a meal it may rise to 7 mmol/L, and after not eating for several hours it may fall to 3.5 mmol/L.

The data in Table 1.23 shows the daily record of blood glucose levels of an 11-year-old boy with Type 1 diabetes, taken during the week that he was on camp. His blood glucose levels were being controlled using daily insulin injections.

7 Plot the data in Table 1.23 on the graph paper provided. Take care to allow for the whole week on the time axis. Label both axes.

Table 1.23 Blood glucose levels of a diabetic boy over seven days

Day	Time	Blood glucose level (mmol/L)
Sunday	5.30 p.m. 10.00 p.m.	3.6 2.4
Monday	2.00 a.m. 7.30 a.m. 5.30 p.m. 10.00 p.m.	10.0 5.6 8.3 3.1
Tuesday	1.00 a.m. 7.30 a.m. 5.30 p.m. 10.00 p.m.	12.1 13.8 6.4 15.5
Wednesday	1.30 a.m. 7.30 a.m. 5.30 p.m. 10.00 p.m.	15.5 9.8 4.1 13.4
Thursday	7.30 a.m. 5.30 p.m. 10.00 p.m.	20.3 5.8 2.0
Friday	1.30 a.m. 7.30 a.m. 5.30 p.m. 10.00 p.m.	15.4 18.4 25.0 2.0
Saturday	1.00 a.m. 7.30 a.m.	21.0 15.0

PRACTICAL ACTIVITY 6

8 On the graph, mark in horizontal lines to indicate the upper and lower range for normal blood glucose readings.

a Summarise the boy's fluctuating blood glucose levels over the week. Comment on any patterns that are observed.

b Suggest reasons that may account for particularly high blood glucose levels for this boy.

c Outline some strategies that may help the boy achieve lower overall blood glucose levels.

9 Hyperglycaemia describes the condition of excessive blood glucose levels that are common in diabetic patients. The administration of insulin is one strategy that helps overcome this problem.

a Suggest a dietary strategy that a diabetic might follow in attempting to achieve relatively even blood glucose levels.

b Explain what is meant by 'hypoglycaemia'.

c Diabetics must be on the alert to avoid episodes of hypoglycaemia. Describe a situation in which a diabetic may be vulnerable to hypoglycaemia.

d Suggest an appropriate action that a diabetic might take to avoid hypoglycaemia when they are aware that an episode is likely to occur.

CONCLUSIONS

10 Summarise the importance of negative feedback mechanisms in the regulation of blood glucose levels.

11 Outline the importance of modern technologies in the management of insulin-dependent diabetes.

PRACTICAL ACTIVITY 7

Australian endotherms and ectotherms—temperature regulation

INTRODUCTION

Ectotherm and *endotherm* are terms that are often used when describing the abilities of different animals to cope with different environmental temperatures. Ectotherms have a limited ability to control their body temperature, which fluctuates according to the temperature of the external environment. Endotherms maintain an internal body temperature that is independent of the external temperature.

Australian animals often have to cope with extreme environmental temperatures and have developed many different adaptations to allow them to do this. These adaptations may be structural, physiological or behavioural, and vary according to the type of animal and the environment in which it lives.

PURPOSE

- To distinguish between ectotherms and endotherms.
- To identify Australian examples of ectotherms and endotherms.
- To describe the adaptations or responses of these organisms that assist in temperature regulation.

Some suggested Australian ectotherms to research include the broad-headed snake, the thorny devil, the Kangaroo Island tiger snake, the blue-tongue lizard, the western swamp tortoise and the desert-dwelling scavenger ants.

PART A TYPES OF TEMPERATURE REGULATION

Five different vertebrate species were subjected to environmental temperatures ranging between 5°C and 40°C. After two hours at each environmental temperature, the animal's body temperature was recorded. The results are shown in Figure 1.47.

1 Write down the meaning of the terms **endotherm** and **ectotherm**. Consult a textbook if necessary.

a endotherm

____

____

b ectotherm

____

____

2 **a** Which animals could be described as true endotherms? Explain.

____

____

b Which animals could be described as true ectotherms? Explain.

____

____

PRACTICAL ACTIVITY 7

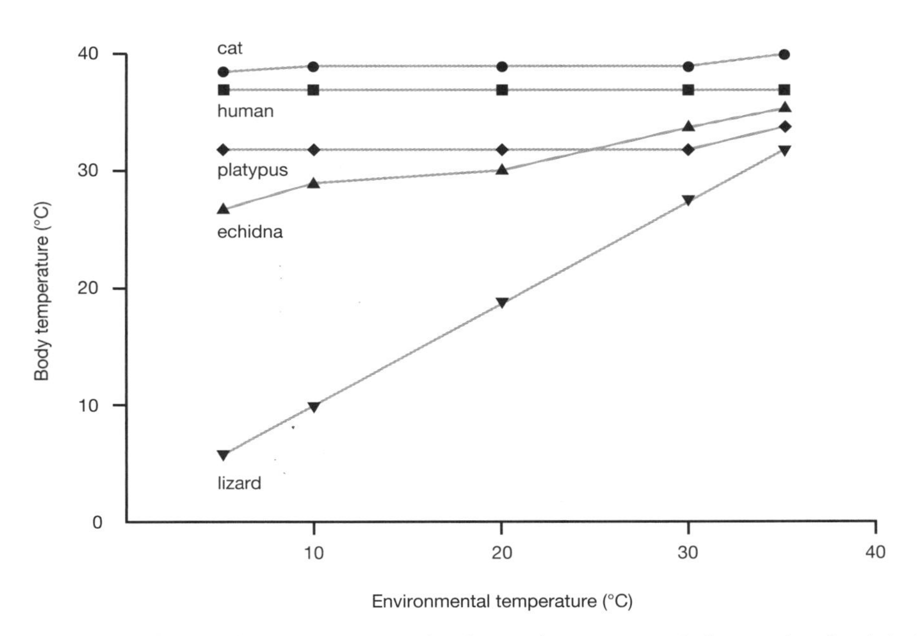

Figure 1.47 Relationship between external and internal temperatures in five species of vertebrate

3 Suggest why there is an advantage to both endotherms and ectotherms in having a warm body temperature (within limits).

____

____

PART B SOME METHODS OF MAMMALIAN TEMPERATURE REGULATION

4 Complete Table 1.24.

Table 1.24 Temperature control in mammals

Observation	Explanation (how the observation relates to the regulation of body temperature)	Type of adaptation (structural, physiological or behavioural)
An echidna living in cold regions hibernates during winter		
Your skin often looks quite flushed on a hot day		
Many Australian marsupials salivate and lick their fur on hot days		
Whales have a thick layer of blubber (fat) under their skin		

Table 1.24 Temperature control in mammals (continued)		
Observation	**Explanation (how the observation relates to the regulation of body temperature)**	**Type of adaptation (structural, physiological or behavioural)**
You tend to feel cooler on a hot, dry day than on a humid day of the same temperature		
A small mammal, with the same body temperature and insulating mechanisms as a larger mammal, loses heat more quickly than the larger mammal		
Dogs pant on a hot day		
Cats often look 'fatter' on a cold day		

PART C EXAMPLES OF AUSTRALIAN ENDOTHERMS

Potoroo

Temperature regulation in marsupials has been the subject of a number of investigations. One such investigation made some interesting discoveries about the long-nosed rat-kangaroo or potoroo (*Potorus tridactylus*). The potoroo is a marsupial mammal about 60 cm long and weighing about 1 kg. It lives mainly along the east coast of Australia in forests and heathlands, where there is relatively thick ground cover. It sleeps by day in a nest of vegetation, and feeds at night, digging for roots, fungi and insect larvae.

The breathing rate of potoroos was measured in response to changing air temperatures. The results are shown in Figure 1.48.

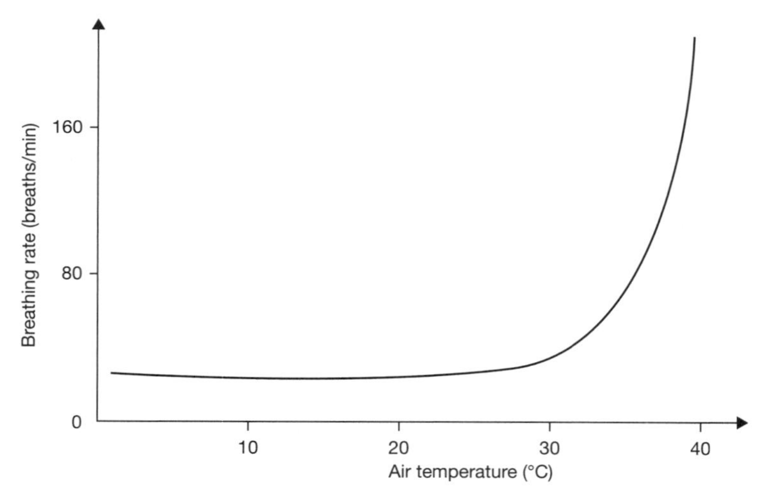

Figure 1.48 Variation in breathing rate with changing air temperature in the potoroo

5 **a** Describe the relationship between air temperature and breathing rate in potoroos, as shown in Figure 1.48.

____

____

b Outline the significance of the relationship between breathing rate and air temperature in terms of temperature regulation in potoroos.

____

____

6 A number of interesting observations not seen in most other marsupials were made about the potoroo. Complete Table 1.25 for these observations.

Table 1.25 Temperature control in the potoroo

Observation	Explanation (how the observation relates to the regulation of body temperature)	Type of adaptation (structural, physiological or behavioural)
The tail lacks hair		
Sweat glands observed in dense rings around the tail		
At high temperatures, the tail appears to be quite wet		
At high temperatures, potoroos continually twitch their tails from side to side		

Echidna

Biologists have studied the behaviour of the Australian echidna (*Tachyglossus aculeatus*) during winter months at high altitudes. Much of their experimental work has been carried out in Kosciuszko National Park. In one experiment they captured five echidnas and implanted a miniature temperature-sensitive radio transmitter into each. These devices transmit a continuous radio signal that carries information about changes in body temperature to radio receivers that record the information.

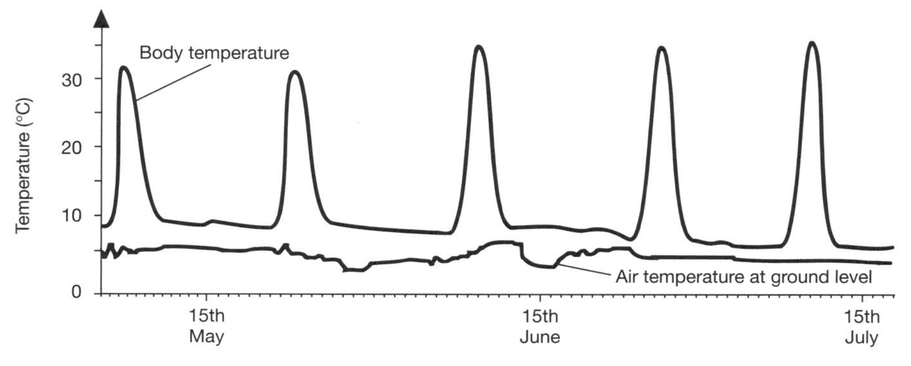

Figure 1.49 Body temperature (upper trace) of a hibernating echidna on Prussian Plain, Kosciuszko National Park, over 10 weeks in winter. The lower trace is ground temperature.

Figure 1.50 An echidna

Figure 1.49 shows the body temperature changes in one echidna (Figure 1.50) over a 10-week period in winter. The other tagged echidnas showed similar temperature fluctuations. The biologists considered these temperatures to be evidence of the echidna entering into states of torpor punctuated by brief periods of activity. (Torpor is when an animal is sluggish and inactive.) It is still unknown what causes the periodic brief return to normal temperature every 20–25 days during winter.

7 Describe the evidence that suggests that the echidna enters a state of torpor.

8 If measurements were made of the echidna's heart rate, oxygen consumption and overall metabolic rate when in torpor, how do you think these would differ from measurements when the echidna was active? Why do you think so?

9 Suggest how the echidna's ability to enter torpor is an adaptation to survival in very cold conditions during winter.

10 List some of the disadvantages of being an ectotherm. Can you think of any advantages?

CONCLUSION

11 Create a visual summary of the adaptations used by Australian endotherms and ectotherms to regulate their body temperature. Include specific examples. Present your answer as a concept map, table, poster or electronic presentation.

PRACTICAL ACTIVITY 8

A tale of two rats—investigating water balance in mammals

INTRODUCTION

To achieve water balance, an organism's water input must equal its water output. Most animals obtain water in two ways—by drinking and through the water content of their food. A few species of desert-adapted animals can achieve water balance in part through the production of metabolic water. This is water that is produced during the process of cellular respiration—that is, as a by-product of food that has been consumed and metabolised in the cells. Water is lost from the body in a variety of ways—through elimination of urine and faeces, sweating, exhalation of moist air from respiratory surfaces and panting. Water balance is critical in animals. If water output is greater than water input, dehydration occurs and death may result.

Kangaroo-rat

Common rat

PURPOSE

- To compare the ability to conserve water between different species of mammal.
- To consider some adaptations featured by a desert-adapted mammal in relation to its particular environment.

BACKGROUND INFORMATION

The kangaroo-rat (*Dipodomys merriami*) is a species of burrowing rodent found in arid regions of North America. It is not a kangaroo, but a kind of placental mammal that has acquired its name because of its long hind legs and hopping motion. Its long, thin body ranges in length from 10 to 20 cm. Its diet is chiefly insects and vegetation, including seeds and fruits. Kangaroo-rats can endure long periods without water and do not need to drink.

The related species of common rat (*Rattus rattus*) which is often bred for laboratory purposes, originated in the more temperate climate of Europe and is now common throughout the world. The common rat is mainly herbivorous and typically nocturnal.

In this experiment, 100 g of barley (which yields 54 mL of water) was fed to two different species of rat—the kangaroo-rat (*Dipodomys merriami*) and the common rat (*Rattus rattus*). The experiment was designed to simulate desert conditions, providing the rats with food but no water. Figure 1.51 illustrates the volume of water input and output for the two species.

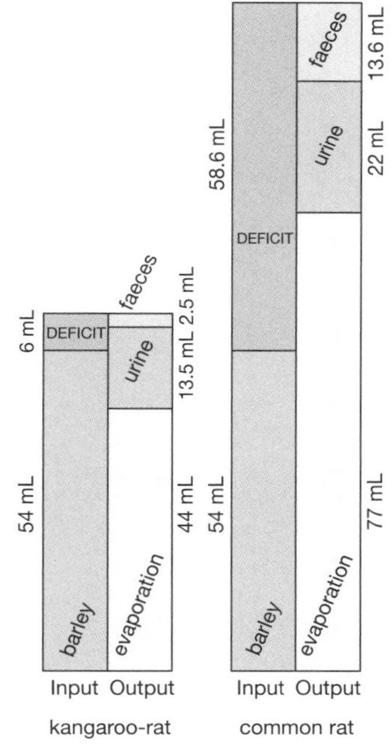

Figure 1.51 A comparison of the water input and output for two rats each fed 100 g of barley

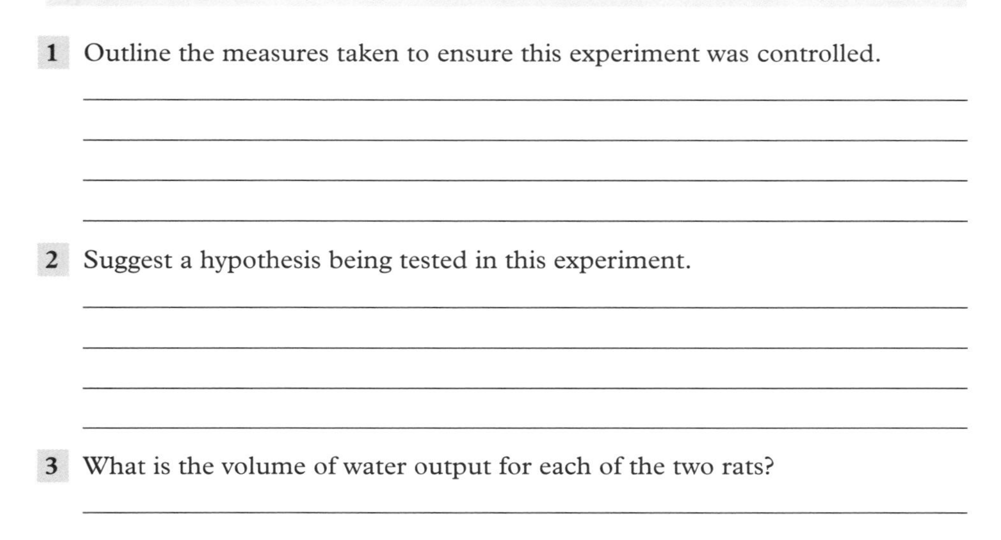

1 Outline the measures taken to ensure this experiment was controlled.

2 Suggest a hypothesis being tested in this experiment.

3 What is the volume of water output for each of the two rats?

4 How does this compare with the total water input in each case?

____

____

____

____

5 Calculate the percentage water loss through evaporation, urine and faeces for each rat species. Enter the data into Table 1.26.

Table 1.26 Percentage water loss

Means of water loss	Rat species	
	Kangaroo-rat	Common rat
Evaporation		
Urine		
Faeces		

6 Describe the experimental evidence that suggests the kangaroo-rat is better adapted than the common rat to arid conditions.

____

____

____

____

____

____

7 In both rats there is a water deficit. However, the kangaroo-rat still manages to achieve water balance. Explain how this is so.

____

____

____

____

8 What measures must be taken by the common rat to achieve water balance?

____

____

One way that desert-adapted mammals contribute to water balance is to produce a small volume of concentrated urine. Study the diagram of a nephron (functional unit of the kidney) in Figure 1.52.

9 **a** Name the structure in the nephron that you would expect to differ between the kangaroo-rat and the common rat. Describe the difference in structure.

____

____

____

____

b Explain how this difference contributes to the production of concentrated urine in the kangaroo-rat.

____

____

____

____

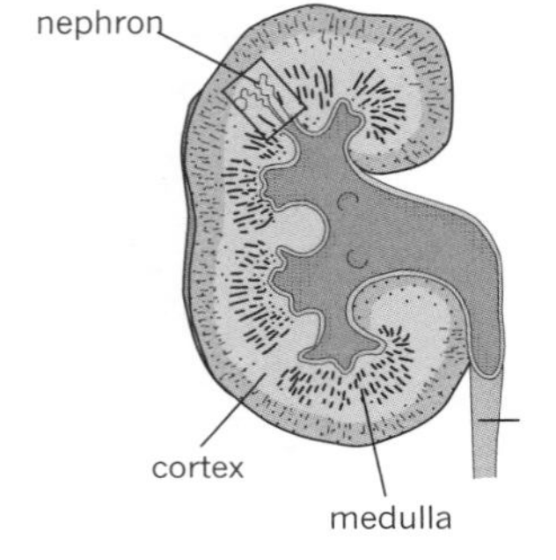

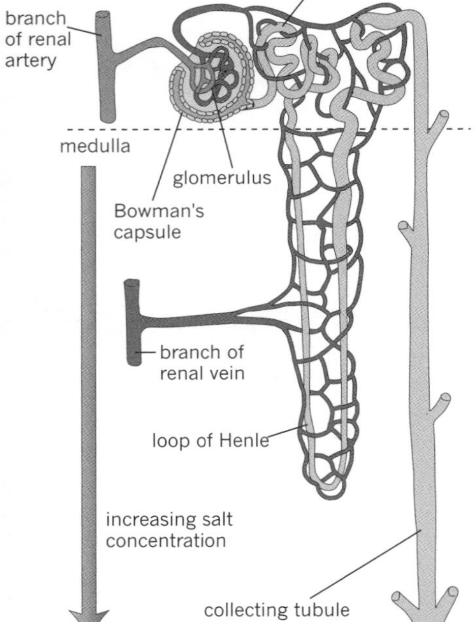

Figure 1.52 Mammalian kidney and nephron

10 Describe at least two behavioural adaptations that may assist the kangaroo-rat in reducing water loss.

CONCLUSIONS

11 Contrast the ability of the two rat species to conserve water.

12 Describe adaptations of the kangaroo-rat that make it well suited to a desert environment. Include:

a a physiological adaptation

b a structural adaptation

c a behavioural adaptation

PRACTICAL ACTIVITY 

Keying out creatures—designing a dichotomous key

INTRODUCTION

Dichotomous keys are tools constructed by biologists to assist in the identification of particular organisms. The key uses a series of pairs of characteristics to subdivide larger groups into smaller groups. The process continues until each group contains a single organism. (A dichotomy is a division of a group into two distinct parts.)

PURPOSE

- To become familiar with the use of dichotomous keys.
- To construct a dichotomous key to assist in the identification of organisms within a selected group.

MATERIALS

- specimens of selected fruits (whole and halved samples), examples:
  - group A: apple, orange, cucumber, tomato, pea pod, bean, quince, almond, walnut
  - group B: plum, peach, nectarine
  - group C: strawberry, pineapple, raspberry, blackberry
- knife
- cutting board
- nutcracker

PART A FILING FRUITS

In this part of the activity you will have some practice at using a dichotomous key to identify particular fruits from a group of fruits. A fruit is defined as the part of a plant that contains the seed.

PROCEDURE

In this part of the activity you will have some practice at using a dichotomous key to identify particular fruits from a group of fruits.

1 Select a fruit specimen from either group A or B fruits.
2 Work through the key in Figure 1.53, beginning at the first box and deciding which of the two alternative subgroups best describes your specimen. Take that route to the next choice. (Note: Figure 1.54 has been included as a reference to help you get started—it is the same key but includes the fruits that have been sorted at each level.)
3 Once again you must decide which alternative best describes your specimen. Keep moving along the dichotomous key branches until you have reached the end of the key.
4 At this stage there are no further alternatives and you are left with one fruit, which you have identified.
5 Look back through the key. The descriptors at each point that determined your choice of pathway are the distinguishing features of your particular fruit specimen—none of the other fruits have the same complete set of features.
6 Work through the key using several other fruits from groups A and B; then try a group C fruit.

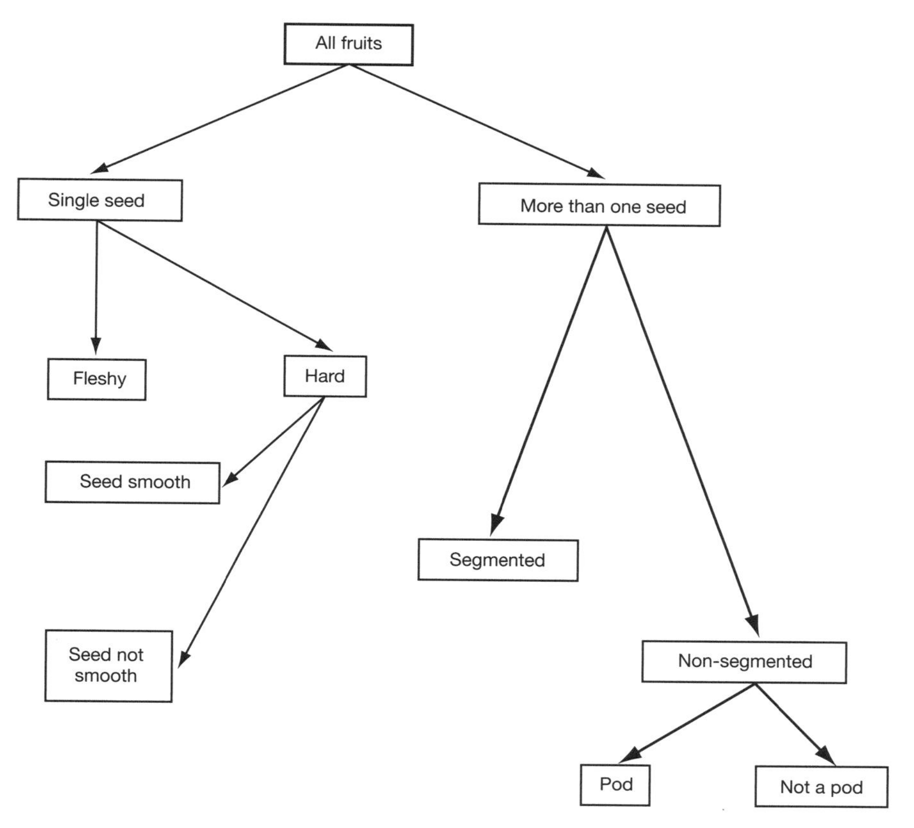

Figure 1.53 Dichotomous key of fruits

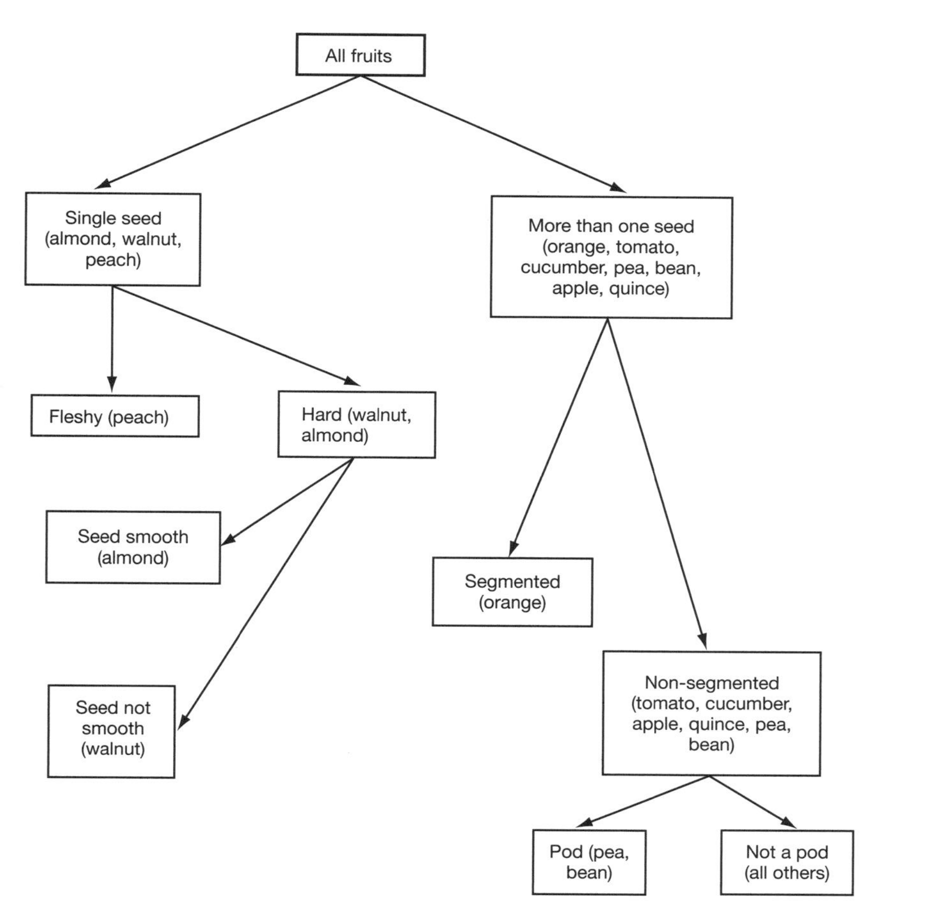

Figure 1.54 Dichotomous key of fruits—in more detail

1 **a** What happened when you tried to identify a Group C fruit, e.g. strawberry, using the key in Figure 1.53?

b Explain why this occurred.

2 If this key was used to identify the following fruits, what would they be identified as? Suggest reasons for your answer.

a avocado

b lemon

7 Keys can also be presented in couplet form, with a choice of two descriptive statements. The following key is written in this way. To use this key you must decide which of the two alternatives best describes the fruit you wish to identify. The number at the end of the line refers you to a further pair of alternatives. When you have reached the subgroup to which the fruit belongs, its name appears at the end of the line.

1a	Fruit with a single seed	2
1b	Fruit with more than one seed	4
2a	Ripe fruit has a fleshy outer layer	Peach
2b	Ripe fruit has a hard outer layer	3
3a	Seed smooth	Almond
3b	Seed not smooth	Walnut
4a	Fruit divides into segments when peeled	Orange
4b	Fruit does not divide into segments when peeled	5
5a		
5b		

3 Add descriptors for the remaining fruits in Figure 1.54 to complete the form of the key shown in 7 above.

CONCLUSIONS

4 Outline the advantages of using a key to identify organisms.

5 Comment on the limitations of keys as tools for identification.

PART B CREATING A KEY

6 Design a dichotomous key that clearly leads to the identification of a selected organism from a larger group of organisms. You will need a sheet of A4 paper for this.

Choose from the following groups:

trees	dogs	flowers	horses	mammals	fish
marsupials	birds	reptiles	dinosaurs	invertebrates	

You may wish to choose another group of organisms—be sure to check in with your teacher before proceeding.

Your dichotomous key should be user-friendly, enabling your audience to make clear choices that will lead to the correct identification of an organism belonging to the group for which the key is designed.

Include:

- a title (one that includes the name of the group)
- alternative descriptors that accurately distinguish the group into two subgroups at each level of separation
- setting out that allows easy arrival at the correct destination.

7 When you have completed your key, invite a class member to use the key to identify an organism from the group. This is a useful approach to evaluating the effectiveness of your key. Make appropriate adjustments so that your key is complete and effective.

PRACTICAL ACTIVITY 10

Plants in their place—using line transects

MATERIALS

- clipboard
- paper and pencil
- measuring tape (at least 10 m long) or a line with distances marked on it
- metre ruler
- labels for plant specimens—masking tape is suitable
- secateurs (optional)
- reference material to assist with identification (optional)
- camera (optional)

INTRODUCTION

When we look around us, we may see a diversity of plants growing in a community. As biologists, it is useful to describe plant communities. This can be done in a variety of ways. We will often give a community a name based on the most obvious or common plant species present (the **dominant species**), e.g. a mountain ash forest. We can make a more detailed description by listing all the plant species present and estimating their **abundance**. This activity and the next look at two different ways of making this estimation:

- an estimation made by looking at the community and making a rough count of the numbers of each species present (Practical activity 11)
- a more detailed estimation by using a line transect (this activity).

BACKGROUND INFORMATION

In the course of their work, many people seek to describe the vegetation patterns of a particular area.

- A forester studies the recovery of an area of bush burnt in a bushfire.
- A wildlife ranger investigates changes in vegetation as a result of increasing kangaroo numbers in the Hattah–Kulkyne National Park.
- A biologist describes an area of tropical rainforest for the first time.
- A farmer wishes to re-establish some cleared marginal land with native vegetation.

The reason for studying vegetation in this way is usually to find the answer to one or more of three questions:

1. What plant species are present in the area?
2. How abundant are the different plant species?
3. How are the different plant species distributed?

This background provides vital information about the community under investigation.

A walk through an area being studied would probably reveal many of the larger plant species, but a detailed investigation will be needed to answer questions about abundance and distribution of all the plant species.

Biologists use several techniques to obtain data from which they can answer these questions.

TRANSECTS

Transects are lines or belts set out through an area as a guide for recording what plant species are present. They provide a useful method for assessing changes in the abundance of a particular species in response to changes in a physical variable in the environment, such as slope or soil moisture content (Figure 1.55).

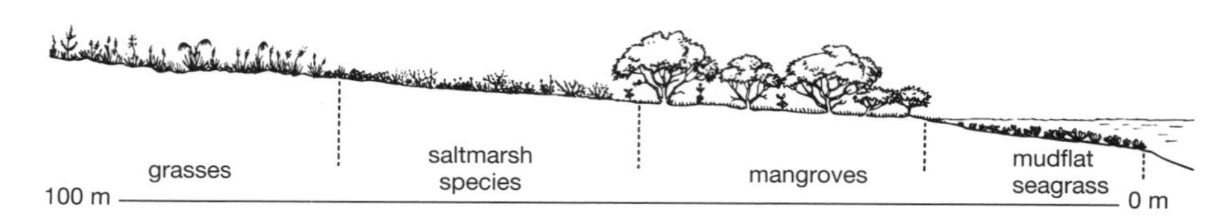

Figure 1.55 Transect line showing location of seagrass, mangrove and saltmarsh plants.

PRACTICAL ACTIVITY 10

Line transect (line intercept transect)

A line transect is made by running out a tape measure or marked line across the area to be sampled. The observer systematically works along the line, recording the name and position of each plant that the line passes over, under or through. The data are recorded on paper on a corresponding line drawn to scale.

Belt transect

This is similar to a line transect except that all the vegetation between two parallel lines is recorded. In a way it is like a long, thin quadrat. (Quadrats are discussed in Practical activity 11.)

A transect can also be used as a location line for quadrats, in which the cover of each species can be estimated. (This can be seen in Figure 1.58 in Practical activity 11, page 102.)

Profile diagram

A profile diagram is a scale drawing of the profile or 'side view' (also called the elevation) of the vegetation along a line. It may also show the shape of the land surface and details of soil type. Care needs to be taken with the choice of the vertical scale so that the drawing is not too distorted.

Profile diagrams are able to show the horizontal layers or strata of the vegetation. Well-drawn profiles are often useful for making qualitative comparisons between different plant communities.

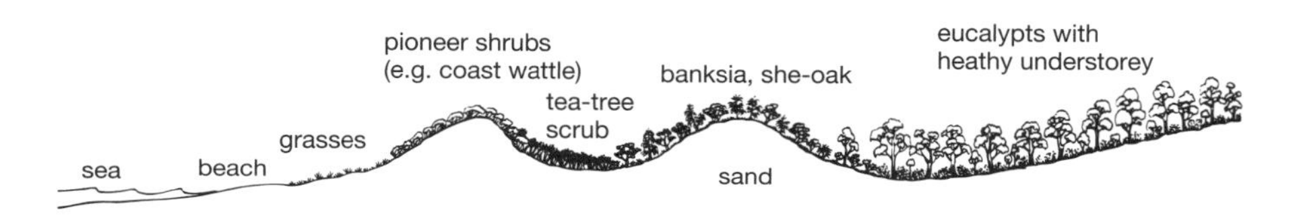

Figure 1.56 (a) Profile diagram of vegetation growing on sand dunes

(b) Detailed profile diagram of a section of a wet sclerophyll forest

IDENTIFICATION OF PLANTS

When studying a plant community it is important to have a ready means of identifying the species present. A commonly used method is to make use of a field herbarium. A field herbarium contains specimens of each of the plants in the area, collected and pressed between newspaper. The important parts to collect are those that are useful for identification in the field, such as leaves, flowers and fruits. When dry, these are mounted on sheets of card, labelled and stored in plastic sleeves. Plants that cannot be readily identified can be labelled as species A, species B, etc.

Good quality colour photographs are also useful aids for identification in the field.

PURPOSE

- To use two different methods to describe the composition of a plant community.
- To make some comparisons between the results obtained by using the different methods.

PROCEDURE

1 Walk through the area you intend to describe and collect samples of each plant species present. *Make sure that you are permitted to collect in the area you have chosen*. Take care when collecting to see that you do not cause unnecessary damage, and use secateurs if they are available. You only need a small piece of each species.

2 Put each plant species into a category that describes its life form. You do not need to identify the species (determine its scientific name).

You might find these categories useful:

Trees: Ecologists define trees as woody plants over 5 m tall, usually with a single stem. Label as 'tree 1', 'tree 2', etc.

Shrubs: Ecologists define shrubs as woody plants less than 5 m tall, frequently with many stems arising at or near the base. Label as 'shrub 1', 'shrub 2', etc.

Herbs: Ecologists define herbs as any non-woody plant. Because the group could be very large, further subdivision into ferns, grasses and broad-leaved plants may be helpful. Label as 'fern 1', 'fern 2', 'grass 1', 'grass 2', 'broad-leaf 1', 'broad-leaf 2', etc.

Climbers: Label as 'climber 1', 'climber 2', etc.

Use whichever categories you find easiest to work with, but be consistent with the categories in which you place the different plants. Label your specimens using your chosen system so that you can refer back to them later.

1 List each plant you have labelled in the 'Species' column of Table 1.27.

Table 1.27 Ranking species

Species	First ranking	Line transect count	Second ranking
Tree 1			
Shrub 1			

3 Each species is to be given a ranking number, in order of abundance. The most abundant (common) species is ranked 1. The least abundant (rarest) species is ranked with the highest number.

Return with your group to the area you are describing and, by group decision, rank each plant listed in Table 1.27 from most common to rarest.

2 Enter the rankings next to the plant names in Table 1.27 under the column headed 'First ranking'.

4 Now run out the tape or line in a straight line through the area. Move along the tape from one end and, for each plant species, count the number of individual plants of that species that the tape passes over, under, or through. The easiest way to do this is to select a particular species and walk along the line counting the number of that species. Then select the next species and repeat the procedure. Continue to do this until all species have been counted.

3 Record your counts for each species listed, in the 'Line transect count' column of Table 1.27.

You have now made a line transect through the study area.

It may be difficult to count the individual grass plants along the transect.

4 Describe another method of comparing the abundance of grasses with that of other species along the line.

______

______

______

5 If time permits, make a second line transect through the same area.

6 Using the same system of ranking as used in step 3, make up a new ranking order based on the data in the 'Line transect count' column of Table 1.27. Some plant species may not show up in your count; ignore these for the moment.

5 Record these rankings in the 'Second ranking' column of Table 1.27.

CONCLUSIONS

6 **a** Describe any differences you noted between your two rankings.

______

______

b Suggest possible reasons for the differences.

______

______

______

7 **a** List any species that were absent from either the first or second rankings.

______

______

b If they were absent, suggest why this might be.

______

______

______

8 Suggest why it is better to collect data from more than one transect.

______

______

______

9 Which method best describes the area you have studied? Explain the reasons for your answer.

______

______

______

PRACTICAL ACTIVITY 11

The flatweed census—population estimation

MATERIALS

- quadrat (1 m square is a suitable size)
- tape measure (10 m)
- clipboard and paper
- weed species chart from your local council or from the internet

INTRODUCTION

Your lawn is covered in weeds. Will regularly digging out the dandelions really reduce their abundance? Does spraying the lawn with weedkiller reduce the number of weeds more effectively than digging? What experimental techniques can you use to answer these questions? How can you accurately record the abundance of weeds in your lawn before and after digging or herbicide treatment?

PURPOSE

- To use quadrats to estimate the population density of a flatweed species in a lawn.
- To use these data to estimate the total population of the flatweed in the lawn.

BACKGROUND INFORMATION

QUADRATS

A quadrat (Figure 1.58) is a square, rectangular or circular frame of convenient size, used to mark out an area in which the vegetation is to be sampled. The shape and size of the quadrat depends on the type of vegetation. A square with 50 cm sides would be suitable for sampling a lawn, while a square with 10 m sides may be used for sampling trees in a forest.

When a quadrat is used to sample vegetation, first a list is compiled of all the plants contained in the quadrat. Repeating this for several quadrats should provide a composite list of the species present in the area. Quadrats can also be used to give an estimate of the abundance of one or more of the species.

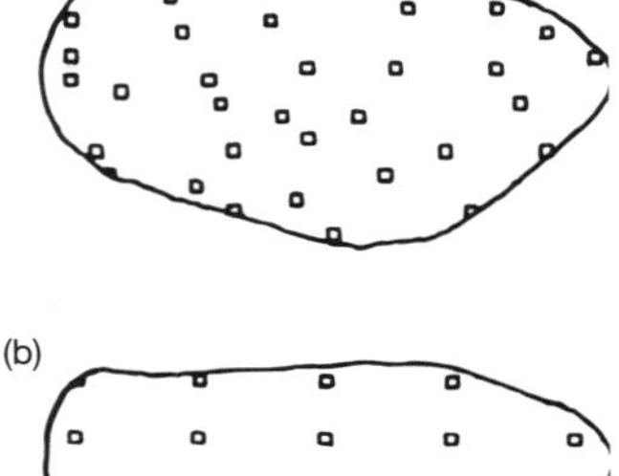

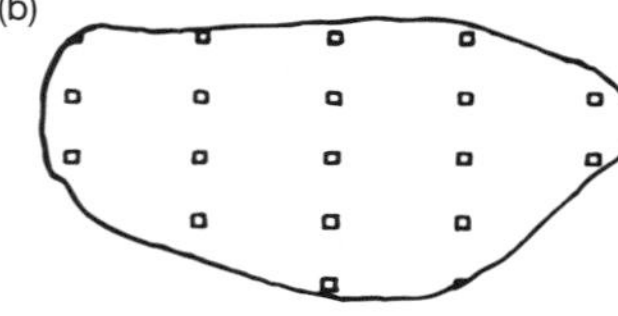

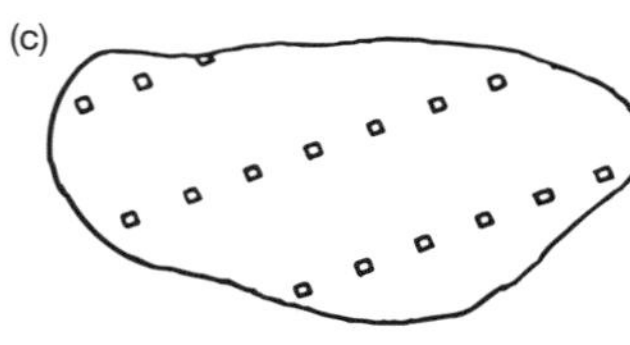

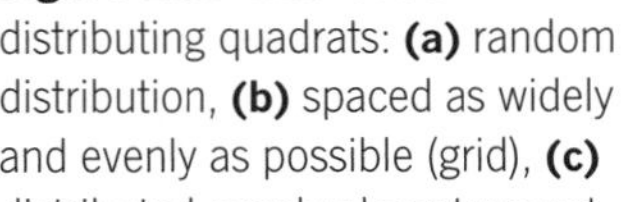

Figure 1.57 Methods of distributing quadrats: **(a)** random distribution, **(b)** spaced as widely and evenly as possible (grid), **(c)** distributed evenly along transect lines.

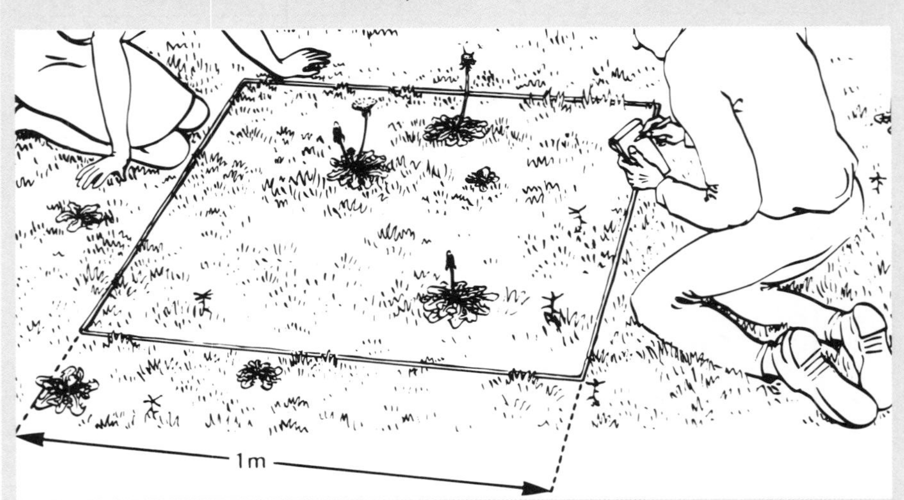

Figure 1.58 A 1 m^2 quadrat in use for sampling an area of 'lawn'. In this case the density of dandelions is 4 per m^2 and the cover is 10%.

Abundance is measured in two ways:

1. Count the number of a particular plant in the quadrat. This gives the density of the plant, e.g. the number of dandelions in a lawn per square metre.
2. Cover is the percentage area of the quadrat covered by a particular plant species, e.g. the area of the quadrat of lawn that is covered by dandelion plants.

Quadrats may be located either randomly over the area being sampled, or at regular intervals along a transect or on a grid (Figure 1.57).

PRACTICAL ACTIVITY 11

PROCEDURE

1 In groups, select a suitable area of 'lawn' that has populations of different flatweed species. Choose the flatweed that you want to count and, using a reference, try to identify it.

1 Record the name of the species you have chosen. Several groups should count the same species so that data can be combined.

2 Work out a way of determining the total area (in square metres) of the lawn you are studying.

2 Describe the method you are going to use.

____

____

____

3 Take the measurements and calculate the area.

3 Record the measurements and do the calculation in your workbook.

4 Discuss the following questions with others in your group:

a What percentage of the total area would you need to sample in order to cover the lawn adequately?

b How many quadrats should be used to do this?

4 a Record the number of quadrats the group agreed upon.

b Explain how you arrived at this number.

5 Discuss with others in your group how you should locate the quadrats.

5 Describe the method your group has chosen to locate the quadrats and explain why you have chosen this method.

____

____

____

____

6 Locate the first quadrat using the method outlined in your answer to point 5.

7 Count the number of flatweed plants in the quadrat. For plants that the quadrat frame touches, use the following method: if more than half the leaf area of a plant is inside the quadrat, then count that plant; if less than half the plant is inside, then do not count that plant.

6 Record the count in Table 1.28.

Table 1.28 Separate group results

Quadrat number	Number of weeds
1	
2	
3	
4	
5	
Total	

8 Repeat step 6 for at least five quadrats.

YOUR GROUP'S CALCULATIONS

7 Use your data from Table 1.28 to calculate the average number of weeds per quadrat.

9 If a 1 m^2 quadrat was used, the average number of weeds per quadrat is the same as the average density, that is, the number of weeds per m^2. If you used a quadrat with 0.5 m sides then multiply your number of weeds by 4 to give average density.

8 What is the average flatweed density?

9 Using your measurement of the area of the lawn, calculate and record your estimate of the size of the flatweed population in the lawn. Show your working.

10 Record the data of other groups who counted the same flatweed species in Table 1.29.

Table 1.29 Combined results for groups using the same flatweed species

	Number of weeds counted (total of all quadrats)	Number of quadrats sampled
Group 1		
Group 2		
Group 3		
Group 4		
Total		

COMBINED GROUPS' CALCULATIONS

11 Complete the totals for the two columns in Table 1.29, and then calculate and record the average number of weeds per quadrat.

12 Using the combined data, calculate and record the estimate of the size of the flatweed population in the lawn.

CONCLUSIONS

13 **a** Describe any differences in the estimates of the population size calculated using your group's data and the combined data.

____

____

b Suggest reasons for any differences.

____

____

c Which of the two estimates of population size do you expect is more accurate? Explain the reasons for your answer.

____

____

14 Outline how quadrats are useful in determining population density.

____

____

15 Evaluate the technique you used.

a Describe any limitations you encountered.

____

____

____

b Suggest how they could be overcome.

____

____

____

PRACTICAL ACTIVITY 12

A numbers game—factors affecting population size

MATERIALS

- graph paper
- calculator (optional)

INTRODUCTION

All living things need resources from their environment, mainly nutrients and oxygen, and need to get rid of wastes into their environment. These environmental resources are always limited. There is a limit to the amount of food that is available in the environment; there is competition for food resources. There is also a limit to the amount of wastes the environment can absorb. As a result, there is usually a limit to the size of a population.

Problems caused by the size of populations really only come to our attention when something appears to be 'out of balance'. Some examples include:

- rabbit, mouse and grasshopper plagues that can cause damage to agricultural productivity
- koala populations becoming too large for the areas set aside for their preservation
- culling of kangaroos in areas where their numbers have become too large
- crown-of-thorns starfish invasions on the Great Barrier Reef.

Factors that affect population size are of two kinds:

- those factors that increase population size—births (b) and immigration (i) to an area
- those factors that decrease population size—deaths (d) and emigration (e) from an area.

PURPOSE

To consider several sets of population growth figures and make some observations about factors that may affect population size.

PART A HYPOTHETICAL POPULATION GROWTH

The simplest type of population growth to investigate is a population of bacteria. Bacteria reproduce by a process of binary fission (splitting in two). In ideal conditions, bacteria can split every 30 minutes.

Assume that there are no factors operating to limit the growth of the population.

1 Complete the population data for bacteria in Table 1.30.

2 Use the grid to draw up a graph representing the data in the table. **Hint:** Plot generation number on the horizontal axis (1 cm = 2 generations) and number of bacteria on the vertical axis (1 cm = 2000 bacteria).

3 What problems did you encounter when you attempted to draw the graph?

____

4 Describe the shape of the curve you have drawn.

____

5 Describe what is happening to the population size as you go from one generation to the next. Outline some of the consequences of this once the population numbers start to become large.

____

____

6 What name is given to growth of this kind? ______________

This type of growth is characteristic of a population in which there are no restraints on growth, and so it is not a particularly good model. There is one important component missing—the environment and its influence.

PRACTICAL ACTIVITY 12

Table 1.30 Bacterial population numbers

Time	Generation number	Number of bacteria
6.30 a.m.	0	1
7.00 a.m.	1	2
7.30 a.m.	2	
8.00 a.m.	3	
8.30 a.m.	4	
9.00 a.m.	5	
9.30 a.m.	6	
10.00 a.m.	7	
10.30 a.m.	8	
11.00 a.m.	9	
11.30 a.m.	10	
12.00 noon	11	
12.30 p.m.	12	
1.00 p.m.	13	
1.30 p.m.	14	
2.00 p.m.	15	

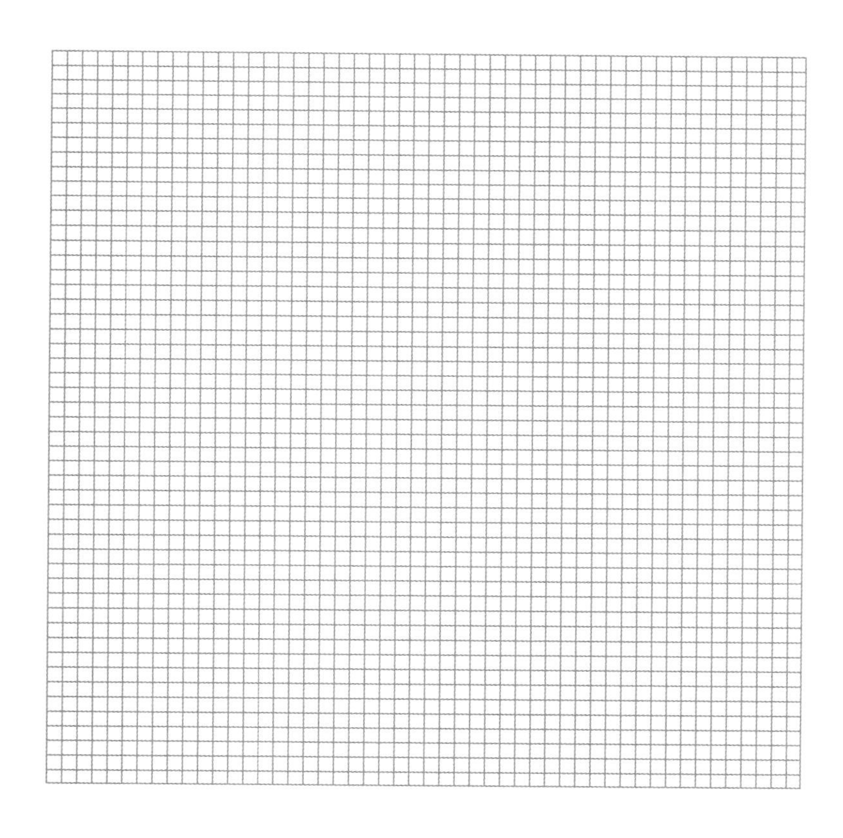

Table 1.31 Beehive population numbers

Time since hive establishment (weeks)	Population of beehive
0	1000
2	2500
4	8000
6	22 000
8	40 000
10	55 000
12	72 000
14	80 000
16	77 000
18	80 000
20	75 000
22	74 000
24	78 000
26	82 000
28	80 000

PART B REAL POPULATION GROWTH

In this activity you will plot the data for two natural populations. These populations differ from the hypothetical population because they are continually interacting with their environment.

Population growth of a natural beehive

Natural beehives are established when a newly emerged queen bee and a number of other castes fly from the original hive and establish in a new location. A study has been done on the number of bees in the hive for 28 weeks from the time of establishment (Table 1.31).

7 Use the grid to plot a graph of the beehive population for the 28 weeks. **Hint**: Plot the time since hive establishment in weeks on the horizontal axis (1 cm = 2 weeks), and population size on the vertical axis (1 cm = 10 000 bees).

Population growth of deer on St Paul's Island

Four male and 21 female European reindeer were introduced as an experiment onto St Paul's Island near the coast of Alaska in 1912. The island was free of predators and environmentally favourable to the deer. The population numbers were monitored until 1950 and are given in Table 1.32.

8 Draw a graph of the deer population data. **Hint**: Plot the year on the horizontal axis (1 cm = 5 years) and the population size on the vertical axis (1 cm = 200 deer).

PRACTICAL ACTIVITY 12

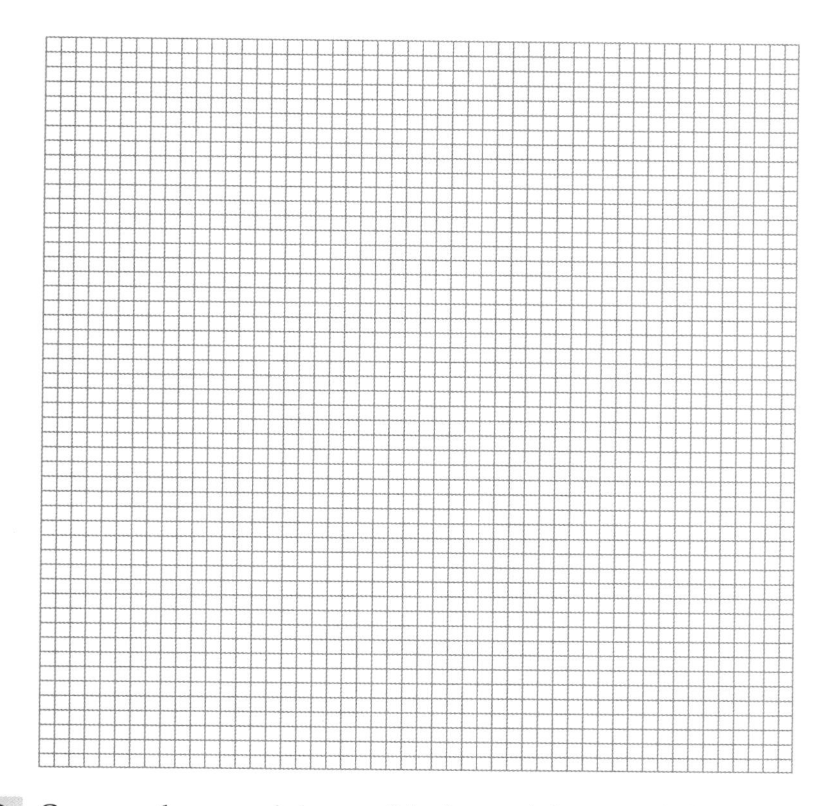

Table 1.32 Deer population numbers	
Year	**Deer population**
1912	25
1915	105
1920	200
1925	315
1930	475
1935	1250
1940	1750
1941	1200
1945	500
1947	300
1948	100
1949	50
1950	8

9 Compare the general shapes of the bee and deer population growth curves.

a In what way are the curves similar? ______________________

____

b In what way are the curves different? ______________________

____

10 From your own observations of natural populations, explain which of these two natural growth curves is likely to be more common.

____

____

11 Suggest an explanation for the changing population in the beehive.

____

____

12 Suggest reasons for the decline of the deer population.

____

____

13 In what way is the hypothetical growth curve for bacteria:

a similar to the two natural curves? ______________________

____

b different from the two natural curves?

____

A number of important points can be made about natural populations:

- The **reproductive potential** of a population is when the maximum number of offspring are produced and survive.
- A population increases in number exponentially until its demands for resources become equal to the environment's capacity to supply these resources. This is the **carrying capacity**.
- When population numbers reach this point, more and more organisms die because of the lack of resources. This is **environmental resistance**.
- Finally, when the number of births plus immigration is approximately equal to the number of deaths plus emigration, the population is in equilibrium.

14 Suggest some factors that might contribute to environmental resistance in:

a the bee population

____

b the deer population

____

CONCLUSIONS

It has been found that the growth curves for most natural populations are very similar in shape. Four stages have been identified and described for this 'S'-shaped (sigmoid) curve. The stages are identified in Figure 1.59.

15 Enter each of the following terms into Table 1.33 so that it corresponds to the correct definition: exponential, negative acceleration, positive acceleration, equilibrium.

16 Complete the labelling by first matching the name of the stage to the correct stage description (Table 1.33) then entering the information in the correct place on the growth curve.

17 Most population data is determined by considering birth rates and death rates. Describe any situations in which the other two factors—immigration and emigration—may have an influence on population size.

____

____

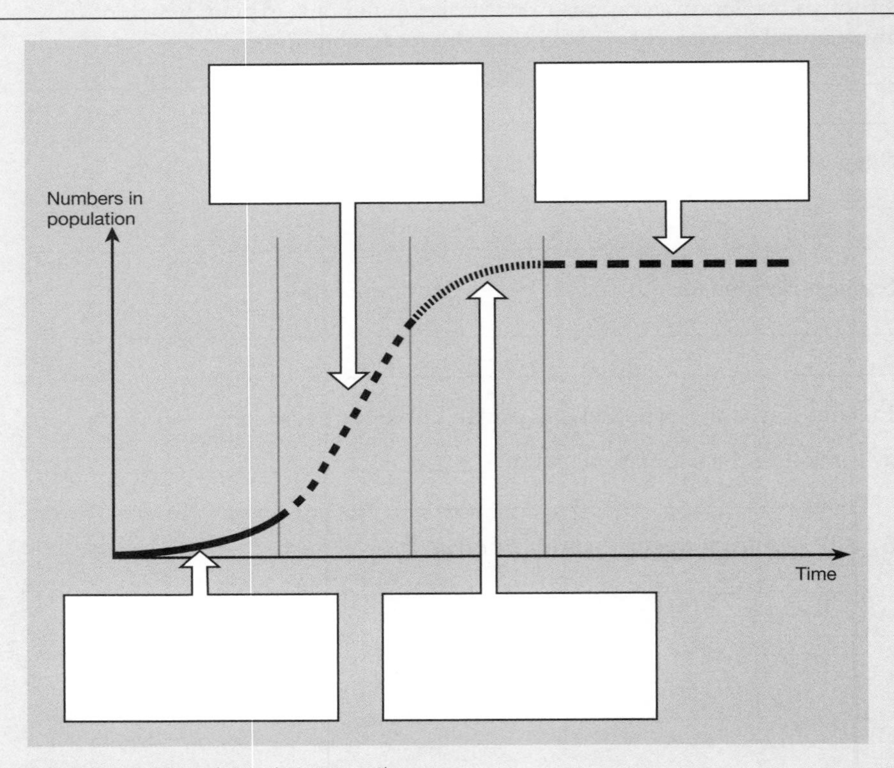

Figure 1.59 Natural population growth curve

PRACTICAL ACTIVITY 12

Table 1.33 Four stages of growth in natural populations

Name of stage	Description of stage
	Carrying capacity reached. Birth rate = death rate. Conditions will continue until there is a change in environmental resistance.
	Full reproductive potential reached. Maximum growth. No environmental resistance.
	As numbers increase, so does environmental resistance, causing either increased death rate, decreased birth rate or both
	Growth increases as reproduction starts. Slow at first. No environmental resistance.

18 At the start of this activity, several examples of population 'problems' were outlined. Suggest which environmental factors might be responsible for:

a a grasshopper plague. What do you think will eventually become of the grasshopper population?

____

____

b the very rapid growth in the crown-of-thorns sea star population. What do you think will eventually become of the sea star population?

____

____

19 Consider the examples of population dynamics you studied in this activity. Write a brief summary that describes:

a the pattern of population change over time, and

b the factors that affect population growth.

____

____

____

____

____

____

____

____

PRACTICAL ACTIVITY 13

In the field—a report on an ecosystem

MATERIALS

- pencils
- measuring tape (at least 10 m long)
- rope or cord
- 1 m × 1 m quadrat
- thermometer or temperature probe
- light meter
- anemometer (or devise a suitable scale, e.g. 5 point)
- pH meter or probe
- secchi disk or turbidity tube
- oxygen meter or probe
- magnifying glass
- field guides, e.g. of grasses, herbs, eucalypts, invertebrates
- extra lined/unlined paper for notes and diagrams, if required

INTRODUCTION

This activity provides an opportunity to conduct a first-hand field study of an ecosystem. A local terrestrial or aquatic ecosystem would be desirable and convenient; however, a field study of an ecosystem in the school grounds or even the classroom may be satisfactory. If you are able to visit a local nature reserve, remember that these are set aside by local authorities to protect native plant and animal species. Be mindful to create the least possible disturbance. Ensure that you have permission from the appropriate authority if you must collect specimens for analysis back in the school laboratory. Monitoring and analysis that can be completed in the field should be done there.

Field guides and keys for the identification of plants and animals will be useful to take along. Take care to protect yourself from stinging or biting insects and spiders when observing particular parts of the ecosystem. For example, use a stick or pencil to gently lift the bark of trees or to lift leaf litter. Rubber gloves may be useful. Ensure rocks that have been upturned during the investigation are returned to their original position.

You need to be familiar with different kinds of aquatic and terrestrial ecosystems, so background reading is recommended. In this activity you will classify the ecosystem you study. You also need to be able to choose and conduct appropriate sampling techniques for estimating population sizes for plant and animal species. Activity 10 'Plants in their place—using line transects' and Activity 11 'The flatweed census—population estimation' will be useful background activities.

You are likely to be working as part of a team, contributing part of the overall data for the ecosystem, and relying on others to provide data as well. Therefore, it is important to keep an accurate record of all of the data you collect.

PURPOSE

- To complete a first-hand field study of a selected ecosystem
- To consider the biotic and abiotic factors that make up an ecosystem
- To estimate the abundance and distribution of selected organisms within an ecosystem and consider the factors that might affect them.
- To consider some of the relationships between species within an ecosystem.

PROCEDURE

In the field you will be actively collecting data. This will involve making notes and diagrams.

In the field

1 When you arrive at the chosen study site, take a few minutes to look around. Observe the main features, prominent landmarks, the kinds of vegetation in the area, dominant plant species and weather conditions.

PRACTICAL ACTIVITY 13

1 Write a general description of the habitat, including abiotic and biotic features. Abiotic features will include geographical characteristics as well as local weather conditions. When describing biotic features, mention the type and density of vegetation. Consider features that will help you classify this ecosystem. For example, for terrestrial ecosystems consider the amount of sunlight that penetrates the foliage of trees to reach the ground. For aquatic ecosystems think about the salt or fresh nature of the water. Is the body of water a lake, stream, river or sea? Give a name to the kind of ecosystem you are studying.

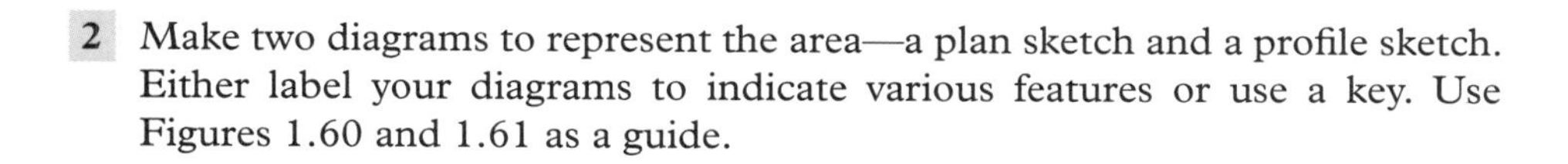

2 Make two diagrams to represent the area—a plan sketch and a profile sketch. Either label your diagrams to indicate various features or use a key. Use Figures 1.60 and 1.61 as a guide.

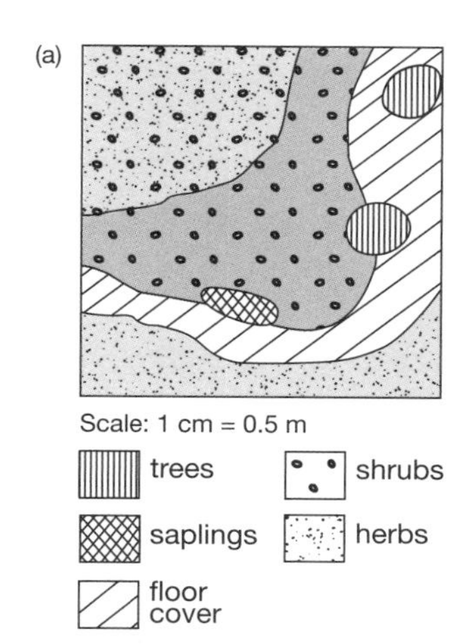

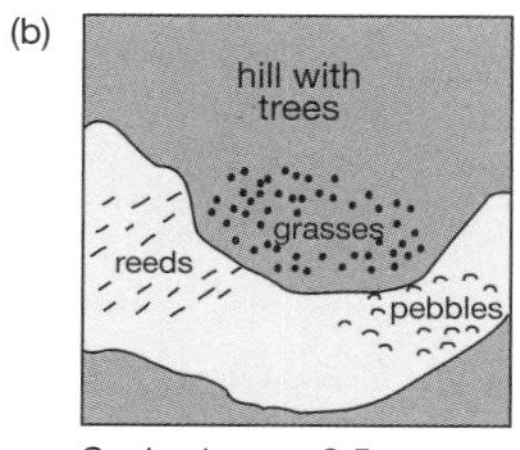

Figure 1.60 Plan sketch of **(a)** a terrestrial and **(b)** an aquatic ecosystem

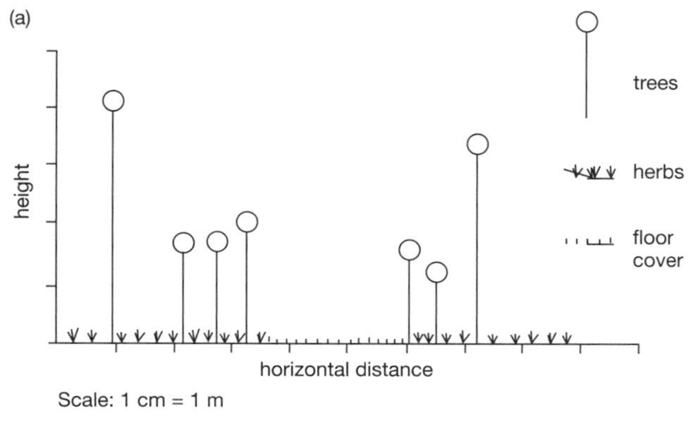

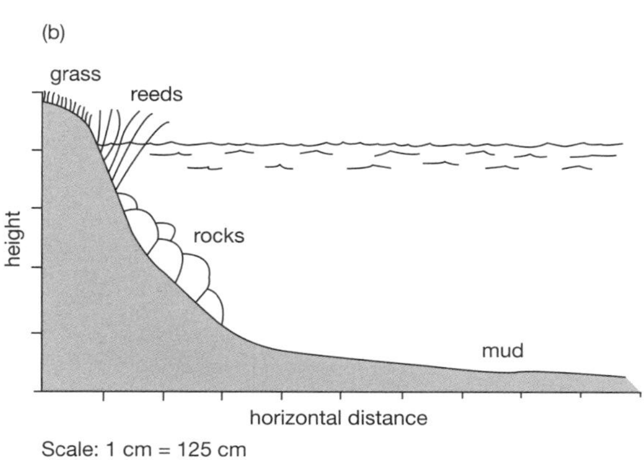

Figure 1.61 Profile sketch of **(a)** a terrestrial and **(b)** an aquatic ecosystem

Abiotic factors

3 Measure as many abiotic factors as possible for your ecosystem. Record the results of each test in Table 1.34 as you go.

Table 1.34 Summary of abiotic factors

Abiotic factor	Measurement
Air temperature • At ground level • At 1 m above ground level	
Soil temperature	
Water temperature	
Light intensity	
Wind speed	
Soil pH	
Water pH	
Water turbidity	
Dissolved oxygen content of water	
Flow rate of water (place an object in the water and measure distance covered over a given time, e.g. metres per minute)	

4 Identify and describe any other abiotic factors in the ecosystem.

____

____

____

____

Biotic factors

2 Observe the ecosystem closely, looking out for any plant and animal life.

5 Write a list of the different kinds of plants in the ecosystem, e.g. trees, grasses, herbs, ferns, mosses, lichens. Also include algae and fungi that may be present. Provide specific names of plants that you are able to identify.

____

____

____

____

____

____

3 Stand or sit quietly (for at least five minutes) to determine the kinds of animals in the ecosystem. Use other senses as well as your sight—listen for sounds. Examine the bark of trees where tiny animals may be hidden or camouflaged. Look for evidence of the existence of animals—e.g. nests, spider webs, scats, footprints, trails, burrows or chewed leaves.

6 Prepare a list of the types of animals present in the ecosystem—identify as many as you can.

____

____

____

____

7 Use your knowledge of interactions between organisms within ecosystems and your observations to draw four different food chains for this ecosystem.

8 Prepare a food web for this ecosystem that includes at least two different plants and at least four different animal species. You could start by combining the food chains you constructed in question 7.

Population abundance and distribution

In this part of the field work you will use some sampling techniques to gather data related to the distribution and abundance of organisms.

4 Use the rope and measuring tape to mark a transect line at least 10 m long through a selected area of the ecosystem. Make sure your transect line runs through an area that varies over the distance selected. For example, the vegetation may change, taking in a body of water and undulations in the landscape.

9 Draw a profile sketch of the ecosystem represented by the transect line (see Figure 1.61).

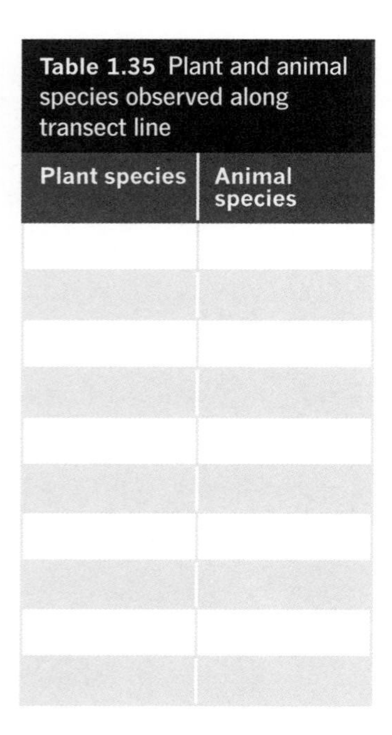

Table 1.35 Plant and animal species observed along transect line

Plant species	Animal species

Table 1.36 Number of plants

Quadrat number	Number of plants

5 Walk the length of the transect line, observing the plants and animals along the way.

10 Complete Table 1.35, entering the different plant and animal species you observe along the transect line.

6 Choose a plant species from your list. Set up a quadrat 1 m × 1 m at one end of the transect line. Count the individual plants of the species within the quadrat.

11 Record your data in Table 1.36.

7 Repeat the procedure for another four quadrats set at intervals along the transect line to give a random selection of the plant type you are investigating. Enter the data into Table 1.36.

8 Discuss with other members of your team how to estimate the 'abundance' of this plant species in the area of the ecosystem you are studying. Decide where to locate another five quadrats in order to achieve meaningful results. Count the plants and add the data to Table 1.36.

12 **a** Describe the distribution of the plant species along the transect line.

b Account for any differences in the distribution you have observed.

13 Use the data in Table 1.36 to calculate the average size of the plant population per quadrat.

14 Estimate the abundance of the plant species in the area.

15 Comment on the variability of the measurements made in different quadrats.

9 Choose a small animal, e.g. an insect species, from the list of animals you compiled in question 10. With the members of your team discuss a suitable way of estimating the abundance of this species in the area.

16 Estimate the abundance of the animal species in the area. Indicate how you arrived at the estimation. Record the date and time you made the estimate, along with a description of particular circumstances that might affect the abundance of the animals at the time.

17 Describe the distribution pattern of this animal species in the area. (**Hint:** Look at the features of the ecosystem that provide the optimum conditions for the species—e.g. shade plants, rocks for shelter, availability of food.)

Human impact

10 Look carefully around the ecosystem for signs of human impact. This may include deliberate change or indirect effects resulting from human activity outside the ecosystem. Examples of human activity could include pollution (air, water, noise), clearing of land, building, fencing, use of water bodies, recreational use of land/water, introduced species of plants and animals.

18 Describe how human activity appears to have impacted on the ecosystem.

SUMMARY

19 Suggest how the abiotic factors in this ecosystem are likely to change over a 24-hour period.

20 Describe how such changes in the abiotic factors are likely to affect the plant and animal life in the ecosystem.

21 Describe an example of each of the following kinds of relationships evident in the ecosystem:

a predator–prey:

b parasite–host:

c mutual benefit:

PRACTICAL ACTIVITY 13

22 Use your knowledge of food webs to explain how energy moves through ecosystems.

23 Outline some factors that might account for the distribution and abundance of organisms in the ecosystem.

24 Prepare a concept map summarising the relationships between organisms within the ecosystem and between the organisms and their non-living surroundings. Include inputs and outputs relevant to the ecosystem.

25 Considering the human impact on this ecosystem discussed earlier in this activity, suggest strategies that might lead to an improvement in the quality of this ecosystem.

____

____

____

____

____

____

UNIT 1

How do living things stay alive?

AREA OF STUDY 3

Practical investigation

Outcome 3

Design and undertake an investigation related to the survival of an organism or species, and draw conclusions based on evidence from collected data.

Key knowledge

- the biological concepts specific to the investigation and their significance, including definitions of key terms, and biological representations
- the characteristics of scientific research methodologies and techniques of primary qualitative and quantitative data collection relevant to the investigation: laboratory work (microscopy), fieldwork (quadrats, transects and field guides) and/or observational studies of animal behavior; precision, accuracy, reliability and validity of data; and minimisation of experimental bias
- ethics and issues of research including identification and application of relevant health, safety and bioethical guidelines
- methods of organising, analysing and evaluating primary data to identify patterns and relationships including sources of error and limitations of data and methodologies
- observations and experiments that are consistent with, or challenge, current biological models or theories
- the nature of evidence that supports or refutes a hypothesis, model or theory
- options, strategies or solutions to issues related to organism or species survival
- the key findings of the selected investigation and their relationship to cytological and/or ecological concepts
- the conventions of scientific report writing including biological terminology and representations, standard abbreviations and units of measurement.

The flatweed census

AUTHOR: ____________

AREA OF STUDY 3
PRACTICAL INVESTIGATION

Students design and undertake an investigation related to the survival of an organism or species, and draw conclusions based on evidence from collected data.

The investigation is related to knowledge and skills developed in Areas of Study 1 and/or 2, and is conducted through laboratory work, fieldwork and/or observational studies. The investigation draws on key knowledge outlined in Area of Study 3 and related key science skills for Biology (see pages 10–11 of the Study Design).

ASSESSMENT FOR OUTCOME 3

A report of a student-designed or adapted investigation related to the survival of an organism or a species using an appropriate format. Formats might include a scientific poster, practical report, oral communication or digital presentation.

USING THIS TEMPLATE

This investigation is drawn from the ecosystem fieldwork in Outcome 2 and represents an adaptation/extension of fieldwork you may have already completed.

In this investigation you will use your understanding of scientific method to:

- develop a question
- design and conduct the investigation
- record data appropriately
- analyse and interpret the data
- arrive at a conclusion that responds to the question under investigation.

It will be important to refer to resources available to guide you through these steps.

The fieldwork report for this first-hand data investigation has used the format of a scientific poster. A scientific poster is a valid and common format for communicating scientific ideas and the outcomes of investigations. Scientific posters follow the same format as a standard laboratory report, but they are succinct and visually informative.

In this student-designed investigation it is important to carefully consider how to monitor the factor under investigation to achieve fair and reliable results. This template is intended to guide you through approaches to planning, conducting and reporting on the task.

INTRODUCTION

Background

Hypochaeris radicata is a flatweed commonly known as the dandelion. Native to Africa, Europe and western Asia, it is now an invasive weed widely distributed in Australia. Quadrat sampling of the flatweed in some lawns reveals irregular distribution. To understand this uneven distribution it will be important to consider various factors operating in the habitat of the lawn. For example, light exposure, light intensity, gradient/water runoff. The impact of these factors can be investigated in turn. This investigation focuses on the impact of light intensity.

The question under investigation is: Why does the flatweed grow more densely in some parts of the lawn than in others?

Aim

To investigate the irregular distribution of flatweed species in a lawn.

Hypothesis

Hypochaeris radicata requires high light intensity to thrive.

MATERIALS AND METHOD

Materials

- quadrats (1 m square is a suitable size)
- tape measure (10 m)
- hand-held light/lux meter
- clipboard and paper
- weed species chart or field guide

Method

Several factors need to be considered in planning this investigation.

- Identify variables.
- How will you keep the investigation controlled?
- How big is the area of lawn?
- How many quadrats will you use?
- Where will these be placed? Give consideration to sunny and shaded areas of the lawn.

Prepare step-by-step instructions. Remember that these instructions should be clear and easy for someone else to follow. They should be written in the third person.

—distribution of a flatweed species

RESULTS

The experimental results will include all of the data collected during the fieldwork and other information relevant to the investigation. This may include:

- sketches of the area in question
- a profile of the area showing further information such as gradient
- notes and lists related to factors observed in the area
- photographs of the weed in question for easy identification
- population data collected from each quadrat
- lux readings for each quadrat.

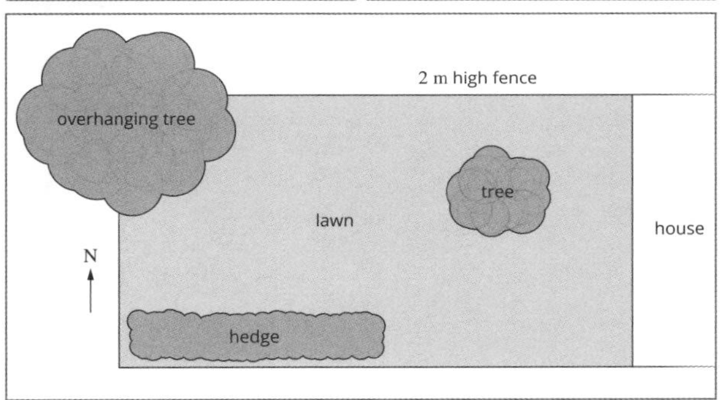

Table 1.37 Lux reading/weed count

Quadrat number	Light intensity (lux)	Number of weeds
1		
2		
3		
4		
5		

DISCUSSION

The discussion involves analysing the data collected and set out in the results. It should address all the experimental data in turn. Usually this would include manipulating the quadrat data to calculate the average population per square metre and projected overall population for the area. For this investigation it will be important to examine patterns of weed density in quadrats across the lawn and any alignment with patterns in light intensity. Account for any such patterns.

The discussion is also the opportunity to evaluate the scientific method used. This includes identifying limitations encountered during the investigation. A discussion of limitations should consider how identified factors have impacted on the investigation, and suggestions about how to reduce or eliminate these in subsequent investigations.

CONCLUSION

The conclusion is a clear and concise statement that summarises the findings of the investigation. The conclusion should respond to the aim of the investigation and state whether the hypothesis is supported or negated, drawing on experimental evidence to support this.

References

Remember to acknowledge any reference material used in the course of the investigation. This may include:

- your log book—raw data and calculations
- worksheets supplied by your teacher
- school website—support material
- field guides
- Internet sources.

When referencing published sources it's important to provide bibliographical data according to accepted protocols, such as Harvard citation style.

Example:

Iewf.org, 'Factsheet—*Hypochoeris Radicata*'. N.p., 2015. Web. 8 Aug. 2015.

UNIT 2

How is continuity of life maintained?

AREA OF STUDY 1

How does reproduction maintain the continuity of life?

Outcome 1

Compare the advantages and disadvantages of asexual and sexual reproduction, explain how changes within the cell cycle may have an impact on cellular or tissue system function and identify the role of stem cells in cell growth and cell differentiation and in medical therapies.

Key knowledge

The cell cycle

- derivation of all cells from pre-existing cells through completion of the cell cycle
- the rapid procession of prokaryotic cells through their cell cycle by binary fission
- the key events in the phases (G1, S, G2, M and C) of the eukaryotic cell cycle, including the characteristics of the sub-phases of mitosis (prophase, metaphase, anaphase and telophase) and cytokinesis in plant and animal cells.

Asexual reproduction

- the types of asexual reproduction including fission, budding, vegetative propagation and spore formation
- the biological advantages and disadvantages of asexual reproduction
- emerging issues associated with cloning, including applications in agriculture and horticulture.

Sexual reproduction

- how an offspring from two parents has a unique genetic identity
- the key events in meiosis that result in the production of gametes from somatic cells including the significance of crossing over of chromatids between homologous chromosomes in Prophase 1 and the non-dividing of the centromere in Metaphase 1
- the biological advantage of sexual reproduction, specifically the genetic diversity in offspring.

Cell growth and cell differentiation

- the types and function of stem cells in human development, including the distinction between embryonic and adult stem cells and their potential use in the development of medical therapies
- the consequences of stem cell differentiation in human prenatal development including the development of germ layers, types of tissues formed from germ layers and the distinction between embryo and foetus
- the disruption of the regulation of the cell cycle through genetic predisposition or the action of mutagens that gives rise to uncontrolled cell division including cancer and abnormal embryonic development.

Cell cycle and cell replication

Cells are in a constant state of activity that includes all the chemical reactions that make up the cell's metabolism, as well as growth and reproduction. Cell growth includes the replication of DNA that will be organised and divided for distribution to daughter cells during cell division. This cyclical activity of cells is called the **cell cycle** (Figure 2.1).

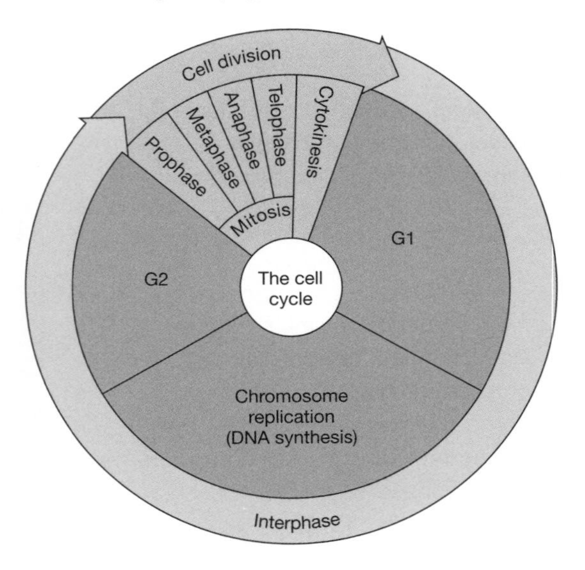

Figure 2.1 The cell cycle takes approximately 24 hours to complete in mammalian cells.

We know from the cell theory that all cells are derived from pre-exisitng cells. Prokaryotic cells replicate by a process known as binary fission in which the cell and its contents are divided into two. Eukaryotic cells replicate by a process known as mitosis (the division of the nucleus) followed by the splitting of the entire cell into two (cytokinesis). In both cases the parent cell divides to form two identical daughter cells. When cells replicate to form identical daughter cells, the resulting cells are called clones.

Cell replication is responsible for the production of new cells within an organism for the purposes of maintenance, growth and repair (Table 2.1).

Table 2.1 Purpose of cell replication

Cell replication contributes to	Example(s)
Maintenance	Replacement of old cells as they 'wear out'
Growth	Enables part of organism or whole organism to increase in size
Repair	Replacement of damaged cells after injury

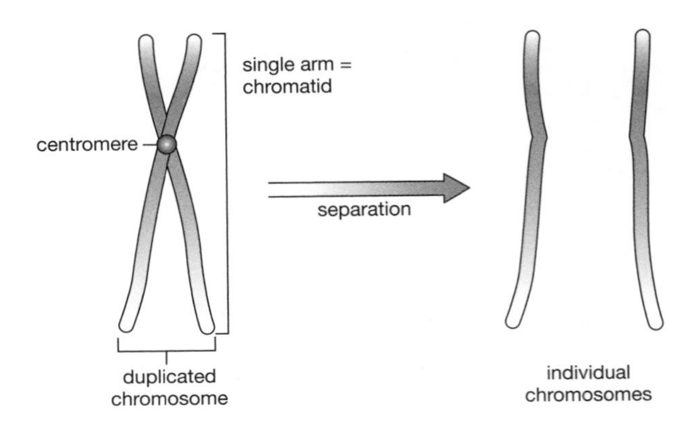

Figure 2.2 Anatomy of a chromosome

DNA replication

During cell reproduction the genetic material is organised so that the resulting daughter cells each receive precisely the same genetic material as the parent cell from which they are derived. Before this can occur, the genetic material must be duplicated. This copying process is called **DNA replication** (Figure 2.6). During DNA replication, the two strands of DNA that make up the double helix 'unzip' or separate. The enzyme **DNA polymerase** then moves along the exposed template strands adding nucleotides according to base-pairing rules to build the new strands.

DNA replication is called **semi-conservative** because the parental strand is *conserved* or retained in the new molecule.

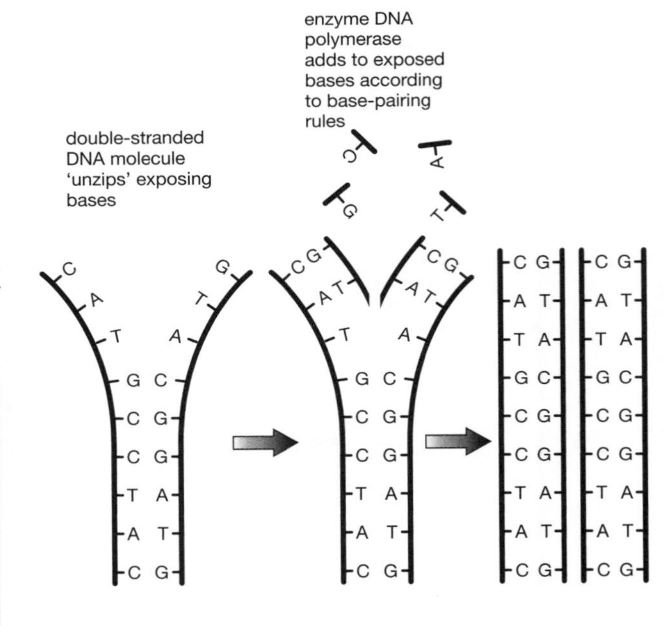

Figure 2.6 DNA replication—DNA polymerase adds nucleotides to build copies of the original DNA strands

KEY KNOWLEDGE

Asexual reproduction and mitosis

Cell replication and nuclear division in eukaryotic cells involves mitosis followed by cytokinesis. Mitosis is divided into phases. **Interphase** is followed by mitosis. Mitosis is divided into **prophase**, **metaphase**, **anaphase** and **telophase** (see Figure 2.3 on page 127). Cytokinesis occurs at the end of telophase.

- **Interphase:** Replication of the chromosomes occurs. Without this, the daughter cells would not receive the appropriate type and number of chromosomes. (Chromosomes, made of DNA, carry all of the information needed for cell structure and function.)
- **Prophase:** Chromosomes shorten and thicken, and become visible under the light microscope. The nuclear envelope dissolves and a structure called the spindle starts to form. The spindle consists of fibres that radiate across the cell from centrioles at each pole.
- **Metaphase:** Chromosomes line up along the equator of the cell. Each chromosome attaches to a spindle fibre by its centromere.
- **Anaphase:** The spindle fibres contract, causing the centromeres to split, pulling the sister chromatids towards opposite poles. (Remember, each chromosome was replicated during interphase and the two copies of each have remained joined until now.
- **Telophase:** New nuclear membranes form around each of the two new groups of chromosomes.
- **Cytokinesis:** The cytoplasm divides forming two individual daughter cells.

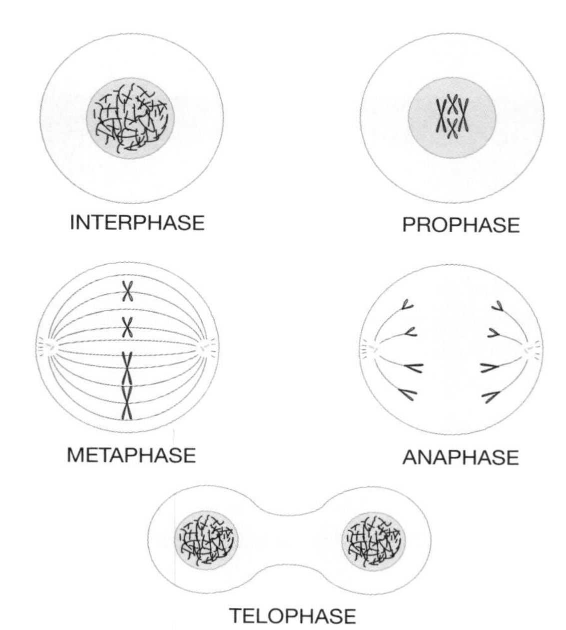

Figure 2.3 Mitosis

Sexual reproduction and meiosis

A different type of cell division gives rise to gametes (sex cells). These resultant cells are not identical. Gamete production involves a special type of nuclear division called **meiosis**.

Unlike somatic cells, **gametes** contain only one set of chromosomes—half the full complement. They are called **haploid**.

Meiosis, also called reduction division, is the process responsible for the production of haploid gametes. Meiosis results in the production of daughter cells, in this case the gametes, which are different from the parent cell from which they arose (see Figure 2.4).

Diploidy (having two sets of chromosomes) is restored at fertilisation.

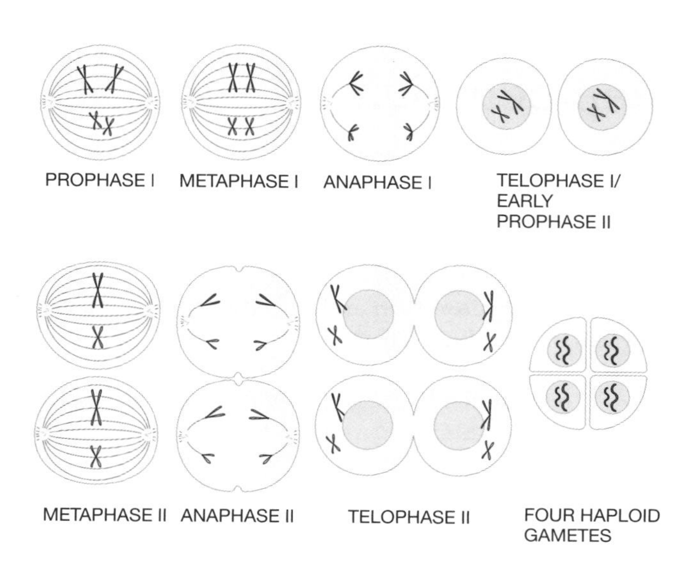

Figure 2.4 Meiosis

VARIATION

Variation in meiosis occurs as a result of independent assortment and crossing over.

Independent assortment: When the chromosomes of a homolgous pair line up together and then segregate to different poles, they do so independently of other homologous pairs.

Crossing over: During early prophase I, when homologous chromosomes pair, they may touch at points called **chiasma**. At chiasmata the homologous pairs may exchange chromosome segments. This results in **recombination** and is responsible for an increase in the variety of gametes formed.

Homologous chromosomes (Figure 2.5 on page 128) are similar chromosomes, that is, they contain the same genes but they may contain alternative forms of those

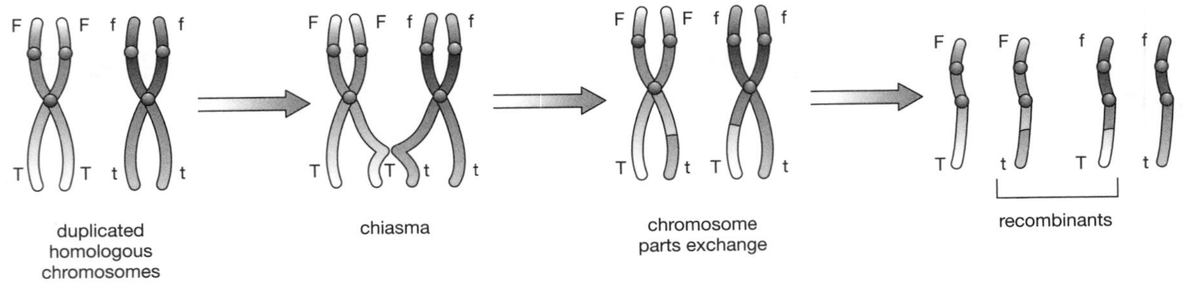

Figure 2.5 Homologous chromosomes

genes. Alternative forms of a gene are called **alleles**. For example, earlobe shape in humans has different forms—free or attached. By convention, letters of the alphabet are assigned to represent the different alleles. F can be used to denote the allele controlling the expression of 'free lobes'. Similarly, the alleles T and t can be used to denote the genetic expression of 'tongue rolling'.

Reproduction

Reproduction allows the survival of a particular species from one generation to the next. There are two types of reproduction—**asexual** and **sexual**.

ASEXUAL REPRODUCTION

Asexual reproduction involves the process of cell division referred to as **mitosis**.

Characteristics of asexual reproduction:

- all new individuals are genetically identical to parent individuals
- does not require another individual (mate).

Asexual reproduction:

- occurs in all single-celled organisms, fungi, simple animals and plants
- results in large numbers of new individuals being produced relatively quickly
- is an advantage in an unchanging environment when individuals are adapted to their environment
- features a lack of **genetic variety** in a **population** of individuals. If conditions become unfavourable, then all individuals could die and the population becomes extinct.

SEXUAL REPRODUCTION

All species of organisms can undergo **sexual reproduction**. Sexual reproduction requires the process of **meiosis** to form **gametes**.

Characteristics of sexual reproduction:

- genetically unique individuals are formed as a result of genetic contribution from two parents
- fusion of haploid gametes in fertilisation to produce diploid zygote
- genetic variety produced in offspring.

The reproductive systems of complex multicellular organisms such as flowering plants and mammals feature specialised structures in which haploid gametes are produced through the process of **meiosis**. Various structures and processes are adapted to allow eggs and sperm to meet so that fertilisation can occur.

Table 2.2 Types of asexual reproduction

Type	Process	Examples
Binary fission	Equal division of parent cell into two new cells	Bacteria Protozoans
Budding	Division of cytoplasm is unequal, new organism grows on parent before breaking away	Yeast Hydra
Fragmentation	Part of organism breaks off and regenerates into new individual	Flatworms Marine worms Echinoderms
Spore formation	Spores released into environment and germinate into new individuals	Fungi Mosses Ferns
Vegetative propagation	Separation of plant to form new, independent plant from leaves, stems and underground stems	Many plants including flowering plants
Parthenogenesis	A type of cloning resulting from the formation of new individual from an unfertilised egg	Insects (wasps, ants) Lizards Birds

The resulting zygote grows and divides, ultimately developing into a new individual.

The primary advantage of sexual reproduction is that it generates **genetic variation** within a population and allows a species to survive in changing conditions.

Disadvantages include:

- need to find a mate
- requires more energy
- may be limited to certain times of the year (seasonal dependence).

Cell growth and differentiation

Cell division is followed by cell growth. As cells mature they develop the features that allow them to take on specialised roles. This is called **cell differentiation**. The structure and features of cells are related to their function. For example, cells lining the small intestine feature microscopic finger-like projections (microvilli) on their surface that increase the surface area to volume ratio of the cells, making them efficient at absorbing nutrients.

Undifferentiated cells are called **stem cells**. These can develop into a multitude of cell types. The zygote formed at fertilisation is **totipotent**—it has the potential to differentiate into any cell type in the body. As development continues from zygote to embryo, the potential of embryonic cells to differentiate into different kinds of cells becomes more limited. After the 16-cell stage, the embryo is no longer totipotent. The differentiating cells form three germ layers: the endoderm, mesoderm and ectoderm. Cells from these different layers are **pluripotent**—they each have the ability to form a range of cell types, but not all cell types.

Adult stem cells are even more limited. Some, such as blood-forming cells, are **multipotent**—they can differentiate into white blood cells, red blood cells and platelets, but not other kinds of cells. Some types of cells, such as skin cells, are **unipotent**—while they can divide repeatedly, they can only reproduce one cell type.

Stem cells are important in therapeutic medicine because their ability to differentiate means stem cells from a healthy person may be used to treat patients with certain diseases. For example, bone marrow (which contains blood stem cells) can be transplanted to donate healthy blood-forming cells to leukaemia patients.

Mutagens are agents that alter the DNA molecule in cells. Since DNA sequences are responsible for controlling cell processes, including growth, development and differentiation as well as programmed cell death (apoptosis), any interference in the structure or sequencing of the DNA can also interfere with its regulatory role. This may mean the formation of developmental abnormalities or cancers.

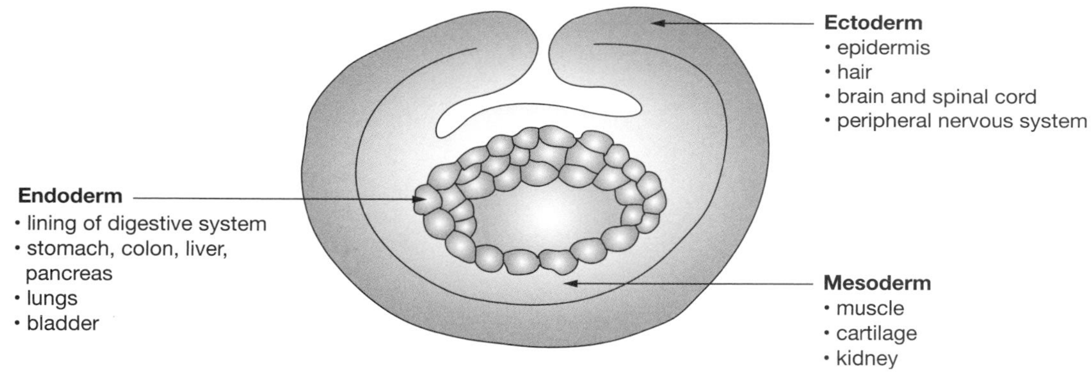

Figure 2.7 Stem cell pluripotency of embryo germ layers

WORKSHEET 25

Cell cycle—replication

1 The genetic material in the nuclei of cells is contained in strands called **chromosomes**. Figure 2.8 shows two chromosomes, one duplicated, the other single-stranded.

a Label the centromere and a chromatid.

b Explain the difference between a chromosome and a chromatid.

____

____

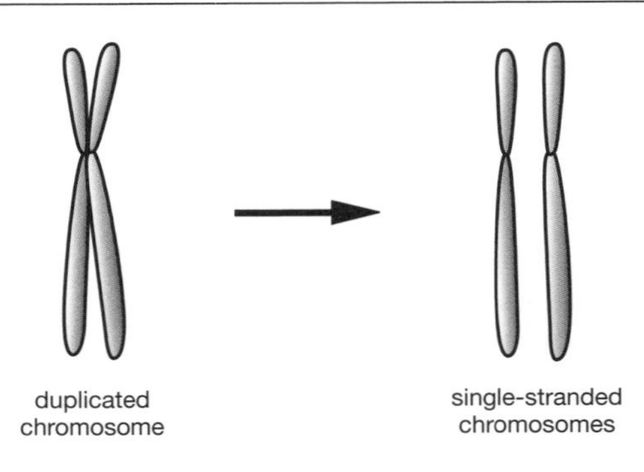

Figure 2.8 Chromosomes

2 Label the stages shown in the cell cycle below. Briefly summarise what occurs at each stage.

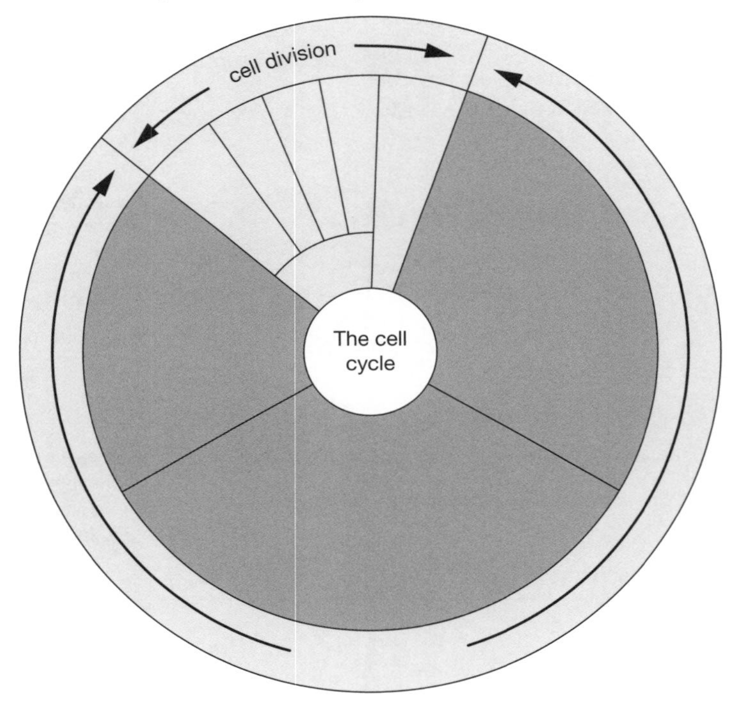

3 Outline the significance of cell replication. Include three key points.

____

____

____

____

____

____

WORKSHEET 26

Mitosis mixer—nuclear division in somatic cells

Mitosis is the kind of nuclear division that occurs in dividing somatic cells during tissue growth and repair. Figure 2.9 was prepared from onion root-tip cells that have been stained to distinguish the DNA.

1 Examine the cells at the different stages of mitosis in Figure 2.9. Some of the cells have been labelled with a letter of the alphabet. Identify the stage of mitosis represented by these cells and record this in the table below.

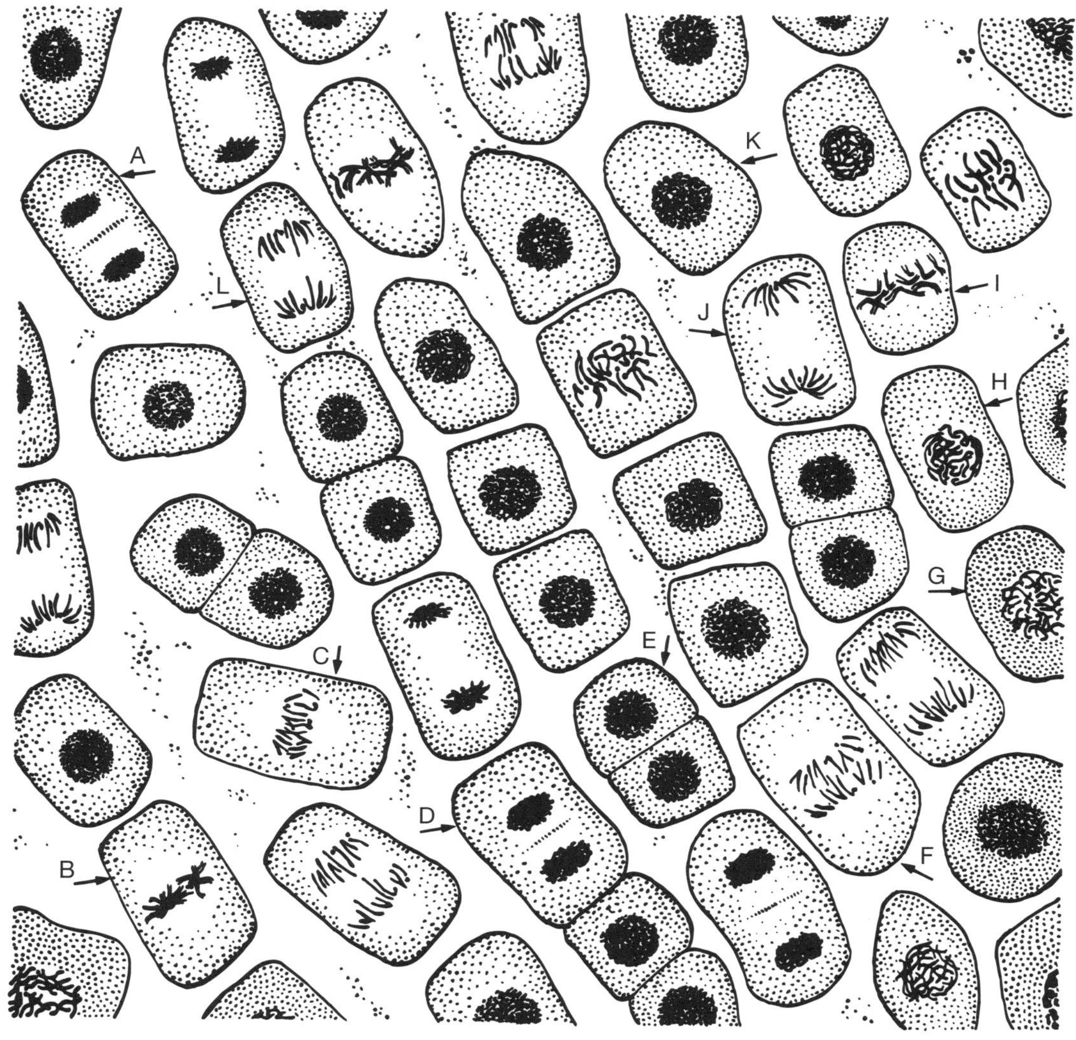

Figure 2.9 Diagram of onion root tip showing cells at different stages of mitosis

Stage of mitosis	Cells in stage
Interphase	
Prophase	
Metaphase	
Anaphase (early)	
Anaphase (late)	
Telophase	

2 In terms of genetic make-up, describe the results of mitosis.

____

____

3 Interphase is sometimes called the 'resting phase' of the cell cycle. This is a misnomer. Outline what is happening in the nuclei of interphase cells.

____

____

____

____

WORKSHEET 27

Super stem cells—cell potential

1 Select appropriate terms from the following list to complete the table. Describe the differentiation potential that occurs at each stage of embryonic development. Note that some terms may be used more than once.

pluripotent	foetus	morula	unipotent
mesoderm	adult stem cell	totipotent	

Type of cell	Diagram	Potency potential	
		Name	Description
Zygote • fertilised egg • 1 cell	fertilised egg (day 1)	Totipotent	
__________ • 16 cells	morula (day 3)		
Blastocyst • endoderm • mesoderm • ectoderm	blastocyst (day 5)		
__________	gastrula (day 12)		
Embryo	embryo (week 3) foetus (week 8)		

2 Explain what happens to the potential of embryonic stem cells to differentiate as the embryo grows and matures.

____

____

____

WORKSHEET 28

Reproductive routines—asexual reproduction

Asexual reproduction is a reproductive strategy that results in offspring that are genetically identical to the parent organism from which they are derived—that is, the offspring are **clones** of the parent. Although asexual reproduction results in identical offspring, the means of asexual reproduction varies between different kinds of organisms.

Consider the different kinds of organisms shown below.

1 Identify and describe the method of asexual reproduction involved in each case.

Bacteria

Process: ______________________________

Description: ______________________________

____

____

____

Hydra

Process: ______________________________

Description: ______________________________

____

____

____

Sea star

Process: ______________________________

Description: ______________________________

____

____

____

Potato tuber

'eye'

Process: ______________________________

Description: ______________________________

____

____

____

2 Describe the circumstances in which asexual reproduction is advantageous to a group of organisms. Explain.

3 Describe the circumstances in which asexual reproduction can place a population at a disadvantage. Explain.

WORKSHEET 29

Ways of reproducing—a concept map

Use the key words listed below to complete the concept map summarising the key ideas about sexual and asexual reproduction. Write along the link lines between words and phrases to show the relationships between ideas in your concept map. Diagrams may be a useful addition.

flower	budding	haploid	stigma	fertilisation	pistil	vegetative reproduction
diversity	mitosis	stamen	gametes	zygote	uterus	clone
pollination	testes	implantation	pollen	ovaries	fission	diploid

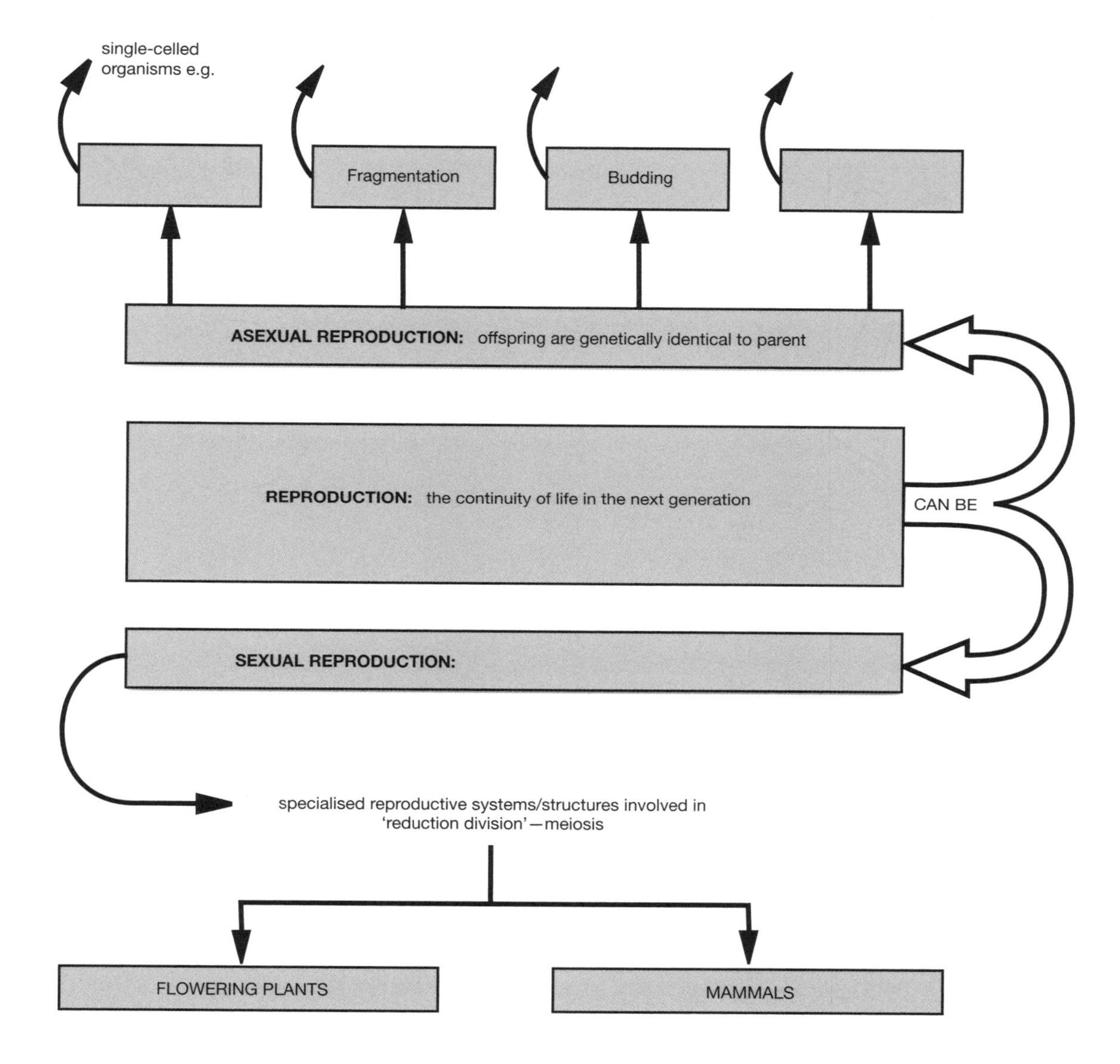

WORKSHEET 30

Mendel's spin on meiosis—Mendel's principles

In his comprehensive experiments breeding the garden pea, Gregor Mendel observed patterns of inheritance that he was able to interpret with skill and accuracy. This was a significant achievement considering he was working 'blind' in a sense, with no knowledge of chromosomes as the carriers of genetic material. Mendel's theories about how the factors that confer phenotypic characteristics are organised during sexual reproduction provide the foundation of our modern understanding of heredity. Today we refer to these theories as:

- The Principle of Segregation
- The Principle of Independent Assortment

1 **The Principle of Segregation** The diagram illustrates the behaviour of chromosomes during segregation. Use the space inside the arrow to explain what is meant by the Principle of Segregation.

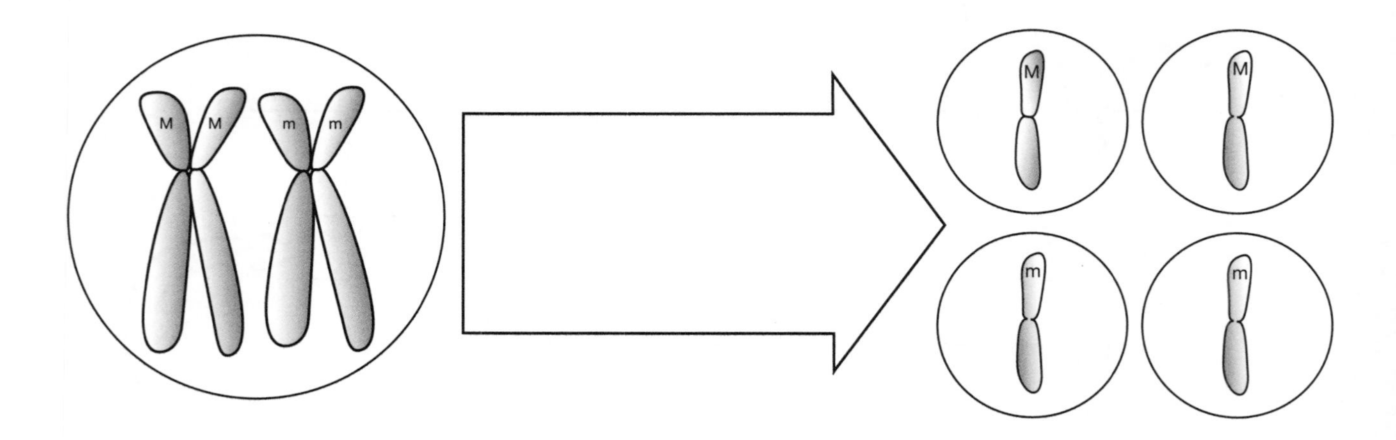

2 **The Principle of Independent Assortment** The germ-line cell shown has a diploid number of four. Meiosis results in independent assortment of the alleles for the different genes. Carry through the notation used to complete the steps illustrating independent assortment of these alleles. Coloured pencils may be useful. Use the boxed space to explain what is meant by the term 'Principle of Independent Assortment'.

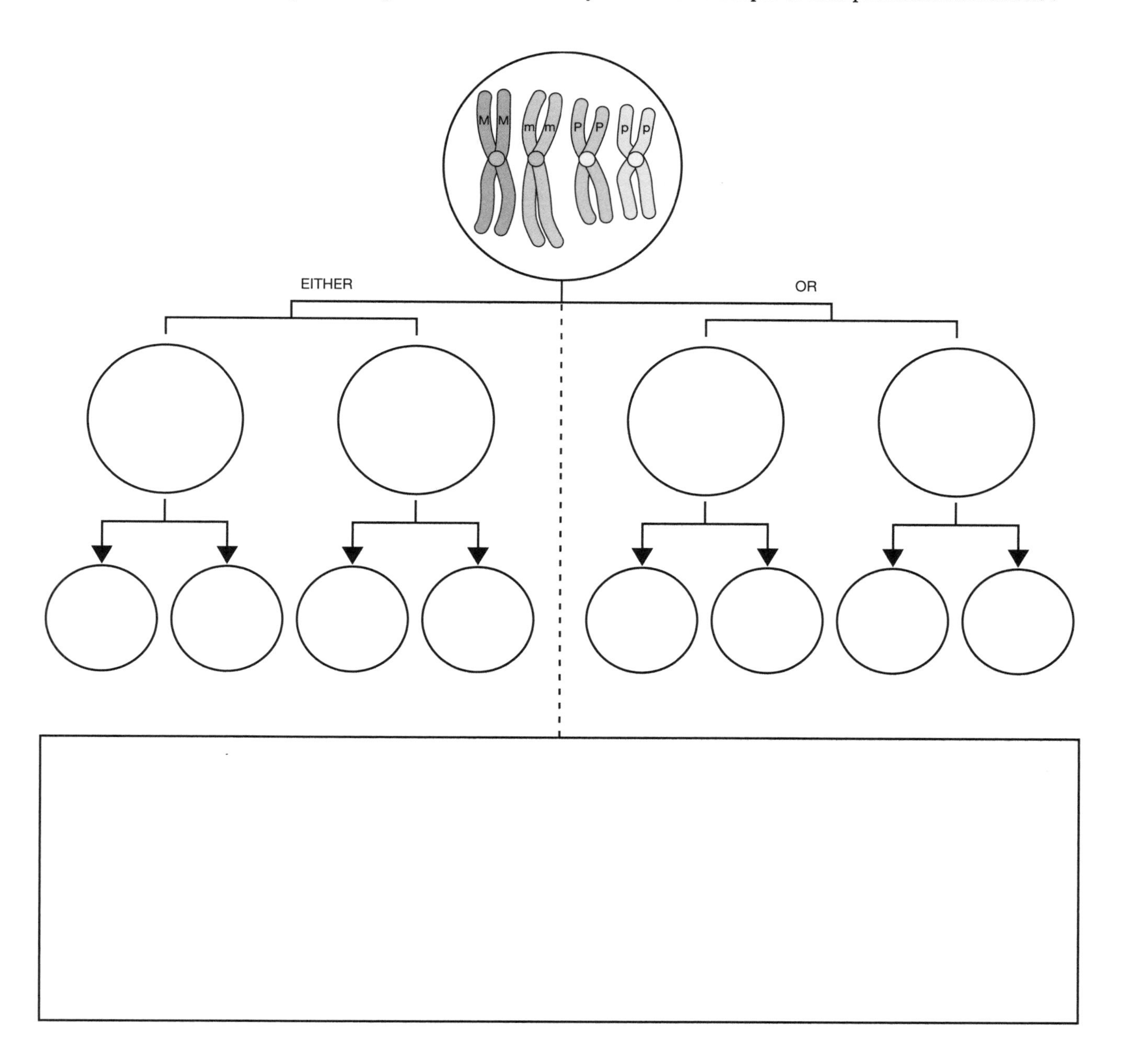

PRACTICAL ACTIVITY 14

Convenient cloning—examining some issues

INTRODUCTION

Dolly the sheep made history as the first cloned mammal in the world. She was born on 5th July 1996 at the Roslin Institute in Scotland. While cloning of plants is age-old, cloning of animals had now arrived in earnest. It set the scene for many potential farming and medical applications but it also hailed a new era of controversy.

PURPOSE

To investigate the emerging issues associated with cloning of organisms in agriculture and horticulture.

DURATION

45 minutes

PROCEDURE

Read each of the following three articles and consider Figures 2.10 and 2.11. Highlight the key ideas and answer the questions associated with each article.

Article one

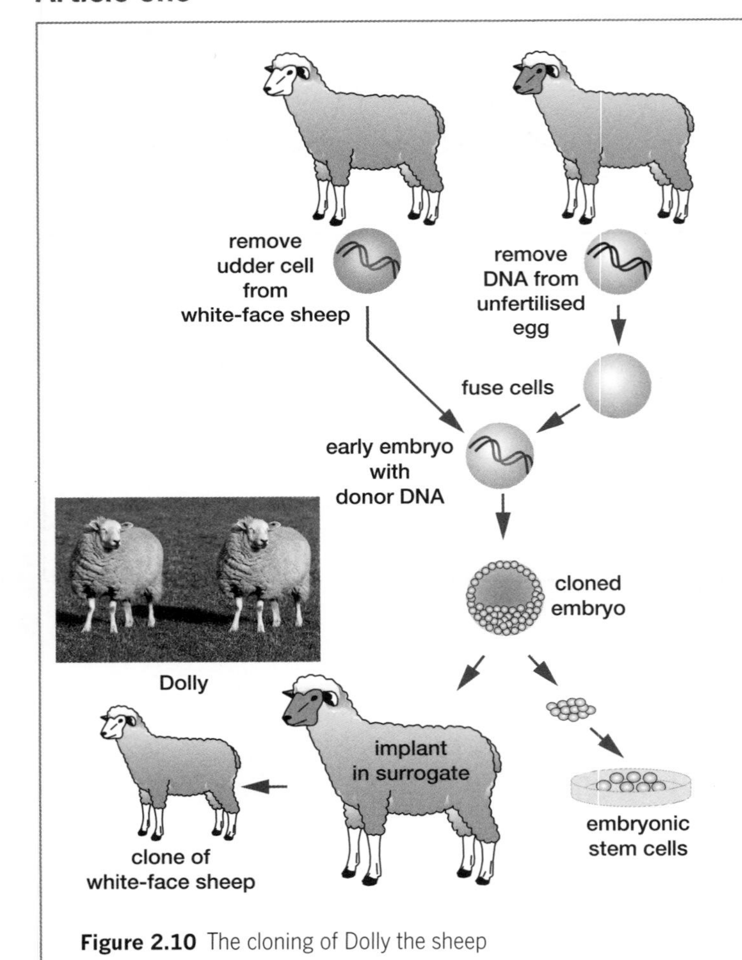

Figure 2.10 The cloning of Dolly the sheep

Remembering Dolly the sheep

On 5th July 1996, Dolly the sheep was born. Dolly was the first mammal created by somatic cell transfer. When the birth of Dolly was published, there was widespread public interest in her life. While this interest waned over the years, it always piqued when Dolly experienced any health issues.

Dolly was euthanized on 14 February 2003, as she had progressive lung disease and arthritis. At nearly 7 years of age, Dolly was young to die; usually, her particular breed will live to around 12 years of age. At the time of Dolly's death, conjecture was rife that the causes of her illness were due to premature ageing, a possible consequence of cloning. However, scientists found little evidence of this in the extensive health assessments carried out on Dolly throughout her life.

Since Dolly, there have been numerous animals cloned using somatic cell transfer. As well as mice, cows and goats, two endangered species, the gaur and mouflon, have also been cloned using this technique. In 2013, human embryonic stem cells were created by using somatic cell transfer. The generated cell lines can be used to treat the patient from which they originate, for example a baby with a rare genetic disorder.

PRACTICAL ACTIVITY 14

1 Suggest why there was such public interest in the life of Dolly the sheep.

2 With reference to Dolly, explain how a clone is similar and how it is different to its parent.

3 The birth of Dolly ignited debate about the potential wider applications of cloning. Outline three ethical issues associated with cloning of animals or other organisms.

Article two

Australian scientists develop genetically modified bananas

A team of scientists at Queensland University of Technology have successfully grown Australia's first genetically modified banana plant. They have been developing the GM banana for about 15 years.

A genetically modified organism (GMO) is one that has had its genetic material transformed. This usually means that genes from other sources have been added to the organism.

Bananas have been cultivated in Australia for more than a century, and are mostly grown in the tropics of Australia. About 95 per cent of the commercial production is bananas of the Cavendish variety. Other varieties, such as Lady Fingers, make up the other five per cent.

The problem is that bananas are clones. Commercial bananas are sterile and farmers cultivate bananas by cloning, including vegetative propagation techniques, such as cutting and replanting older plants. Since bananas are clones, there is little genetic variation in them, making them extremely susceptible to pests and diseases.

A recent outbreak of a fungal pathogen, the Fusarium fungus, wiped out banana production in the Northern Territory. Similar fungi were responsible for wiping out the banana industry in South and Central America in the 1940s.

Currently, the battle against fungi is being fought with a huge amount of fungicides. Not only is this costly, it also has negative effects on local ecosystems.

The GM banana the QUT scientists developed is resistant to Fusarium fungus. The resistant gene has been harvested from a variety of wild banana from Indonesia that has developed resistance to the Fusarium fungus.

Figure 2.11 A wild banana

At the moment, the GM bananas have only been grown in the laboratory, but trials are planned for the bananas to be grown in a trial crop in Darwin in 2011.

Source: http://www.abc.net.au/catalyst/stories/2544893.htm

4 Cloning in plants is a form of vegetative propagation. Explain what is meant by the phrase 'vegetative propagation'.

5 Name and describe three types of vegetative propagation in plants. Provide one example of each.

6 List some advantages and disadvantages of Cavendish (cloned) bananas over wild bananas.

Advantages	Disadvantages

7 Unlike Cavendish bananas, the wild fruit do not require the application of large amounts of fungicides. Suggest how fungicides may be harmful to both consumers and the environment.

Article three

You might be eating that again

Around the world, cloning techniques are increasingly being used in agriculture to clone animals. In the UK, for example, meat from cloned animals has entered the food supply chain, as has milk from the offspring of cloned animals.

Cloning is a type of reproductive technology that is used to create an organism that is an exact genetic copy of another organism.

Cloning is not the same as genetic modification. Unlike genetic modification, which sees the insertion of a gene from one organism into another to introduce new characteristics, cloning does not alter the genetic material of an organism. Since cloning does not modify the genome, food from a cloned animal is not regulated in the same way as genetically modified organisms.

In Australia, cloned animals have not entered the food chain yet. The use of cloning is limited to elite breeding stock in an attempt to continue genetic lines beyond the reproductive life of the original donor animal.

Animal cloning is extremely expensive. This is one of the reasons cloned animals are unlikely to end up as food on your plate. At the moment, cloned cattle are bred in Australia solely for scientific purposes. However, tests have shown that the meat and milk products from the offspring of cloned cattle are suitable for human consumption.

The US food and Drug Administration and the European Food Safety Authority have both released reports concluding that edible products from cloned animals and their offspring are safe to eat. Food Standards Australia and New Zealand concur with these conclusions.

Source: http://www.foodstandards.gov.au/consumer/foodtech/clone/Pages/default.aspx

8 Identify and describe two potential benefits to producers of cloning cattle to increase the herd rather than using traditional methods of sexual reproduction.

9 Identify and describe two potential benefits to consumers of cloning cattle for milk and beef production.

10 Suggest why there may be reluctance on the part of consumers to purchase food products such as beef and milk from cloned cattle.

11 Comment on the statement in the article that 'Cloning is not the same as genetic modification'.

CONCLUSION

12 Summarise the advantages and disadvantages of cloning organisms in agriculture and horticulture.

PRACTICAL ACTIVITY 15

Marvellous meiosis—a mixture of gametes

INTRODUCTION

At fertilisation we receive a single set of chromosomes from each parent—a maternal set and a paternal set. However, during meiosis the chromosomes behave independently of one another, creating a large number of possibilities for gamete formation. As there is a total of 46 chromosomes arranged in 23 pairs, the number of combinations is staggering. The result is variation in the gametes and variation in the resulting offspring.

In this activity you will consider just six chromosomes arranged in three pairs, i.e. $2n = 6$. You will need:

- 6 poppit bead chromosomes—two different colours, three of each colour
- a large sheet of paper to represent a meiotic cell—draw a broken line down the centre of the cell to represent the equator.

PURPOSE

- To simulate the stages of meiotic cell division.
- To consider the consequences of meiosis.

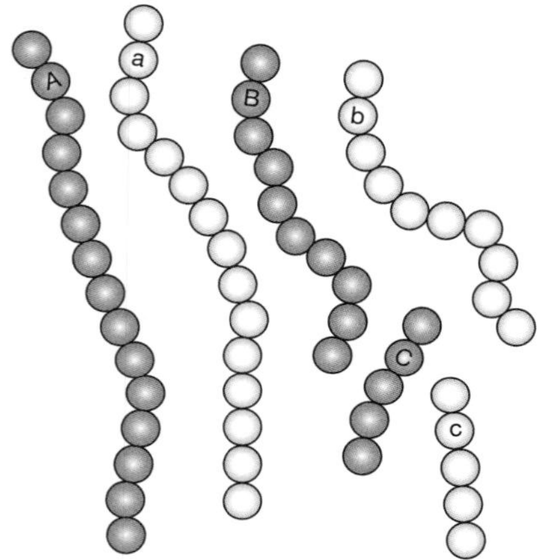

Figure 2.12 Poppit bead chromosomes

PROCEDURE

1. Arrange the poppit beads into two sets representing the maternal set and the paternal set of chromosomes.
2. Each set should include one chromosome at least 15 beads long, one at least 10 beads long, and one at least 5 beads long, as shown in Figure 2.12.
3. Use a marker pen and upper case lettering to mark a bead near the end of each maternal chromosome with the letters 'A', 'B' and 'C'. Mark the paternal homologues with the corresponding lower case lettering 'a', 'b' and 'c' at the same loci.

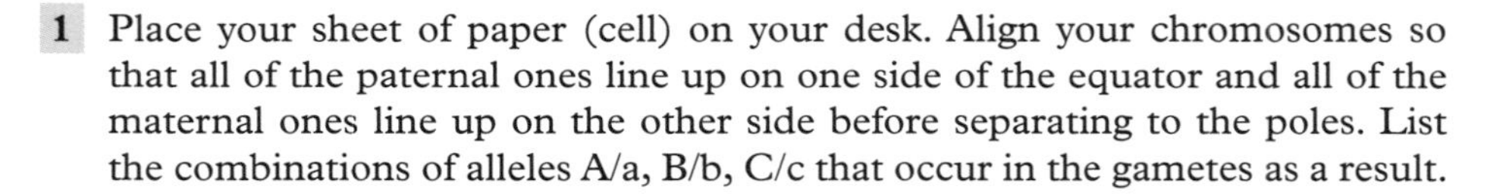

1 Place your sheet of paper (cell) on your desk. Align your chromosomes so that all of the paternal ones line up on one side of the equator and all of the maternal ones line up on the other side before separating to the poles. List the combinations of alleles A/a, B/b, C/c that occur in the gametes as a result.

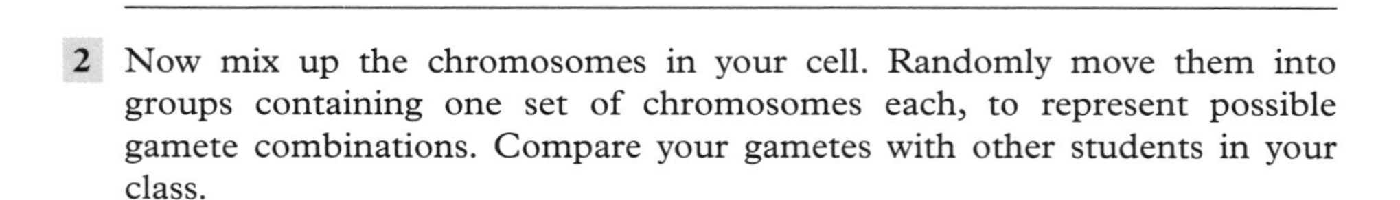

2 Now mix up the chromosomes in your cell. Randomly move them into groups containing one set of chromosomes each, to represent possible gamete combinations. Compare your gametes with other students in your class.

Comment on the kinds of gametes produced. Are they all the same?

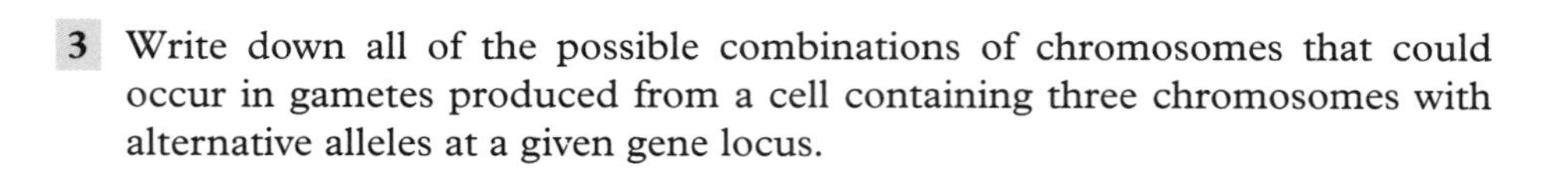

3 Write down all of the possible combinations of chromosomes that could occur in gametes produced from a cell containing three chromosomes with alternative alleles at a given gene locus.

4 The formula for calculating the possible number of combinations, and therefore the possible number of different gametes, is 2^x, where x = number of gene loci, and the base number 2 represents the number of chromosomes in a homologous pair. This formula gives us a total of $2^3 = 8$ different kinds of gametes in **3**.

Calculate the number of possibilities when there are:

a four chromosome pairs, i.e. four gene loci: ______________________

b five chromosome pairs: ______________________

c ten chromosome pairs: ______________________

Imagine the number of possibilities for 23 chromosome pairs! Add to this the large number of gene loci on each chromosome together with their alternative alleles!

VALUE-ADDED VARIETY

4. Use the marker pen to add a second gene locus at the other end of each chromosome. For example, write 'D' at the other end of the maternal 'A' chromosome and 'd' at the other end of the 'a' paternal chromosome.
5. Collect another set of chromosomes to represent duplicated chromosomes.
6. Mark them accordingly and use an elastic band to hold duplicated chromosomes together at their centromeres.

   Experiment with these duplicated chromosomes to show crossing-over events (Figure 2.13).

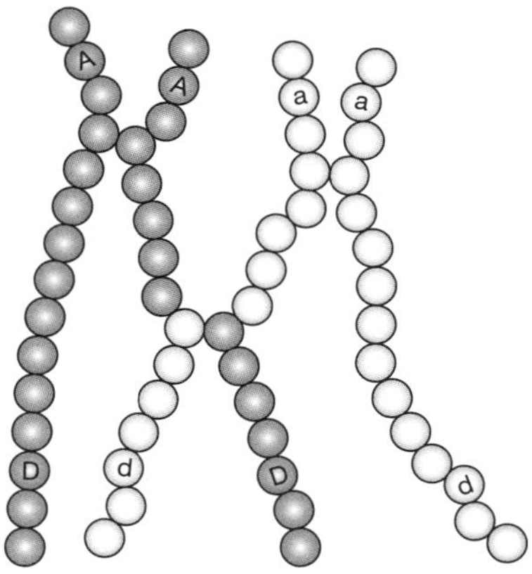

A A a a D d D d

Figure 2.13 Homologous chromosomes at a chiasma

5 What is the point of contact called for chromosomes undergoing a crossing-over event?

____

6 At what stage of meiosis does this event occur?

____

7 How does crossing-over affect the kinds of chromosomes produced?

____

CONCLUSIONS

8 Outline the significance of meiosis.

____

____

____

9 Summarise the processes occurring during meiosis that contribute to the variety of gametes produced.

____

____

____

PRACTICAL ACTIVITY 16

Skin deep—stem cells in medical therapies

BEFORE

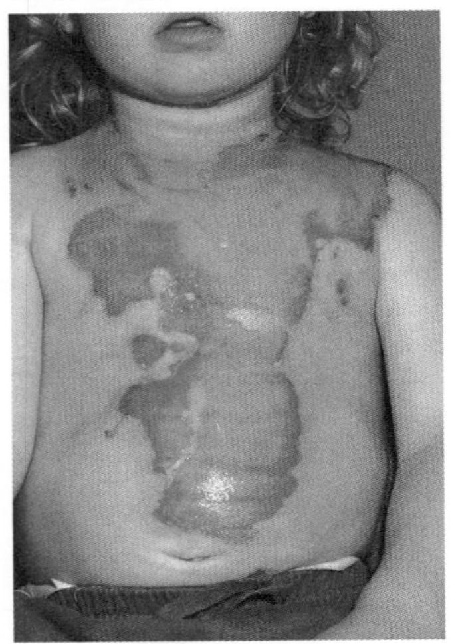

Figure 2.14 Severe burns on a child's chest

AFTER

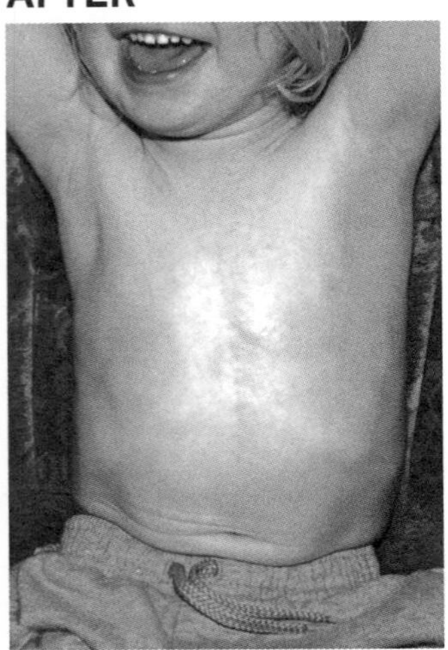

Figure 2.15 The same child after spray-on skin was used in treatment of the burn

INTRODUCTION

On 12th October 2002 two bombs were detonated in the tourist precinct of Kuta on the Indonesian island of Bali. Citizens of 21 different countries died in the blasts, including 88 Australians. Many of those who survived suffered horrific burns injuries. Twenty-eight of the most seriously injured survivors were airlifted to Western Australia's Royal Perth Hospital where they were placed under the care of Professor Fiona Wood. Professor Wood had previously been credited with developing 'spray-on skin' technology, a technique that proved to be instrumental in the recovery of the surviving patients.

PURPOSE

To consider some applications and associated issues related to stem cell technologies in medical therapies.

PROCEDURE

Read the article below about spray-on skin technology and consider Figures 2.14 and 2.15 before answering the questions that follow.

Treating burns with spray-on skin

Spray-on skin is a new technique developed in Australia to treat burns. Scientist Marie Stoner and plastic surgeon Dr Fiona Wood developed the technique in Perth.

Traditionally, treatment for burns victims involved harvesting healthy skin from another section of the body and grafting it onto the burn site. While this is an effective process, it causes more pain for the patient and also generates a second site that requires healing.

Spray-on skin can be used to treat second-degree burns where only the first and second layers of the skin are damaged. Third degree burns, in which all three layers of the skin are damaged, are too severe to treat with the new technique; skin grafts are still required to treat such burns.

The new technique reduces skin culturing time from 21 days to five days. The spray-on skin is made from a skin biopsy from the patient. Surgeons harvest skin basal cells—stem cells within the epidermis—and use them to create a solution that can be sprayed directly onto the burn. The results are comparable to those from traditional skin grafts.

While Stoner and Wood have received much praise for the development of the technique, there has been some controversy as the spray-on skin technique had not been subjected to clinical trials before being used on patients. The technology is currently approved for use in many countries, including Australia, Canada and China, as well as in Europe.

1 Explain the difference between second- and third-degree burns.

____

____

2 Summarise the advantages of using spray-on skin to treat burns victims over more traditional skin grafts.

____

____

____

____

PRACTICAL ACTIVITY 16

3 Basal cells are a type of 'unipotent' adult stem cell in the skin. What does 'unipotent' mean?

4 Why are basal cells harvested and cultured for use in spray-on skin rather than any kind of skin cells?

5 How are adult stem cells different from embryonic stem cells?

6 Outline some of the issues raised by the harvesting and use of embryonic stem cells.

7 Outline some advantages and disadvantages of embryonic and adult stem cells in therapeutic medicine by completing the table below.

Cell type	Advantages	Disadvantages
Embryonic stem cells		
Adult stem cells		

8 Find out how spray-on skin has impacted on the recovery rate for burns victims.

Other stem cell applications

Stem cell therapy also has an important role in treating patients with blood disorders such as leukaemia. In this instance the patient's own bone marrow is damaged and a bone marrow transplant is required to donate healthy stem cells to the patient. In successful bone marrow transplants the transplanted cells continue to reproduce healthy cells in the recipient.

9 Suggest one advantage and one disadvantage of using donor bone marrow stem cells to treat a leukaemia patient.

Cord blood taken from the umbilical cord of newborns is a rich and robust source of stem cells. Cord blood can be harvested and stored for later use, either to be donated to other patients or used by the person from whom it has come.

10 Explain why cord stem cells are defined as adult stem cells.

11 Suggest an advantage of harvesting stem cells from cord blood with the intention of using it to treat the same patient.

CONCLUSION

12 a Comment on the contribution of stem cell technology in the treatment of medical conditions.

b Comment on the value of embryonic and adult stem cells in medical therapies.

UNIT 2

How is continuity of life maintained?

AREA OF STUDY 2

How is inheritance explained?

Outcome 2

Apply an understanding of genetics to describe patterns of inheritance, analyse pedigree charts, predict outcomes of genetic crosses and identify the implications of the uses of genetic screening and decision making related to inheritance.

Key knowledge

Genomes, genes and alleles

- the distinction between a genome, gene and allele
- the genome as the sum total of an organism's DNA measured in the number of base pairs contained in a haploid set of chromosomes
- the role of genomic research since the Human Genome Project, with reference to the sequencing of the genes of many organisms, comparing relatedness between species, determining gene function and genomic applications for the early detection and diagnosis of human diseases.

Chromosomes

- the role of chromosomes as structures that package DNA, their variability in terms of size and the number of genes they carry in different organisms, the distinction between an autosome and a sex chromosome and the nature of a homologous pair of chromosomes (one maternal and one paternal) as carrying the same gene loci
- presentation of an organism's set of chromosomes as a karyotype that can be used to identify chromosome number abnormalities including Down, Klinefelter and Turner syndromes in humans.

Genotypes and phenotypes

- the use of symbols in the writing of the genotypes for the alleles present at a particular gene locus
- the distinction between a dominant and recessive phenotype
- the relative influences of genetic material, environmental factors and interactions of DNA with other molecules (epigenetic factors) on phenotypes
- qualitative treatment of polygenic inheritance as contributing to continuous variation in a population, illustrated by the determination of human skin colour through the genes involved in melanin production or by variation in height.

Pedigree charts, genetic cross outcomes and genetic decision-making

- pedigree charts and patterns of inheritance including autosomal dominant, autosomal recessive, X-linked and Y-linked traits
- the determination of genotypes and prediction of the outcomes of genetic crosses including monohybrid crosses, and monohybrid test crosses
- the inheritance of two characteristics as either independent or linked, and the biological consequence of crossing over for linked genes
- the nature and uses of genetic testing for screening of embryos and adults, and its social and ethical implications.

KEY KNOWLEDGE

Genes and DNA

The common thread weaving through all living organisms is the **DNA (deoxyribonucleic acid)** contained within their cells. This genetic material contains the genes that are responsible for the inherited features of organisms.

- **Gene:** unit of inheritance; composed of DNA
- **Genome:** the complete set of genes contained within an individual organism, measured in base pairs in a hapolid set of chromosomes.

Nuclear material is arranged in strands of DNA called **chromosomes.**

The DNA is composed of a double helical structure. This helix is like a rope ladder that has been twisted (Figure 2.16). Each strand of the DNA helix is made up of a series of linked subunits called **nucleotides**.

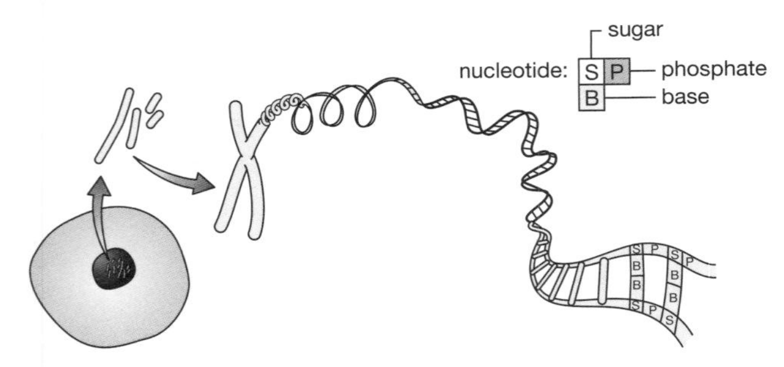

Figure 2.16 The DNA contained in the nucleus unravels to reveal the double helix

There are four different kinds of nucleotides in DNA. Common to each is a **deoxyribose sugar** (5-carbon) molecule and a **phosphate** component. Nucleotides vary in the base unit they contain **adenine, thymine, guanine** or **cytosine**.

The vertical backbone of the DNA helix is composed of the sugar–phosphate groups. The rungs of the 'ladder' are represented by the bases. The bases occur in **complementary pairs**, with *adenine* (A) pairing with *thymine* (T) and *cytosine* (C) pairing with *guanine* (G) as in Figure 2.17.

The complementary strands in a molecule of DNA are referred to as **antiparallel** because one runs 5′→3′ while the other runs 3′→5′ (Figure 2.17).

The number of chromosomes in the **somatic cells** of organisms is characteristic of particular species. Somatic cells are body cells other than **sex cells**. Sex cells are called **gametes**. In animals, these are the ova and sperm.

Somatic cells are typically **diploid**. That is, they contain two sets of chromosomes.

Table 2.3 Diploid numbers

Species	Diploid number
Humans	46
Chimpanzee	48
Cat	38
Blowfly	12
Eucalypt	22

Gametes are **haploid**. That is, they contain only one set of chromosomes—half the full set.

Table 2.4 DNA features

	Feature	Examples
Purines	Double ring structure	Adenine, guanine
Pyrimidines	Single ring structure	Thymine, cytosine

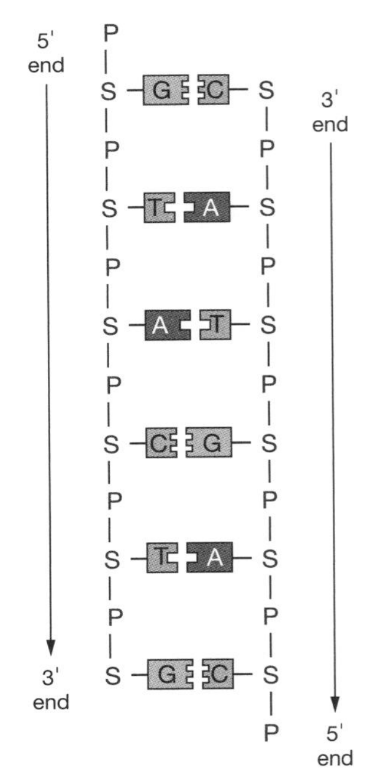

Figure 2.17 Nucleotides arranged in complementary base pairs

Genetic technologies

A range of technological advances in genetics allows scientists to investigate, measure and manipulate the genetic information of species. These include tools to sequence genomes, clone organisms, genetically transform or modify organisms, and diagnose and treat genetic conditions.

DNA sequencing is a process that is used to determine the order of nucleotide bases along a segment of DNA. Bases are 'tagged' so that each appears a different colour when viewed under fluorescent light. Chromatography is used to observe the tagged bases in a series of coloured peaks. The order of the coloured

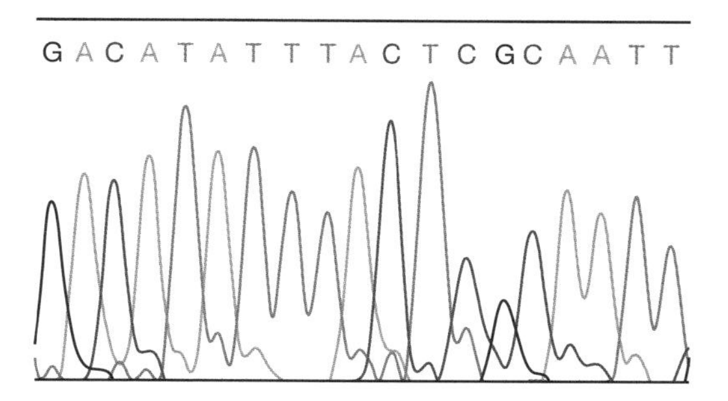

Figure 2.18 In DNA sequencing, each peak reflects a particular nucleotide base.

peaks reflects the order of the bases in the DNA strand (Figure 2.18). Identifying the base sequence of the human genome in the Human Genome Project is a classic example of the use of this technology.

Gene cloning literally makes many copies of a particular gene. This technology involves the production of **transgenic** (or **recombinant**) bacteria. A foreign gene is inserted into a bacterial plasmid and the bacteria are allowed to reproduce, thereby making many copies or clones of the required gene. The cloned genes can then be delivered to the target tissue, e.g. using a disabled virus.

Gene cloning is used in the production of human insulin for the treatment of diabetes.

Gene therapy is a process used to treat patients with certain genetic diseases, such as cystic fibrosis. A normal gene from a healthy individual is inserted into the DNA of a vector, such as a disabled virus. The vector is then used to deliver the normal gene into the cells of the affected person. Transcription of the normal gene results.

Cloning technology allows the production of genetically identical individual organisms. Plant clones are easy to achieve using asexual reproduction. Animal cloning involves inserting the nucleus of a mature body cell into an emptied ovum that is ready for fertilisation. After a period of laboratory incubation, the new embryo is implanted into the uterus of an adult female where development proceeds in the usual way.

Cloning applications include the production of crops and stock with desirable characteristics, e.g. pest-resistant crops. Therapeutic cloning produces compatible tissue for transplanting in humans, e.g. to treat burns victims with new skin.

Karyotyping is a process of sorting chromosomes according to size (Figure 2.19). In a karyotype, chromosomes are arranged in **homologous** (similar) pairs and usually organised in order from largest to smallest. Karyotypes are used to determine gender and to diagnose chromosomal abnormalities, e.g. Down syndrome, in which there are three number 21 chromosomes instead of two (Figure 2.20).

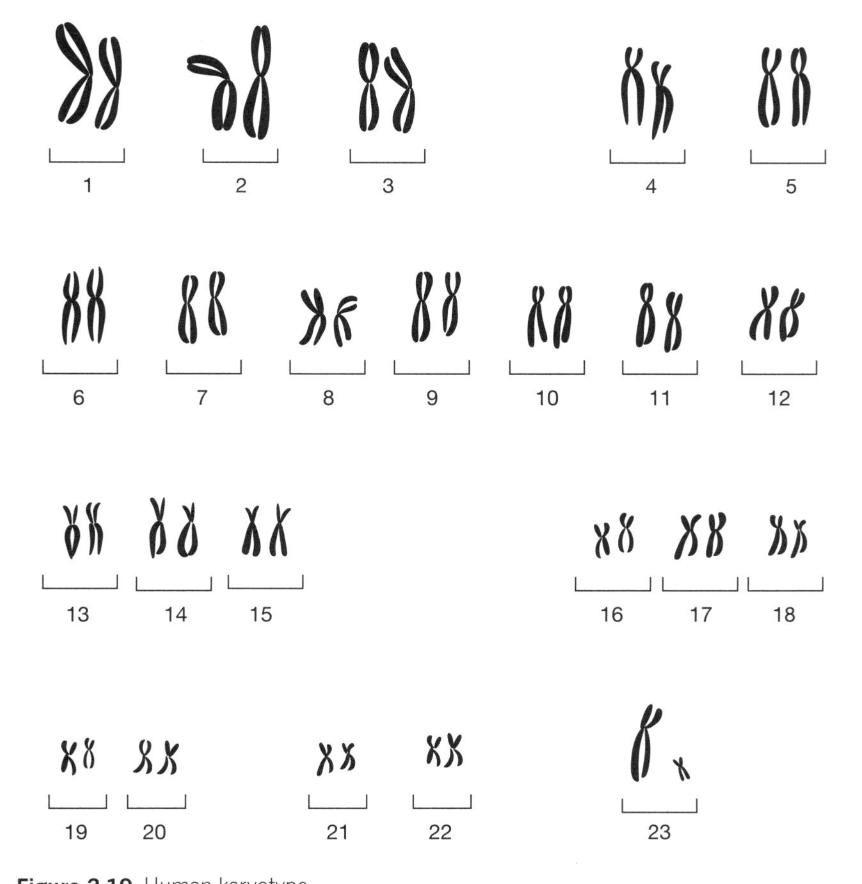

Figure 2.19 Human karyotype

Figure 2.20 Homologous chromosomes

FISH (**fluorescent in situ hybridisation**), also called chromosome painting, identifies particular entire chromosomes by applying a 'colour tag' that is specific for each homologous pair. Homologous pairs of chromosomes are easily identified according to colour using the fluorescent dyes. This technique also allows the order of homologous pairs to be established in karyotyping.

Errors in meiosis

Non-disjunction occurs when chromosomes fail to separate during meiosis. This results in some gametes having two copies of a particular chromosome, and others missing that chromosome altogether.

When a chromosome with the incorrect chromosome number is involved in fertilisation, a zygote is formed that has either one too many or one too few chromosomes. This can have serious repercussions for the well-being of an individual.

Down syndrome is an example of **trisomy 21**, that is, the individual has three copies of chromosome 21 in each of the somatic cells. Individuals with Down syndrome have characteristic facial features, are relatively short in stature and display delayed physical development and intellectual impairment.

Translocation Down syndrome occurs when the number 21 chromosome in a cell is joined to the number 15 chromosome. During meiosis, gametes are formed that contain a normal number 21 chromosome as well as a chromosome 15–21, effectively two copies of chromosome 21. During fertilisation, trisomy 21 occurs.

Chromosomes and sex determination

- **Sex chromosomes** are chromosomes that are involved in sex determination (see Figure 2.21). In humans, these are the X and Y chromosomes—XX: female; XY: male.
- **Autosomes** are chromosomes that are not involved in sex determination.
- Diploid cells in humans contain 46 chromosomes, arranged in 23 pairs.
- There are 22 homologous pairs—the autosomes—and 1 pair of sex chromosomes.
- Females are **homogametic**, that is, the sex chromosomes are homologous.
- Males are **heterogametic**, that is, the sex chromosomes are not a homologous pair.
- Unlike humans, female birds are heterogametic and males are homogametic.

Genotype and phenotype

Gregor Mendel is credited with laying the foundations of our modern understanding of genetics. He carried out breeding experiments with various aspects of garden pea in a successful attempt to understand and interpret the patterns of inheritance that he observed.

- An organism's **genotype** is the combination of alleles that make up its genetic information.
- The **phenotype** of an organism is the observable expression of its genotype.
- An organism's phenotype is influenced by both its genotype and environmental factors.

phenotype = genotype + environment

- **Genes** are the units of heredity.
- **Alleles** are alternative forms of genes.

The chromosomes of an homologous pair may carry the same or different alleles for a given gene.

- **Homozygous** describes the state of an organism that carries the same alleles for a particular gene on both chromosomes of an homologous pair.
- **Heterozygous** refers to the state of an individual that carries alternative alleles for a given gene.

Example: In humans, 'handedness' is a genetic trait controlled by a gene with two alternative alleles. Right-handedness is dominant to left-handedness.

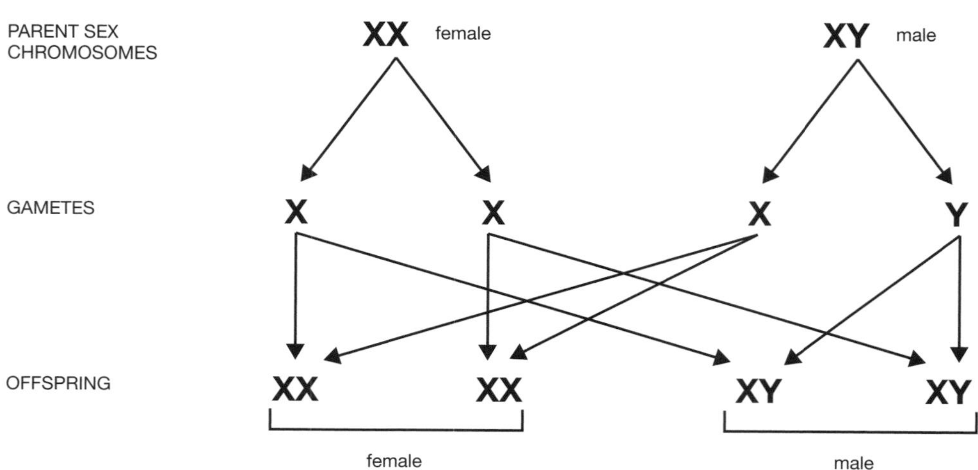

Figure 2.21 Sex determination in humans

KEY KNOWLEDGE

Notation for handedness: *R*: right-handed
r: left-handed
RR: homozygous right-handed individual
Rr: heterozygous right-handed individual
rr: homozygous left-handed individual

- Phenotypic traits can be described as **dominant** or **recessive**.

A trait is **dominant** when it appears in the phenotype of a heterozygote.

Recessive traits only appear in the phenotype of homozygotes; they do not appear in the phenotype of a heterozygote.

Pedigree analysis provides the opportunity of tracking the pattern of inheritance of particular traits from one generation to the next in families. This is a useful method of establishing the mode of inheritance for characteristics.

Using the information provided in the legend, together with appropriate allelic notation, allows genotypes to be assigned to at least some individuals in the pedigree. Such an approach is useful in determining the *mode of inheritance* of a particular characteristic.

The pedigree in Figure 2.22 illustrates that right-handedness is inherited as an **autosomal dominant trait**. Its inheritance pattern is not linked to gender (so the gene is carried on an autosome) and the trait appears in individuals who are heterozygous (making it fit the definition of dominance).

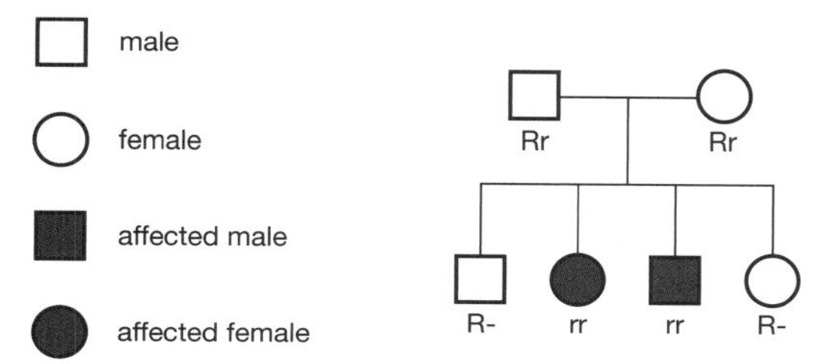

Figure 2.22 Right-handedness is inherited as an autosomal dominant trait.

Some traits do not show simple dominance or recessiveness. There are instances in which both alleles are expressed to varying degrees in the phenotype. This is called co-dominance. The ABO blood grouping system is an example—a single gene locus features multiple alleles, I^A, I^B and i. Individuals carrying alleles for both A antigens and B antigens express both in the phenotype with blood type AB.

Genotype	Phenotype (blood type)
I^AI^A, I^Ai	A
I^BI^B, I^Bi	B
I^AI^B	AB
ii	O

Flower color in snapdragons is another example. When red-flowered snapdragons (homozygous) are crossed with white-flowered snapdragons (homozygous), they produce pink-flowered offspring. In this instance both the alleles for red color and white color are partially expressed.

Genetic explanation: *R*: red
W: white
Parents: *RR* (red) × *WW* (white)
Offspring: all *RW* (pink)

When the pink-flowered snapdragons are crossed, they produce three different phenotypes. A **Punnett square** can be used to show this.

gametes	R	W
R	RR	RW
W	RW	WW

¼ red : ²⁄₄ pink : ¼ white

A **1 : 2 : 1 phenotypic ratio** is typical of the second generation in a cross involving traits that are co-dominant.

ENVIRONMENTAL IMPACT ON GENOTYPE

Chocolate-point Siamese cats demonstrate the impact of the environment on phenotype. This breed of cat carries genetic information that results in the production of dark pigment in the extremities, i.e. the tips of the ears, snout, tail and paws. In temperate climates, the chocolate points are evident. However, when Siamese cats are raised in hot climates, the fur that grows at the extremities lacks the dark pigment.

Other examples of an interplay between genotype and environment can be observed in individuals diagnosed with phenylketonuria whose health is managed by diet; fur colour in Himalayan rabbits; and correction of tooth gap using braces in humans.

MONOHYBRID CROSSES

A **monohybrid** cross is a cross that involves a single gene locus.

Example: Inheritance of colour in pea seeds

Yellow pea colour is dominant to green pea colour.

Notation: *Y*: yellow (dominant)
y: green (recessive)
F_1: first filial generation (offspring)
F_2: second generation

Two pure-breeding plants are crossed.

Parents: *YY* (yellow) × *yy* (green)
F_1: *Yy* (all yellow)

A **Punnett square** is used to calculate the ratio of genotypes and phenotypes in the F_2 generation.

gametes	*Y*	*y*
Y	*YY*	*Yy*
y	*Yy*	*yy*

¾ of the offspring will be yellow; ¼ of the offspring will be green.

KEY KNOWLEDGE

A **3 : 1 phenotypic ratio** is typical of a cross between heterozygotes in a monohybrid cross where the gene under investigation has two allelic forms.

DIHYBRID CROSSES

A **dihybrid cross** is a cross that involves two gene loci.
Example: Inheritance of colour and shape in pea seeds

Round pea shape is dominant to wrinkled pea shape.

Yellow pea colour is dominant to green pea colour.

Notation: *R*: round (dominant)
r: wrinkled (recessive)
Y: yellow (dominant)

When pure-breeding round, yellow pea producing plants are crossed with pure-breeding wrinkled, green pea producing plants, all the offspring produce round, yellow peas.

Parents: *RRYY* (round, yellow) × *rryy* (wrinkled, green)

F_1: *RrYy* (all round, yellow)

Punnett square to calculate the F_2 ratio:

gametes	*RY*	*Ry*	*rY*	*ry*
RY	*RRYY*	*RRYy*	*RrYY*	*RrYy*
Ry	*RRYy*	*RRyy*	*RrYy*	*Rryy*
rY	*RrYY*	*RrYy*	*rrYY*	*rrYy*
ry	*RrYy*	*Rryy*	*rrYy*	*rryy*

This reveals a phenotypic ratio of 9⁄16 round, yellow: 3⁄16 round, green: 3⁄16 wrinkled, yellow: 1⁄16 wrinkled, green.

A **9 : 3 : 3 : 1 phenotypic ratio** is typical of a dihybrid cross between heterozygotes where the traits under investigation are controlled by genes with two alleles.

TEST CROSSES

A **test cross** is a cross between an individual displaying the dominant phenotype and a homozygous recessive individual. Test crosses are carried out to determine whether the individual with the dominant phenotype is homozygous or heterozygous. If offspring displaying the recessive phenotype are produced, the individual must be heterozygous. If all offspring show the dominant phenotype, this suggests the individual is probably homozygous. The larger the number of offspring, the more reliable the results.

Monohybrid test crosses reveal a phenotypic ratio of 1 : 1.

gametes	*R*	*r*
r	*Rr*	*rr*

Dihybrid test crosses reveal a phenotypic ratio of 1 : 1 : 1 : 1.

gametes	*RY*	*Ry*	*rY*	*ry*
ry	*RrYy*	*Rryy*	*rrYy*	*rryy*

GENE LINKAGE

Genes located on the same chromosome and that are likely to be inherited together form a **linkage group**. **Linkage** refers to the tendency for alleles located on the same chromosome to be inherited together.

Example: Consider linked genes *P* and *Q*, represented by alleles *P*, *p* and *Q*, *q* respectively.

Notation: *PQ* denotes that alleles *P* and *Q* are located on one chromosome and *pq* denotes alleles *p* and *q* are located on the other

During meiosis, two kinds of gametes are expected to be produced, *PQ* and *pq*. These are called **parental types** (also called parental gametes).

The further apart the gene loci are located on the chromosome, the more likely that **crossing over** will occur between them. Crossing over will rearrange the genetic material, resulting in new combinations of alleles. Such gametes are called **recombinants**. Crossing over increases variation in the kinds of gametes produced.

Genes are considered to be linked if less than 50% of the gametes produced are recombinant. When a dihybrid test cross deviates from the expected 1 : 1 : 1 : 1 ratio, it indicates the gene loci in question are linked.

SEX LINKAGE

Genes located on the sex chromosomes are said to be **sex-linked**. This is because the phenotype is linked to the gender of the individual. Tracking the pattern of inheritance of characteristics in pedigree analysis is a useful method of establishing whether or not genes are sex-linked.

Colour-blindness and haemophilia in humans are sex-linked characteristics; genes controlling both characteristics are located on the X-chromosome (Figure 2.23).

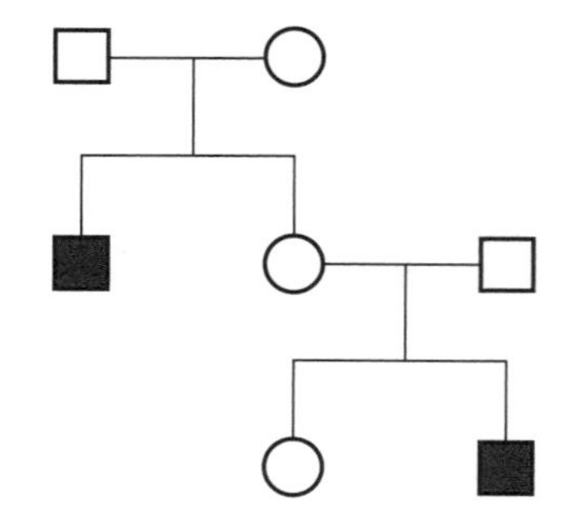

Figure 2.23 Colour-blindness is inherited as a sex-linked recessive trait.

X-linked dominant characteristics: An affected male will pass the trait to all his daughters but not his sons.

X-linked recessive characteristics: An affected female will pass the trait to all her sons.

Y-linked characteristics: Pattern of inheritance is always father to son.

CONTINUOUS AND DISCONTINUOUS VARIATION

Many characteristics come under the control of more than one gene. This is called **polygenic inheritance**.

Continuous variation: Traits are controlled by **polygenes** and characterised by a range of phenotypes; their distribution can be represented graphically by a typical bell curve.

Examples include the inheritance of height, eye colour and skin colour.

Discontinuous variation: Traits are typically controlled by a single gene, usually with two allelic forms and characterised by distinct phenotypes.

Examples:

- Handedness—individuals are either right-handed or left-handed.
- Flower colour in snapdragons—two alleles result in three distinct phenotypes.
- ABO blood grouping—three different alleles result in four distinct phenotypes.

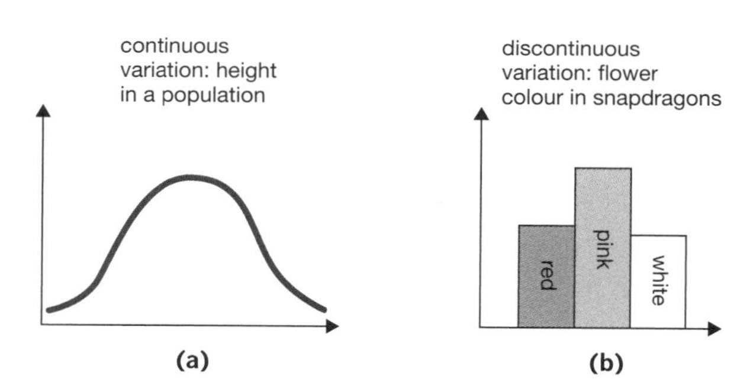

Figure 2.24 **(a)** Continuous variation **(b)** Discontinuous variation

TRACKING GENETIC PEDIGREE

Stud books are records outlining breeding relationships over a number of generations. They represent a useful way of tracking the individuals that have been bred, their characteristics and their relationships with one another. Stud books are kept for thoroughbred race horses, and for breeding cats and dogs. They are important in breeding livestock, particularly in the selection of animals identified with desirable characteristics. Stud books are also important record-keeping tools in breeding programs for wildlife management, especially in relation to endangered species, where maintaining genetic variation and avoiding inbreeding are paramount.

WORKSHEET 31

Crossword—genotype, phenotype and crosses

Complete the crossword puzzle to help you check your knowledge and understanding of key terms and processes related to genotypes, phenotypes and genetic crosses.

Across

2 Describes the characteristic that is observed in the phenotype of an individual homozygous for a particular allele, but not observed in the heterozygote. [9]
4 Physical expression of genotype. [9]
6 Nitrogenous base complementary to adenine in DNA. [7]
10 Cross between individuals that takes into account one particular characteristic. [15]
12 A unit of hereditary information that determines the characteristics of an organism. [4]
15 The full complement of genes in an individual organism. [6]
16 The structural unit of nucleic acids. [10]
17 Nitrogenous base complementary to cytosine in DNA. [7]
18 Alternative form of a gene. [6]

Down

1 Describes the status of an individual that carries two different forms of a gene in relation to a particular characteristic. [12]
3 Cross between an individual displaying a dominant phenotype and an individual displaying a recessive phenotype (homozygous) for the purposes of determining the genotype of the individual with the dominant phenotype. [9]
5 Describes the arrangement of the two complementary strands in a DNA molecule as they run in opposite directions. [12]
7 Describes the status of an individual's genotype when identical alleles are present. [10]
8 Describes the alternative forms of a characteristic that are either fully or partially expressed in the phenotype of an individual. [11]
9 Nitrogenous base complementary to guanine in DNA. [8]
11 Genetic make-up of an individual in relation to one or more genes. [8]
13 Describes a characteristic that is observed in the phenotype of a heterozygote. [8]
14 Nitrogenous base complementary to thymine in DNA. [7]

WORKSHEET 32

Nuclear puzzle—same pieces, different species

Millions of different species of organisms have evolved on Earth—plants, animals, algae, fungi, protists, bacteria and more. Within a single species there is also enormous diversity. And yet, we account for every individual using the same fundamental threads of genetic material—DNA. Not only this, the DNA that codes for the staggering number of different organisms and the features that make each one unique comes in only four different forms. The pieces of the DNA puzzle, the nucleotides, are characterised by a different base molecule—**adenine**, **thymine**, **cytosine** or **guanine**. It is the infinite number of combinations that gives us such a titanic degree of variety.

1 Nucleotides are composed of the same three components. Name the molecule represented by

P: ____________________ S: ____________________

A, T, C, G: ____________________

2 The nucleotide sequence in Figure 2.25 is part of the human β-haemoglobin gene.

Use coloured pencils to colour-code the nucleotide bases in the legend.

Follow your code to colour the different bases along the base sequence.

3 Use appropriate symbols and colour-coding to draw the complementary DNA strand against this template strand.

4 Look carefully at the details of your double-stranded DNA. Describe two features of DNA that ensure complementary base-pairing occurs.

Feature 1: ____________________
____
____

Feature 2: ____________________
____
____

5 Add another symbol to the base legend in Figure 2.24 that will allow the construction of an RNA molecule.

6 Use the space at the right of the DNA template strand in Figure 2.25 to draw in the complementary RNA strand.

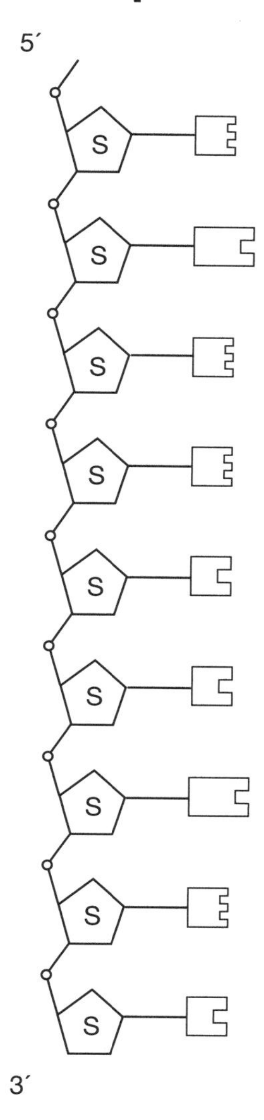

LEGEND

A

T

C

G

Figure 2.25 Sequence of nucleotide bases in the human haemoglobin gene

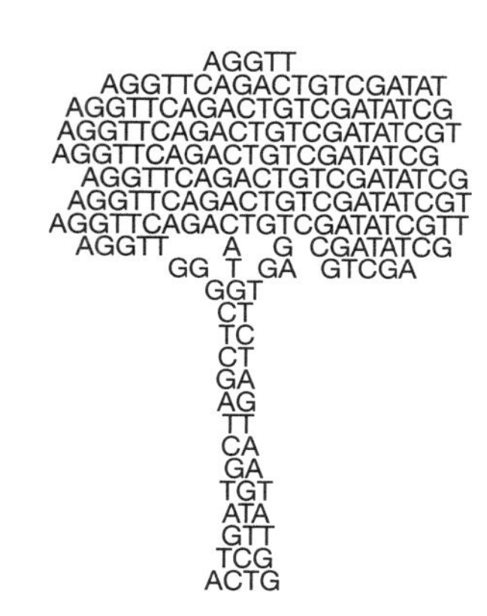

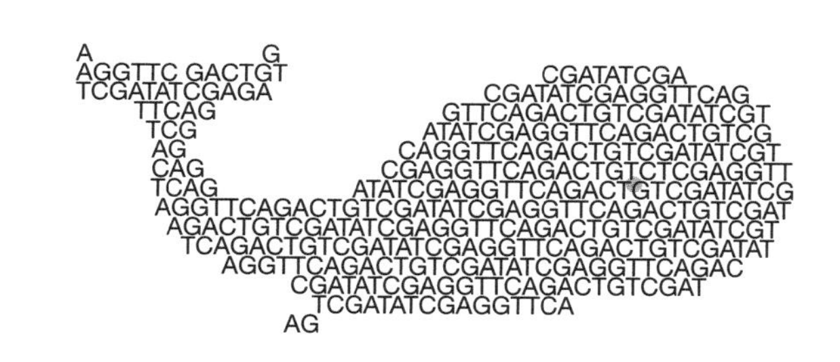

WORKSHEET 33

Counting on karyotypes—chromosomal diagnoses

A karyotype is a visual display of an individual's chromosomes set out in homologous pairs—pairs are arranged in order of length, usually longest to shortest.

1 Examine each of the karyotypes displayed. In the space below each, write information that can be determined about the individual from the chromosomal information provided. Include the general genotype in each case, e.g. 46XY.

INDIVIDUAL A

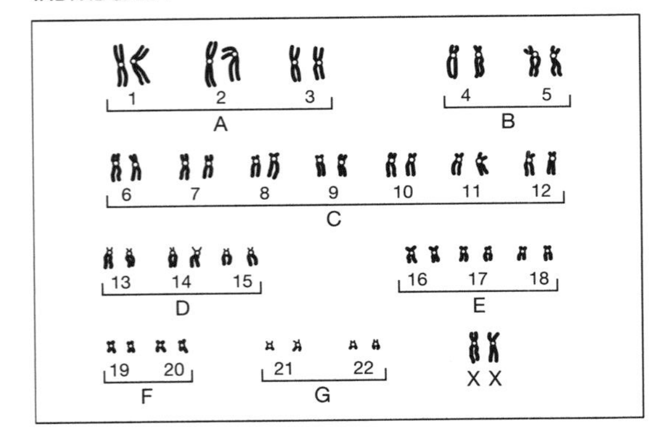

INDIVIDUAL B

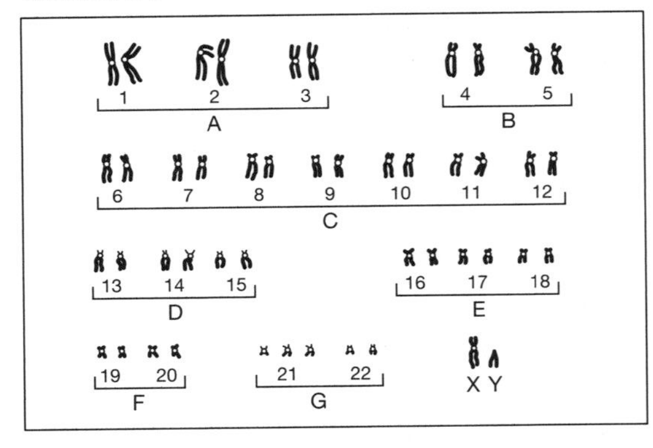

INDIVIDUAL C

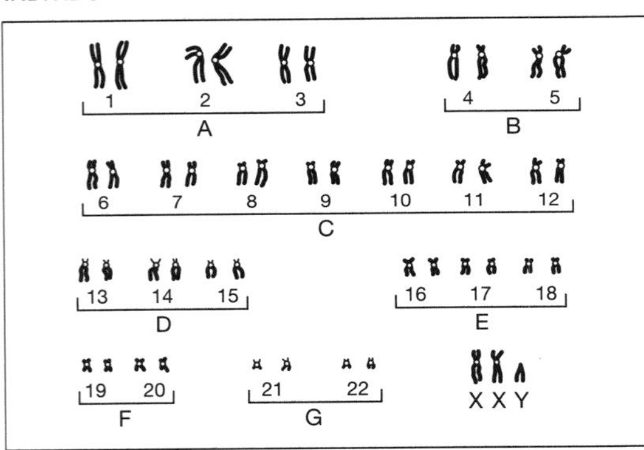

INDIVIDUAL D

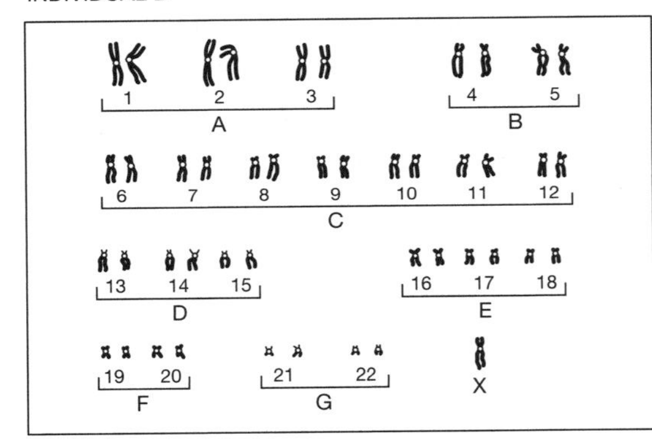

2 Describe the kind of information that karyotyping provides about an individual.

3 What kind of genetic information is not available from karyotype analysis?

4 Outline a technique that may be used in conjunction with karyotyping that allows geneticists to arrange and interpret chromosomes with greater accuracy.

WORKSHEET 34

Counting characteristics—variations in a group

A glance around your classroom reveals an enormous degree of variation in a small group of humans. There is variation in the form of hair colour and texture, eye colour, skin colour and texture, gender and height. You may add many more just by brief observation.

In this exercise, you will collect data about the number of people with varying forms of some characteristics in your class.

1 What is the sample size for your class? $n =$ ______

2 Take each characteristic in turn. Count the number of individuals who display the different forms.

a Enter the data into the table.

b Use the data and the formula provided to calculate the frequency of each characteristic for your class.

Frequency F (%) $= \frac{x}{n} \times \frac{100}{1}$, where x = number of individuals with a particular form of a characteristic, and n = total number of individuals in sample.

c Convert the percentages of the alternative forms of characteristics into the simplest ratio. Enter this into the table, e.g. 77% : 23% approximates a 3 : 1 ratio.

Trait	Frequency (%)	
Tongue rolling ability	Can roll tongue: $x =$ F =	Cannot roll tongue: $x =$ F =
	Ratio	
Hand clasping	Left thumb on top: $x =$ F =	Right thumb on top: $x =$ F =
	Ratio	
Earlobe shape	Free lobes: $x =$ F =	Attached lobes: $x =$ F =
	Ratio	

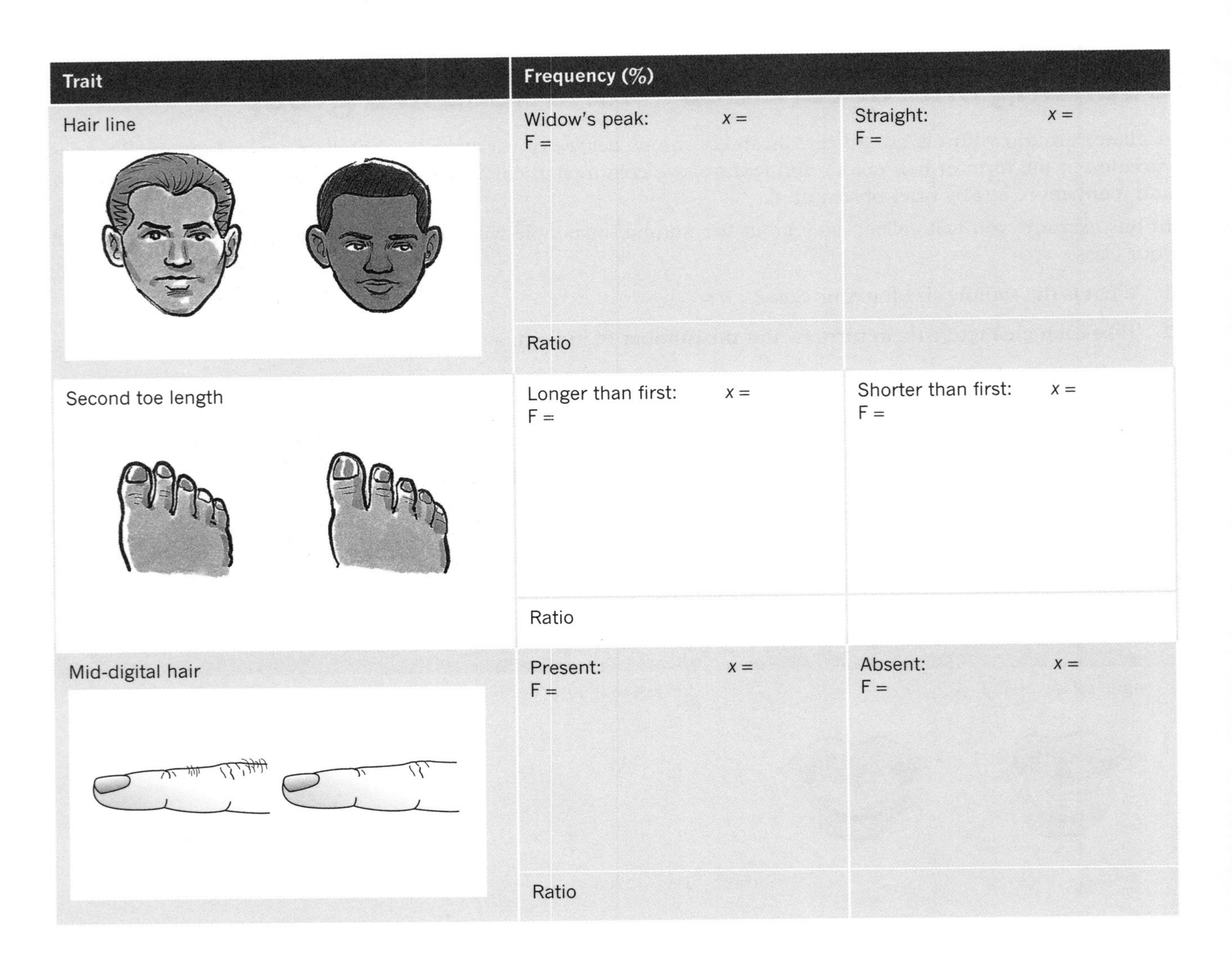

Trait	Frequency (%)	
Hair line	Widow's peak: $x =$ F =	Straight: $x =$ F =
	Ratio	
Second toe length	Longer than first: $x =$ F =	Shorter than first: $x =$ F =
	Ratio	
Mid-digital hair	Present: $x =$ F =	Absent: $x =$ F =
	Ratio	

3 Outline any consistencies that became apparent in the statistics for your class.

____

____

____

4 Explain why a larger sample size is likely to provide more reliable results.

____

____

____

WORKSHEET 35

Linkage and pedigrees—a summary

Make a selection from the list to fill in the missing words in each summary statement.

X-linked	gene complex	continuous	pedigree	sex linkage
polygenic	linkage	crossing over	stud books	Y-linked
discontinuous	recombinant	dominant	recessive	

- When two or more genes are located on the same chromosome they are referred to as a ____________ group. The more closely such genes are situated on a given chromosome, the greater the likelihood that they will be inherited together.
- ________________ gametes are formed as a result of ______________________ at a chiasma during prophase I in meiosis.
- Genes that are so closely linked on a chromosome that crossing over between them is a rare event are referred to as __________________ __________________.
- ____________ ____________ refers to the presence of genes on either of the sex chromosomes. In this case, the inheritance of characteristics is linked to the sex of the individual.
- Colour-blindness is an example of an ____________ characteristic. The mode of inheritance for this condition is X-linked recessive—transmission is typically from female parent to male offspring. X-linked characteristics appear less often in females because there are two X-chromosomes. When one X-chromosome is carrying the affected allele, it may be masked by a normal allele on the second X-chromosome. Males are more often affected because the allele is present on their only X-chromosome.
- _____________ inheritance shows a pattern of transmission from father to son. Characteristics that follow this mode of inheritance are never observed in females.
- ____________ analysis is a strategy that allows geneticists to track the pattern of inheritance of particular characteristics. This provides important information about the mode of inheritance of characteristics and can be useful in calculating the likelihood of genetic diseases occurring in families.
- Animal breeders looking to breed desirable characteristics avoid inbreeding and maintain genetic variation by keeping records called _________ _________ to track breeding stock over generations.
- When alternative forms of a particular characteristic can be clearly placed into non-overlapping groups, _______________ variation is said to exist. Such characteristics are typically governed by single genes.
- _____________________ variation describes the kinds of characteristics that show wide variation across a range. Such characteristics are typically governed by a number of genes and are referred to as __________________ traits.
- Characteristics that appear in the phenotype of a heterozygote are described as _________________.
- Characteristics that do not appear in the phenotype of the heterozygote are described as _________________.

WORKSHEET 36

Puzzling pedigrees—analysing family histories

BLOOD RELATIVES

The ABO blood group of an individual can be determined by identifying the kinds of proteins (antigens) that are present on the surfaces of red blood cells. The single gene locus that codes for the production of these antigens has three alleles (I^A, I^B and i). The genotypes and phenotypes of respective individuals are shown in the Table 2.5.

Table 2.5 ABO blood groups

Genotype	Phenotype
I^AI^A	A
I^Ai	A
I^BI^B	B
I^Bi	B
I^AI^B	AB
ii	O

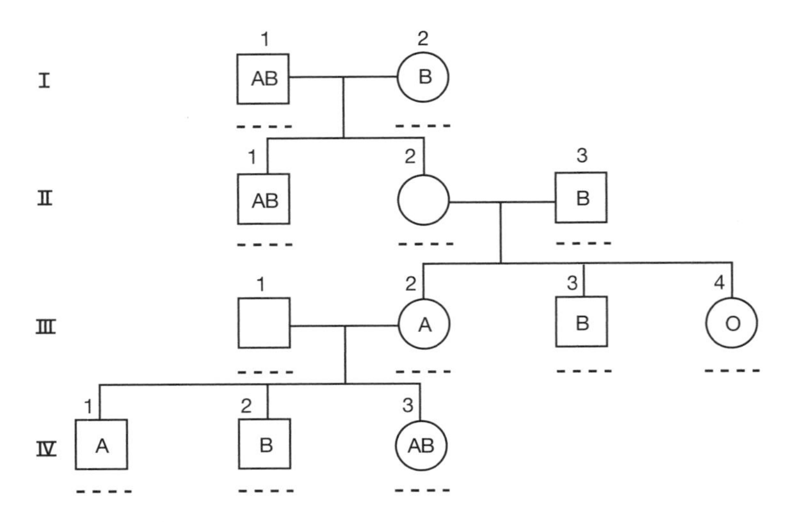

Figure 2.26 ABO blood group pedigree

1 The pedigree in Figure 2.26 on page 161 indicates the blood type for some individuals. Use your understanding of inheritance and the alleles above to assign genotypes and blood types to individuals II-2 and III-1.

2 Outline the relationship between the phenotypic expression of the I^A, I^B and i alleles.

____

____

ROYAL BLOOD

The pedigree in Figure 2.27 represents part of the family tree for a European royal family. It also tracks the inheritance of haemophilia, a blood disorder that leaves sufferers without an important clotting factor, leading to uncontrolled bleeding after even minor injury. Today, haemophiliacs are successfully treated with blood transfusions, but in the past individuals born with this disorder usually did not survive childhood.

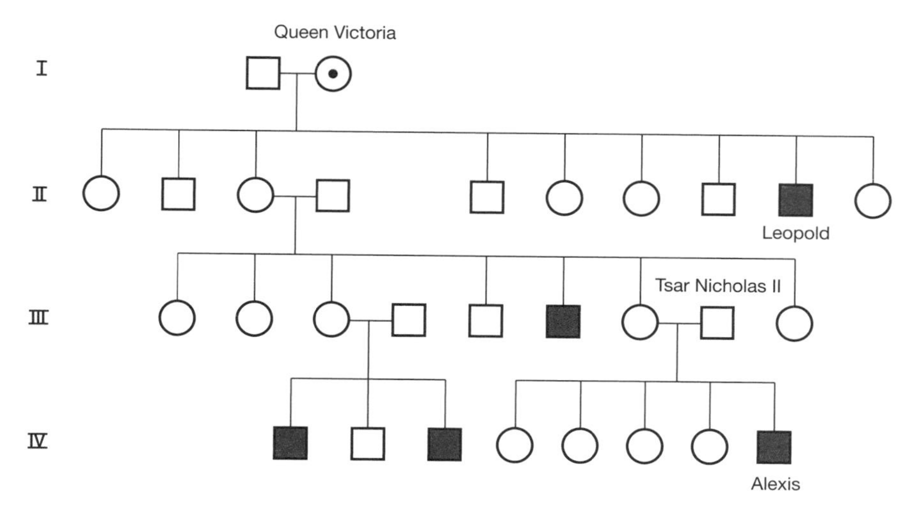

Figure 2.27 Pattern of inheritance of the blood disorder haemophilia in a European royal family

3 Suggest why only males in this family tree are affected by haemophilia.

4 Queen Victoria's son, Leopold, was the first person in the family's history to have been diagnosed with the condition. The cause of the disease in this family is attributed to a mutation that occurred early in the embryological development of Queen Victoria or in a germ-line cell from one of her parents. Describe the evidence from this family tree that points to Queen Victoria as the origin of haemophilia in the family, and not her son Leopold.

5 In the pedigree, Queen Victoria's status as a carrier is denoted by the dot symbol. Use the same notation to identify all of the other carriers of haemophilia in this family.

PRACTICAL ACTIVITY 17

DNA distillery—extracting DNA

MATERIALS

- 1 level teaspoon wheat germ
- 20 mL hot water (about 50°C)
- 1 mL dishwashing detergent
- meat tenderiser powder
- methylated spirits or ethanol
- 50 mL beaker
- 50 mL glass measuring cylinder
- glass stirring rod
- glass hook
- pipette
- 10 mL measuring cylinder

PURPOSE

To extract DNA from the nuclei of wheat germ cells.

PROCEDURE

1 Place the teaspoon of wheat germ in the beaker, add the hot water and stir for about 5 minutes (not too vigorously).

2 Add the detergent then stir VERY GENTLY every minute or so for the next 5 minutes. Be careful to avoid creating any foam. If any foam does form, use a pipette to remove it.

3 Add the meat tenderiser. Again, stir through VERY GENTLY every minute or so for the next 2 or 3 minutes.

4 Gently pour the mixture into the measuring cylinder.

5 Tilt the measuring cylinder a little and very carefully pour some methylated spirits down the inside of the cylinder until it forms a layer about 2 cm deep above the wheat germ–detergent mixture.
IMPORTANT NOTE: Slow and careful addition of the methylated spirits will help prevent the methylated spirits penetrating the wheat germ mixture.

6 Leave the preparation on the bench for 10 minutes. Check your preparation every few minutes.

DISCUSSION

1 Describe your observations. Include a diagram of your complete preparation.

2 The white material that has emerged at the top of the mixture is the DNA that has been extracted from the wheat germ cells. Use the glass hook to gently lift some of this from the surface of the mixture. Describe its appearance.

3 Suggest the reason for adding:

a detergent:

b meat tenderiser:

(Hint: Think about the role of detergents in removing grease, and the role of meat tenderiser in meat preparations. How can these be related to the cells of the wheat germ?)

4 Describe any limitations you encountered in this activity.

5 What measures could you take to reduce these limitations next time?

PRACTICAL ACTIVITY 18

Modelling DNA—simulating the structure

MATERIALS

- 2 different colours of plasticine or similar
- set of 2 different coloured beads (approximately 10 of each)
- set of nucleotides photocopied from template provided (at least 4 of each A, T, G, C)
- scissors
- material to fix nucleotide 'cut-outs' to paper

INTRODUCTION

DNA, or deoxyribonucleic acid, is often referred to as the 'blueprint' for life; a universal code that provides the instructions for protein synthesis in all living organisms.

The building blocks of DNA are nucleotides, composed of three parts—a deoxyribose sugar, a phosphate component and a nitrogenous base (one of either adenine, thymine, guanine or cytosine). The nucleotides link together to form two strands running in an antiparallel arrangement with complementary base pairing between adenine and thymine and between guanine and cytosine.

A single DNA molecule may measure over a metre in length when fully unwound. In order to fit within the nucleus of a cell and maintain order to the code, the DNA coils tightly to form a chromosome.

PURPOSE

To investigate the structure of DNA through a modelling activity.

DURATION

40 minutes

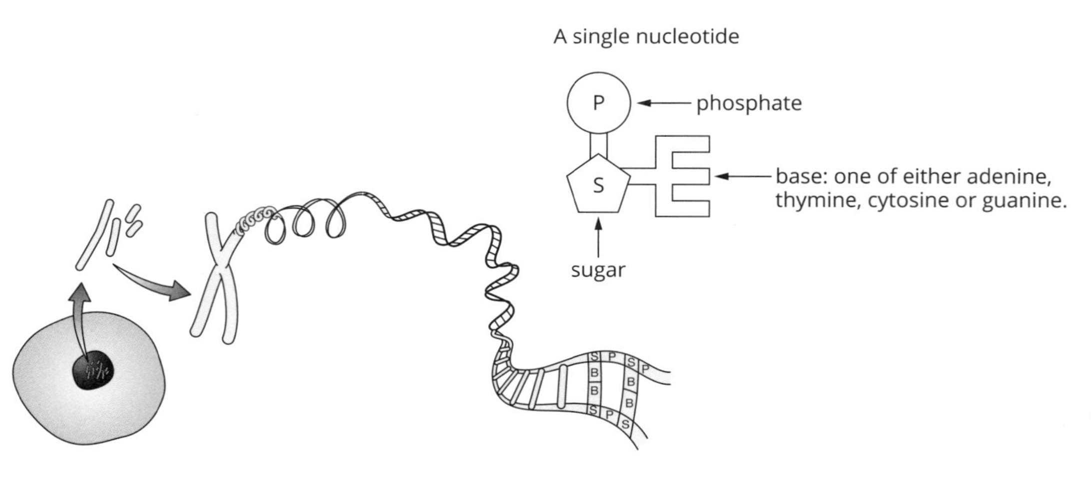

Figure 2.28 The DNA contained in the nucleus unravels to reveal the double helix

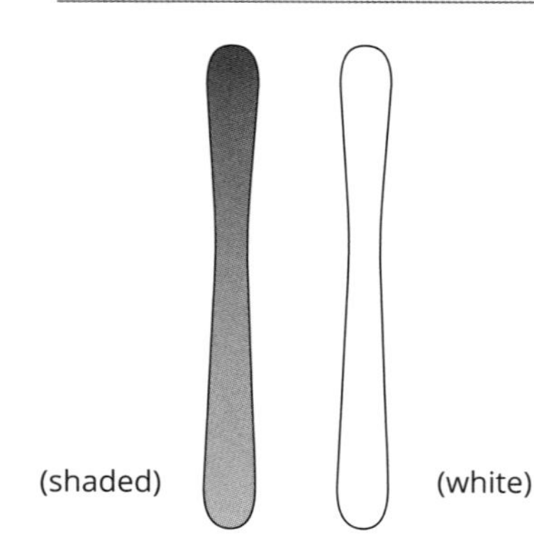

Figure 2.29 Single-stranded chromosomes

PROCEDURE

PART A MODELLING DNA AT THE CHROMOSOMAL LEVEL

1 Using two different colours of plasticine, roll out two single-stranded chromosomes, one of each colour. Ensure that the size is similar. This represents a homologous pair. The different colours represent the maternal and paternal inheritance of each chromosome.

1 Describe how the chromosomes in the homologous pair are similar and different to each other.

____

____

____

____

2 Use the coloured beads provided to mark two gene loci on your plasticine model. For one locus, show identical alleles and for the other show different alleles.

2 Outline the difference between a 'gene' and an 'allele'.

____

____

3 Explain what is meant by the terms 'homozygous' and 'heterozygous'.

____

____

3 During DNA replication, the double helix produces an identical copy in preparation for cell division. At this point of the cell cycle, the duplicated chromosome is held together by a centromere. Add another plasticine roll to each single chromosome to model a duplicated homologous pair.

4 Add further beads to your duplicated pair to show the alleles now present on each chromatid.

4 Sketch a diagram of your duplicated pair of homologous chromosomes. Use colour coding and the following terms to add labels:

duplicated chromosome	chromatid	centromere
gene loci	homozygous	heterozygous

5 Identify and describe a feature of DNA which is clearly demonstrated by your chromosome model.

____

____

6 Share your response to Question 5 with others. Are the responses of your classmates similar or different to your suggestion? Explain.

____

____

PART B MODELLING DNA AT THE BIOMOLECULAR LEVEL

In part B we are going to zoom in on the DNA structure as the chromosome unwinds. When the double helix is completely unwound, the nucleotides appear in two complementary strands that resemble a ladder, with the ribose sugar and phosphate groups forming the uprights and the nitrogenous bases forming the rungs of the ladder.

5 Allocate a colour for each of the four nucleotides and colour in each nucleotide accordingly. Note how each of the four types of nucleotides are similar and different from each other.

6 Cut out the photocopied templates provided for each of the four types of nucleotides. You should have four of each type, so 16 individual nucleotides in total.

7 Arrange a strand of nucleotides to resemble a single strand of DNA running in the 5' to 3' direction as per the image below. Consider the order of your nucleotides. What does the order that you selected represent?

8 Fix the nucleotides in position downwards along the length of the page on the blank space provided on pages 168 and 169.

9 Arrange corresponding nucleotides to demonstrate the complementary base pairing in the other strand. Fix the nucleotides in position.

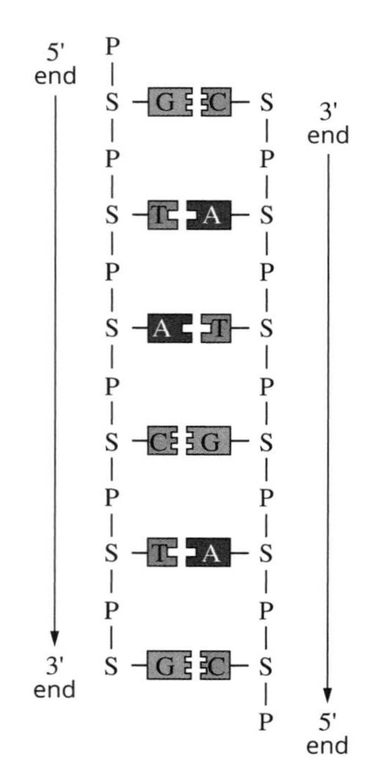

Figure 2.30 Nucleotides arranged in complementary pairs

7 Look carefully at the arrangement of the two complementary DNA strands you have constructed. Explain why the DNA molecule is described as 'antiparallel'.

____

____

8 Describe two features of DNA that ensure complementary base pairing is maintained between the strands.

____

____

9 One of the limitations of this modelling activity is that it does not accurately demonstrate the three-dimensional structure of the double helix. Suggest how you could modify your model to more accurately reflect the three-dimensional structure of the double helix.

____

____

10 Identify and describe another limitation of your model in demonstrating the structure and/or function of the DNA molecule.

____

____

CONCLUSIONS

11 The DNA molecule is composed of threads of nucleotides. Name the three main components of a single nucleotide.

____

12 Summarise the way nucleotides are arranged to form the double helix of the DNA molecule.

____

____

____

PRACTICAL ACTIVITY 18

Photocopiable templates

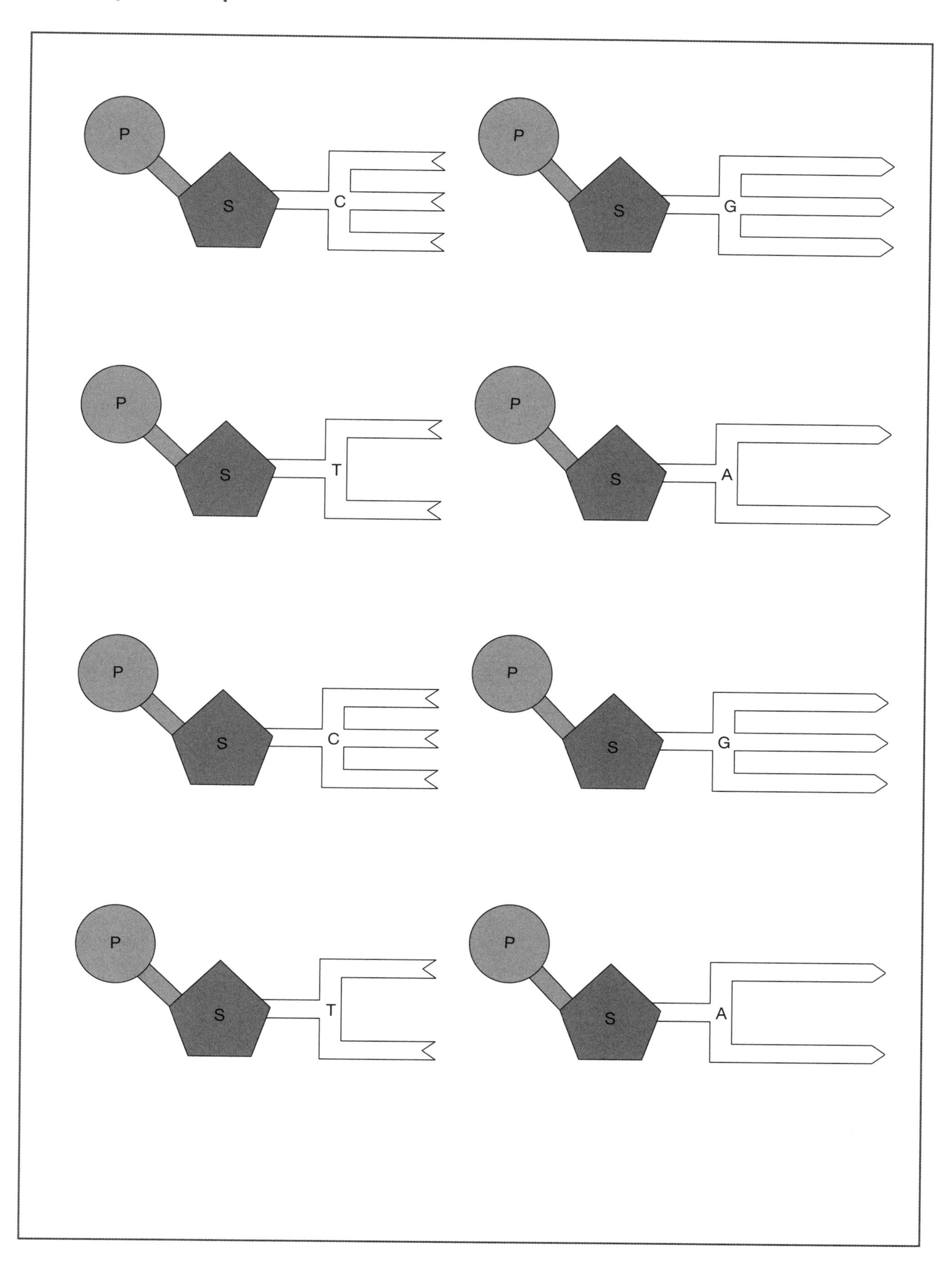

PRACTICAL ACTIVITY 18

PRACTICAL ACTIVITY 19

Genetic roulette—people and pedigrees

INTRODUCTION

A look around your class illustrates many similarities between unrelated individuals—we share hair, eyes, ears, nose, arms, legs, and many other characteristics. Of course, there are many differences in the form of these characteristics between members of the group. For example, hair can be blond, brown, red or black; it can be straight, wavy or curly; it may be fine in some individuals and coarse in others. There are enormous variations in eye colour. But look within a single family—there are more similarities between related individuals within a family than there are between unrelated members of your class. For example, fair skin and reddish hair are likely to be shared by individuals within one family. These characteristics are also likely to be shared by other generations within the family. Why is this? Family trees or pedigrees provide a useful way of analysing information that is inherited from one generation to the next within a family. Analysis of pedigrees gives us a clue about the way characteristics are inherited, and their pattern or mode of inheritance. They can also be used to determine the genetic make-up, or genotype, of an individual, and to predict the chances of children having particular features.

PURPOSE

- To analyse selected pedigrees to determine the mode of inheritance of genetic traits.
- To predict the possible outcomes in children born of particular partnerships in relation to inherited diseases.
- To construct pedigrees from family histories in order to determine modes of inheritance.

PROCEDURE

Carefully read the foundation ideas in the background notes on page 171. This will familiarise you with the symbols used in pedigree analysis. The information in Table 2.6 outlines the key features that distinguish the modes of inheritance for different phenotypic characteristics. Use the information to help you answer the questions related to each of the pedigrees presented in part A and the problems raised in part B of this activity.

Table 2.6 Observed patterns for different types of traits

Pattern of inheritance	Key features
Autosomal dominant	Gene loci on chromosomes other than sex chromosomes; either sex can be affected. Characteristic appears in the phenotype of a heterozygote. Affected individuals must carry at least one allele for the dominant trait. Unaffected parents will not produce affected offspring (unless a new mutation occurs).
Autosomal recessive	Gene loci on chromosomes other than sex chromosomes; either sex can be affected. Characteristic does not appear in the phenotype of the heterozygote. Affected individuals are homozygous recessive. Unaffected parents can produce affected offspring.
X-linked dominant	Affected males pass trait to all their daughters and none of their sons.
X-linked recessive	Affected females produce only affected sons. Expect half the sons of unaffected female carriers to be affected. Affected males produce only unaffected sons.

PRACTICAL ACTIVITY 19

BACKGROUND

In pedigree analysis, symbols are used to provide specific information about individuals in a clear and simple way. Use the following legend as a guide to interpreting the pedigrees in this activity.

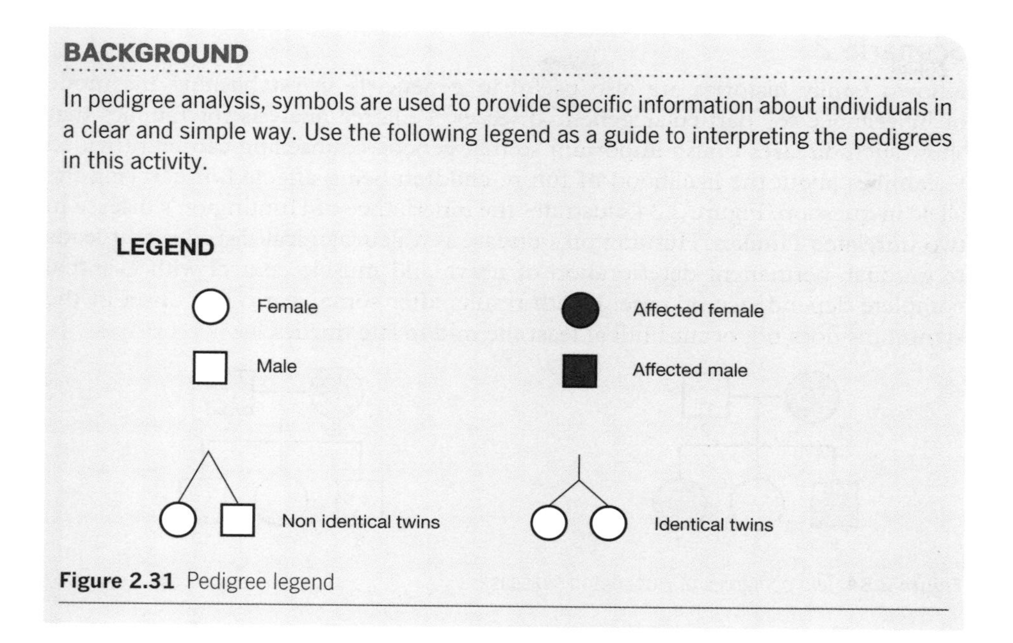

Figure 2.31 Pedigree legend

Scenario 1

The pedigrees in Figures 2.32 and 2.33 show the inheritance pattern of earlobe shape in two different families. 'Free lobes' are dominant to 'attached lobes', which are recessive. The gene responsible for earlobe shape has two alternative alleles represented by E (free lobes) and e (attached lobes).

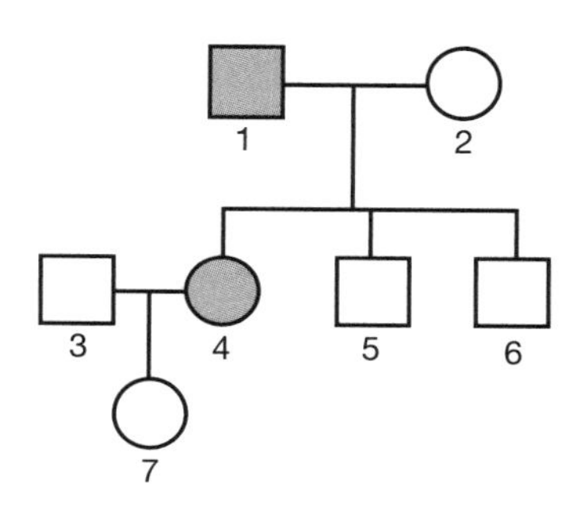

Figure 2.32 Pedigree of earlobe inheritance

PART A PEDIGREE ANALYSIS

1. Assign genotypes to as many individuals as possible in Figure 2.32.
2. Describe the pattern or mode of inheritance for earlobe shape in humans.

   ____

   ____

   ____
3. Examine the pedigree in Figure 2.33. Assign genotypes to as many individuals as possible.
4. Why is it difficult to do this with confidence for individuals 1 and 3?

   ____

   ____

   ____
5. How can you be sure of the genotypes of individuals 6 and 7?

   ____

   ____

   ____

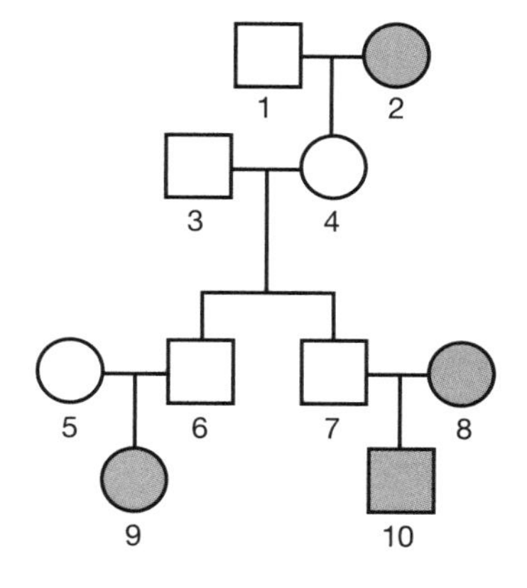

Figure 2.33 Pedigree of free and attached earlobe inheritance in a family

Scenario 2

Known family histories are also useful to geneticists in establishing the mode of inheritance for particular genetic diseases. Pedigree analysis for families that show such diseases is also important so that genetic counselling can be provided to families about the likelihood of future children being affected or carrying the allele in question. Figure 2.34 illustrates the inheritance of Huntington's disease in two unrelated families. Huntington's disease is a neurological disorder that leads to gradual, permanent deterioration of nerve and muscle control with eventual complete dependence on care. Death results after some years. The onset of the symptoms does not occur until at least the mid to late thirties.

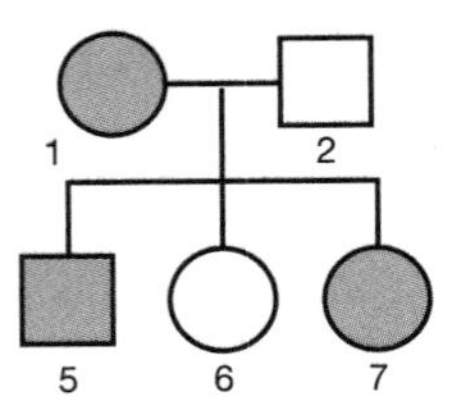

3
4
8
9
10

Figure 2.34 Two pedigrees of Huntington's disease

6 Assign genotypes to each person in both pedigrees.

7 Name the mode of inheritance for Huntington's disease. Explain your choice.

Individuals 7 and 8 are engaged to be married. Both individuals are keen to raise a family.

8 **a** What are the chances of any children from this union developing Huntington's disease? Show your working.

b Suggest options that a genetic counsellor might discuss with such a couple.

Scenario 3

People with galactosaemia are unable to digest milk sugar (galactose).

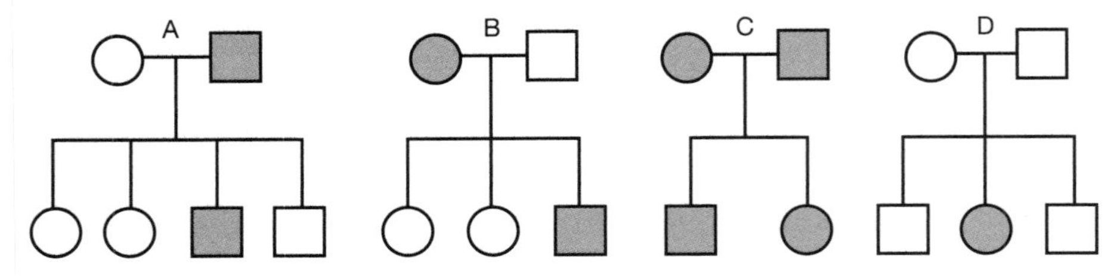

Figure 2.35 Four families with galactosaemia

9 From the evidence of the pedigrees shown in Figure 2.35, suggest which pedigree shows beyond doubt that galactosaemia is inherited as an autosomal recessive condition. Explain your reasoning.

Scenario 4

Red–green colour blindness is a relatively common condition, inherited as an X-linked recessive trait. Figure 2.36 shows the pedigrees of three families in which this condition occurs.

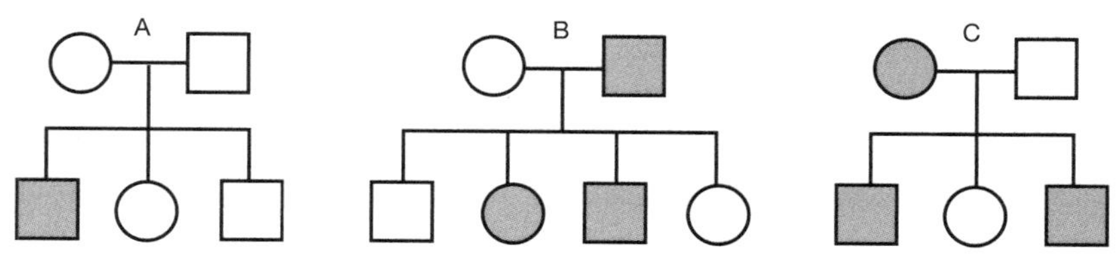

Figure 2.36 Pedigrees of red–green colour blindness.

10 Which of the three pedigrees best establishes the mode of inheritance for this trait? Explain your reasoning.

PART B PICTURING PEDIGREES

Prepare a pedigree chart in the space provided for each of the scenarios described below.

11 **a** An affected child is born to parents, neither of whom shows the characteristic.

b Determine the mode of inheritance. Explain.

12 **a** A man displaying a characteristic inherited as an X-linked trait marries an unaffected female. They have two affected daughters and two unaffected sons.

b Explain whether the trait is inherited as dominant or recessive.

13 **a** A woman showing a trait that has an X-linked recessive mode of inheritance has twins, a girl and a boy, followed by another girl and another two boys. Her partner is unaffected.

b Assign genotypes to all individuals in the pedigree.

CONCLUSION

14 Describe the feature of a pedigree that establishes the mode of inheritance for a particular characteristic as:

a autosomal dominant:

b autosomal resessive:

c X-linked dominant:

d X-linked recessive:

PRACTICAL ACTIVITY 20

Betting on barley—a monohybrid cross

BACKGROUND

Pigmentation in barley is controlled by a single gene with two alternative alleles. In the heterozygote, expression of green pigment masks the effect of the allele coding for no pigment (albino). The genetic barley used in this experiment is the result of a cross between plants heterozygous for the gene locus in question.

This activity recommends that a total of around 200 barley seeds be grown by the class. Your teacher will assign a number of seeds to your group, depending on the number of groups in your class.

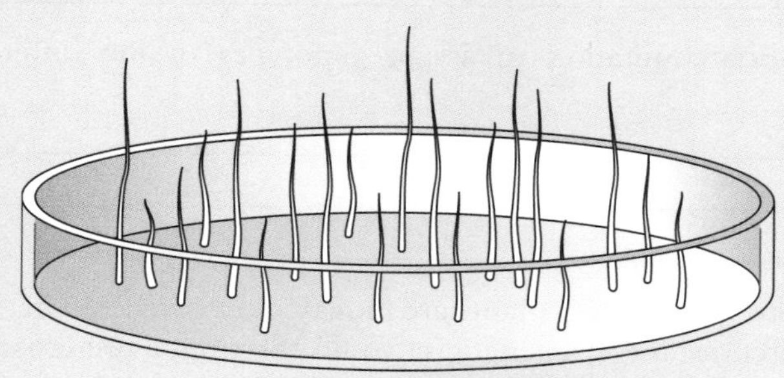

Figure 2.37 Germinating barley seedlings

PURPOSE

To investigate the mode of inheritance of a genetic trait in a monohybrid cross using genetic barley.

MATERIALS

- 20 seeds genetic barley
- sheet of cotton wool
- large Petri dish
- water spray dispenser
- forceps

PROCEDURE

1 Lay a sheet of cotton wool inside the Petri dish and spray generously with water until the cotton wool is quite damp.
2 Use the forceps to arrange the barley seeds on the cotton wool so that they are evenly spaced about 1 cm apart.
3 Spray a little more water to ensure the seeds are dampened.
4 Leave the Petri dish on a bench near a window.
5 Spray the seeds twice daily to ensure they do not dry out. You should continue to do this after initial germination until the barley seedlings are at least 2 cm tall. This is likely to take a couple of weeks.

TWO WEEKS LATER

1 Count the number of different coloured seedlings and enter your results into the table below..

2 Collate the class data. A spreadsheet, whiteboard or overhead projector will be useful for this. Enter the class data into the table.

	Number of seedlings of each colour		Total
	Green	Albino	
Own data			
Class data			

3 Calculate the ratio of green seedlings to albino seedlings for:

a your own data: ______________________

b the class data: ______________________

4 **a** How does the ratio for your own data compare with the ratio for the class data?

____

____

b Which set of data is likely to be more reliable? Explain.

____

____

5 Use appropriate notation to assign genotypes to the different coloured seedlings.

____

____

____

6 Homozygous green barley plants are indistinguishable from heterozygotes. In ordinary circumstances, a geneticist would carry out a test cross to determine the genotype of an individual that shows the dominant characteristic.

a Describe a test cross.

____

____

____

____

____

____

b Outline how a test cross is useful in determining the genotype of such an individual. Use a worked example to illustrate your answer.

____

____

____

____

____

____

SUMMARY REPORT

Summarise your findings in this activity. You should include the following items in your discussion:

- Identify the mode of inheritance for green pigmentation in barley.
- Use a model to explain how the data supports your theory.

UNIT 2

How is continuity of life maintained?

AREA OF STUDY 3

Investigation of an issue

Outcome 3

Investigate and communicate a substantiated response to a question related to an issue in genetics and/or reproductive science.

Key knowledge

- the characteristics of effective science communication: accuracy of biological information; clarity of explanation of biological concepts, ideas and models; contextual clarity with reference to importance and implications of findings; conciseness and coherence; and appropriateness for purpose and audience
- the biological concepts specific to the investigation: definitions of key terms; use of appropriate biological terminology, conventions and representations
- the use of data representations, models and theories in organising and explaining observed phenomena and biological concepts, and their limitations
- the nature of evidence and information: distinction between opinion, anecdote and evidence, weak and strong evidence, and scientific and non-scientific ideas; and validity, reliability and authority of data including sources of possible errors or bias
- the influence of social, economic, legal and ethical factors relevant to the selected biological issue.

Changing conceptions

AUTHOR: ____________________

AREA OF STUDY 3
INVESTIGATION OF AN ISSUE

Students investigate and communicate a substantiated response to a question related to an issue in genetic and/or reproductive science.

In this investigation students apply and extend knowledge and skills developed in Areas of Study 1 and/or 2.

The increasing uses and applications of genetic knowledge and reproductive science provide benefits for individuals and populations. They also raise social, economic, legal and ethical questions in society. Examples of relevant scientific applications that challenge social and ethical norms include:

- human cloning
- genetic modification of organisms
- use of forensic DNA databanks
- assisted reproductive technologies
- prenatal and predictive genetic testing.

ASSESSMENT FOR OUTCOME 3

A report of an investigation into genetics and/or reproductive science using an appropriate format. Formats might include a digital presentation, oral communication or written report.

INTRODUCTION

Scientific research continues to make new technologies available in many areas of health and reproductive medicine. Advances in the fields of genetics and reproductive technology continue to have a huge impact on infertile couples and those who have a family history of genetic disease and are faced with the difficult decision of whether or not to undertake a pregnancy that might result in a seriously ill or disabled child.

Pre-implantation genetic diagnosis or **PGD** is a prenatal and predictive genetic technique developed in the 1980s that offers choice for such families. Combined with IVF technology it allows embryos to be screened for genetic diseases—only 'healthy' embryos are selected for implantation.

PGD is one of a suite of genetic and reproductive technologies that are something of a double-edged sword. They offer choice to families but also raise community debate around social, economic, legal and ethical considerations.

On 25th July 1978 Louise Brown made medical history when she was the first infant born using IVF technology. At the time, the technique was hailed a medical miracle by some and condemned as 'playing God' by others. Despite the controversy, this form of assisted reproductive technology has since become commonplace with over a million IVF births worldwide.

Today debate continues to prevail around a range of genetic and reproductive technologies, with the focus shifting as new tools and techniques emerge. CRISPR presents one such example—it is a tool that allows scientists to edit the DNA of almost any organism. The implications of this newest cutting-edge technology are far-reaching, particularly considering its potential application in correcting 'faulty' genes in fertilised human eggs. CRISPR casts a whole new dimension on our understanding of 'designer babies'.

INVESTIGATING THE ISSUE

The following article, which appeared in *The Age* newspaper in September 2004, continues to represent a classic example of genetic and reproductive technologies that both solved problems and raised issues. The case follows a family for whom PGD combined with IVF technology was used to produce a healthy child free of a devastating genetic disease that afflicted their first child. A bonus for the couple was that the technology not only screened embryos for the disease, it also screened for an embryo that would be a compatible bone marrow donor for their sick son.

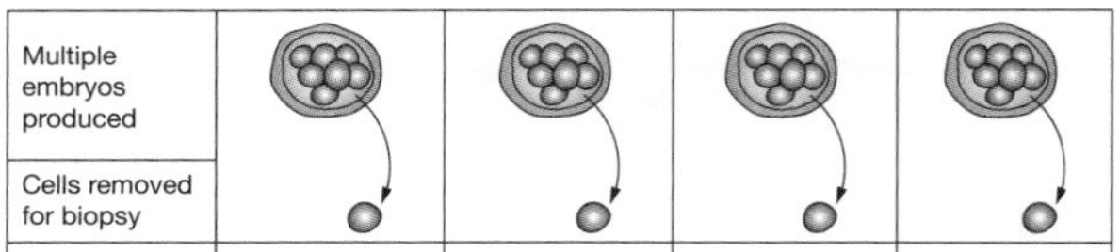

Multiple embryos produced				
Cells removed for biopsy				
Affected	✓	×	✓	×
Compatible bone marrow	×	×	✓	✓
Implanted	×	×	×	✓

Read the article and reflect upon it before responding to the questions. The questions are intended to guide you in this investigation. Develop your own further lines of inquiry to fully address the issues.

—a look at assisted reproductive technologies

Changing conceptions

By Rachel Browne

26th September 2004

AN Australian couple who created medical history and sparked a storm of controversy about their decision to have a 'designer' baby to save their seriously ill son have spoken out about their choice in a new film.

The Tasmanian couple, known only as Stephen and Leanne, welcomed their life-saving baby boy, CJ, last month.

CJ was conceived using a contentious technique called PGD (Preimplantation Genetic Diagnosis) in which embryos are screened for genetic disorders before being implanted in the mother's uterus.

While debate ranges about the ethics of the technique, for Stephen and Leanne it provided the only lifeline for their four-year-old son BJ, who has a rare immune deficiency known as hyper IgM syndrome.

BJ's condition, which affects about 30 children in Australia, meant he had almost no immune system, leaving him open to serious infections. His only chance at a normal life was a bone marrow transplant but nobody in his family could provide a direct tissue match.

So Stephen and Leanne made the difficult decision to conceive a child who would be free from hyper IgM, as well as a tissue match for BJ. Their emotional journey, in which they made Australian medical history, is captured in the Film Australia documentary Who's Afraid of Designer Babies?

Over the past two years, the couple spent about $20,000 and produced 36 embryos in their quest to save BJ, with medical aid from Sydney IVF, a large IVF clinic.

Leanne said she would do it all over again, despite the financial and emotional toll.

"I'm sure there are people who would not choose to go down the path we have taken," said the 34-year-old. "I think a lot of people probably would because you don't know the capacity you have for love until you have a child."

Sydney IVF is the only clinic in Australia that uses PGD to screen embryos for tissue match for an existing sibling and it took the medical team 18 months to develop a test to screen embryos, created by fertilising eggs from Leanne with Stephen's sperm, for hyper IgM.

The technique, a first for Australia, led to heated argument in medical quarters, with some believing it would lead to a genetic underclass.

"I know there are other people who probably would look at this and not understand why we are doing it," Stephen said. "But until you put yourself in the same position, I don't think there would be a parent out there who wouldn't do what they could for their child."

Stephen and Leanne gave a human face to the debate, according to the film's writer-direction Sean Cousins. "People have widely divergent views on the subject," he said.

"There is no simple way of dealing with the question of PGD. It's not a case of good versus evil. It's much more complex than that."

Producer Tony Wright hoped the documentary would encourage community discussion about 'designer' babies. "Science is getting ahead of the debate," he said. "That is one of the reasons why we wanted to make the documentary, to extend the debate more widely."

GUIDING QUESTIONS

1 a What does pre-implantation genetic diagnosis mean?
  b Explain why PGD needs to be used in conjunction with IVF technology.

2 Describe the double benefits to the family in the article as a result of PGD application.

3 Debate surrounding embryo screening continues in Australia and around the world. Write a list of issues that arise from the application of this technology. Include social, economic, legal and ethical concerns.

4 Consider carefully the positions of people on different sides of the PGD debate. Identify some of the stakeholders and prepare arguments from their points of view.

5 Write an editorial article for a newspaper in which you respond to some of these issues. It will be important to draw on the benefits and disadvantages as well as the relevance and importance of the technology in substantiating your response.

REFERENCES

Remember to acknowledge any reference material used in the course of the investigation. This may include:

- scientific journals
- medical articles and texts
- Internet sources
- newspaper articles.

When referencing published sources it's important to provide bibliographical data according to accepted protocols, such as Harvard citation style.

Examples:

Ivf.com.au,. 'Preimplantation Genetic Diagnosis Testing | IVF Australia'. N.p., 2015. Web. 8 Aug. 2015.

Infante, Andre et al. 'Biotech Breakthrough Opens Door To Designer Babies: Here's What You Need To Know'. *MakeUseOf*. N.p., 2015. Web. 8 Aug. 2015.